Contents

Solutions for End-of-Chapter Problems

Chapter 1
Introduction

Section 1-1 Atomic Structure

1.   An atom with an atomic number of 6 has **6 electrons** and **6 protons**

2.   The third shell of an atom can have $2n^2 = 2(3)^2 = $ **18 electrons**

Section 1-2 Semiconductors, Conductors, and Insulators

3.   The materials represented in Figure 1-40 in the textbook are
      (a)   insulator   (b)   semiconductor   (c)   conductor

4.   An atom with four valence electrons is a **semiconductor**.

Section 1-3 Covalent Bonds

5.   In a silicon crystal, each atom forms **four** covalent bonds.

Section 1-4 Conduction in Semiconductors

6.   When heat is added to silicon, more free electrons and holes are produced.

7.   Current is produced in silicon at the **conduction** band and the **valence** band.

Section 1-5 N-Type and P-Type Semiconductors

8.   Doping is the carefully controlled addition of trivalent or pentavalent atoms to pure (intrinsic) semiconductor material for the purpose of increasing the number of majority carriers (free electrons or holes).

9.   Antimony is a pentavalent (donor) material used for doping to increase free electrons. Boron is a trivalent (acceptor) material used for doping to increase the holes.

Section 1-6 The Diode

10.   The electric field across the *pn* junction of a diode is created by donor atoms in the *n* region losing free electrons to acceptor atoms in the *p* region. This creates positive ions in the *n*-region near the junction and negative ions in the *p* region near the junction. A field is then established between the ions.

11.   The barrier potential of a diode represents an energy gradient that must be overcome by conduction electrons and produces a voltage drop, not a source of energy.

Chapter 1

Section 1-7 Biasing the Diode

12. To forward-bias a diode, the positive terminal of a voltage source must be connected to the **p region**.

13. A series resistor is needed to **limit the current** through a forward-biased diode to a value which will not damage the diode because the diode itself has very little resistance.

Section 1-8 Voltage-Current Characteristic of a Diode

14. To generate the forward bias portion of the characteristic curve, connect a voltage source across the diode for forward bias , and place an ammeter in series with the diode and a voltmeter across the diode. Slowly increase the voltage from zero and plot the forward voltage versus the current.

15. A temperature increase would cause the barrier potential to decrease from 0.7 V to 0.6 V.

Section 1-9 Diode Models

16. (a) The diode is reverse-biased.   (b) The diode is forward-biased.
     (c) The diode is forward-biased.   (d) The diode is forward-biased.

17. (a) $V_R = \left(\dfrac{50\,\mathrm{M\Omega}}{50\,\mathrm{M\Omega} + 10\,\Omega} \right)(5\,\mathrm{V} - 8\,\mathrm{V}) \cong -3\,\mathrm{V}$

    (b) $V_F = 0.7\,\mathrm{V}$

    (c) $V_F = 0.7\,\mathrm{V}$

    (d) $V_F = 0.7\,\mathrm{V}$

Section 1-10 Testing a Diode

18. (a) Since $V_D = 25\,\mathrm{V} = 0.5V_S$, the diode is **open.**
    (b) The diode is forward-biased but since $V_D = 15\,\mathrm{V} = V_S$, the diode is **open.**
    (c) The diode is reverse-biased but since $V_R = 2.5\,\mathrm{V} = 0.5V_S$, the diode is **shorted.**
    (d) The diode is reverse-biased and $V_R = 0\,\mathrm{V}$. The diode is **operating properly.**

19. $V_A = V_{S1} = \textbf{+25 V}$
    $V_B = V_{S1} - 0.7\,\mathrm{V} = 25\,\mathrm{V} - 0.7\,\mathrm{V} = \textbf{+24.3 V}$
    $V_C = V_{S2} + 0.7\,\mathrm{V} = 8\,\mathrm{V} + 0.7\,\mathrm{V} = \textbf{+8.7 V}$
    $V_D = V_{S2} = \textbf{+8.0 V}$

EWB/Multisim Troubleshooting Problems

The solutions showing instrument connections for problems 20 through 28 are available in the Solutions folder for Chapter 1 on the CD-ROM provided with the textbook. The solutions may be accessed using the password *ED5FLOYD*. The faults in the circuit files may be accessed using the password *book* (all lowercase).

20. Diode shorted

21. Diode open

22. Diode open

23. Diode shorted

24. No fault

25. Diode shorted

26. Diode leaky

27. Diode open

28. Diode shorted

Chapter 2
Diode Applications

Section 2-1 Half-Wave Rectifiers

1. See Figure 2-1.

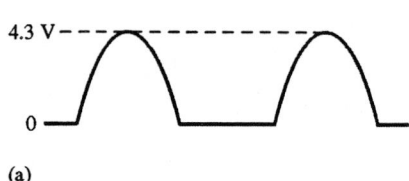

(a)

(b)

Figure 2-1

2. (a) $I_F = \dfrac{V_{(p)in} - 0.7\,\text{V}}{R} = \dfrac{5\,\text{V} - 0.7\,\text{V}}{47\,\Omega} = \dfrac{4.3\,\text{V}}{47\,\Omega} = \textbf{91.5 mA}$

   (b) $I_F = \dfrac{V_{(p)in} - 0.7\,\text{V}}{R} = \dfrac{50\,\text{V} - 0.7\,\text{V}}{3.3\,\text{k}\Omega} = \dfrac{49.3\,\text{V}}{3.3\,\text{k}\Omega} = \textbf{14.9 mA}$

3. $V_{sec} = nV_{pri} = (0.2)115\,\text{V} = \textbf{23 V rms}$

4. $V_{sec} = nV_{pri} = (0.5)115\,\text{V} = 57.5\,\text{V rms}$

   $V_{p(sec)} = 1.414(57.5\,\text{V}) = 81.3\,\text{V}$

   $V_{avg(sec)} = \dfrac{V_{p(sec)}}{\pi} = \dfrac{81.3\,\text{V}}{\pi} = 25.9\,\text{V}$

   $P_{L(p)} = \dfrac{\left(V_{p(sec)} - 0.7\,\text{V}\right)^2}{R_L} = \dfrac{(80.6\,\text{V})^2}{220\,\Omega} = \textbf{29.5 W}$

   $P_{L(avg)} = \dfrac{\left(V_{avg(sec)}\right)^2}{R_L} = \dfrac{(25.9\,\text{V})^2}{220\,\Omega} = \textbf{3.05 W}$

Section 2-2 Full-Wave Rectifiers

5. (a) $V_{avg} = \dfrac{V_p}{\pi} = \dfrac{5\,\text{V}}{\pi} = \textbf{1.59 V}$

   (b) $V_{avg} = \dfrac{2V_p}{\pi} = \dfrac{2(100\,\text{V})}{\pi} = \textbf{63.7 V}$

   (c) $V_{avg} = \dfrac{2V_p}{\pi} + 10\,\text{V} = \dfrac{2(10\,\text{V})}{\pi} + 10\,\text{V} = \textbf{16.4 V}$

   (d) $V_{avg} = \dfrac{2V_p}{\pi} - 15\,\text{V} = \dfrac{2(40\,\text{V})}{\pi} - 15\,\text{V} = \textbf{10.5 V}$

6.   (a) Center-tapped full-wave rectifier

(b) $V_{p(sec)} = (0.25)(1.414)110\text{ V} = \mathbf{38.9\text{ V}}$

(c) $\dfrac{V_{p(sec)}}{2} = \dfrac{38.9\text{ V}}{2} = \mathbf{19.4\text{ V}}$

(d) See Figure 2-2. $V_{RL} = 19.4\text{ V} - 0.7\text{ V} = 18.7\text{ V}$

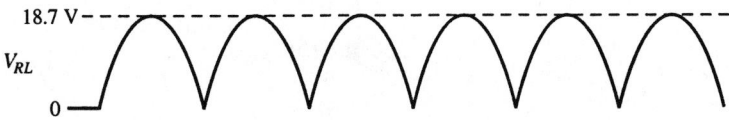

Figure 2-2

(e) $I_F = \dfrac{\dfrac{V_{p(sec)}}{2} - 0.7\text{ V}}{R_L} = \dfrac{18.7\text{ V}}{1.0\text{ k}\Omega} = \mathbf{18.7\text{ mA}}$

(f) PIV $= 19.4\text{ V} + 18.7\text{ V} = \mathbf{38.1\text{ V}}$

7. $V_{avg} = \dfrac{110\text{ V}}{2} = 55\text{ V for each half}$

$V_{avg} = \dfrac{V_p}{\pi}$

$V_p = \pi V_{avg} = \pi(55\text{ V}) = \mathbf{173\text{ V}}$

8.   See Figure 2-3.

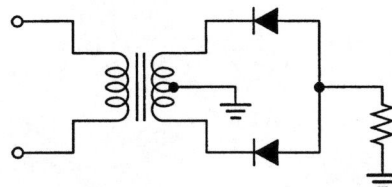

Figure 2-3

9.   PIV $= V_p = \dfrac{\pi V_{avg(out)}}{2} = \dfrac{\pi(50\text{ V})}{2} = \mathbf{78.5\text{ V}}$

10.   PIV $= V_{p(out)} = 1.414(20\text{ V}) = \mathbf{28.3\text{ V}}$

11.   See Figure 2-4.

Figure 2-4

Chapter 2

Section 2-3 Power Supply Filters and Regulators

12. $V_{r(pp)} = (1.414)(0.5 \text{ V}) = 707 \text{ mV pp}$

$r = \dfrac{V_{r(pp)}}{V_{DC}} = \dfrac{707 \text{ mV}}{75 \text{ V}} = \mathbf{0.00943}$

13. $V_{r(pp)} = \dfrac{V_{p(in)}}{fR_L C} = \dfrac{30 \text{ V}}{(120 \text{ Hz})(600 \, \Omega)(50 \ \mu\text{F})} = \mathbf{8.33 \text{ V pp}}$

$V_{DC} = \left(1 - \dfrac{1}{2fR_L C}\right) V_{p(in)} = \left(1 - \dfrac{1}{(240 \text{ Hz})(600 \, \Omega)(50 \ \mu\text{F})}\right) 30 \text{ V} = \mathbf{25.8 \text{ V}}$

14. $\%r = \left(\dfrac{V_{r(pp)}}{V_{DC}}\right) 100 = \left(\dfrac{8.33 \text{ V}}{25.8 \text{ V}}\right) 100 = \mathbf{32.3\%}$

15. $V_{r(pp)} = (0.01)(18 \text{ V}) = 108 \text{ mV}$

$V_{r(pp)} = \left(\dfrac{1}{fR_L C}\right) V_{p(in)}$

$C = \left(\dfrac{1}{fR_L V_r}\right) V_{p(in)} = \left(\dfrac{1}{(120 \text{ Hz})(1.5 \text{ k}\Omega)(180 \text{ mV})}\right) 18 \text{ V} = \mathbf{556 \ \mu\text{F}}$

16. $V_{r(pp)} = \dfrac{V_{p(in)}}{fR_L C} = \dfrac{80 \text{ V}}{(120 \text{ Hz})(10 \text{ k}\Omega)(10 \ \mu\text{F})} = 6.67 \text{ V}$

$V_{DC} = \left(1 - \dfrac{1}{2fR_L C}\right) V_{p(in)} = \left(1 - \dfrac{1}{(240 \text{ Hz})(10 \text{ k}\Omega)(10 \ \mu\text{F})}\right) 80 \text{ V} = 46.7 \text{ V}$

$r = \dfrac{V_{r(pp)}}{V_{DC}} = \dfrac{6.67 \text{ V}}{46.7 \text{ V}} = \mathbf{0.143}$

17. $V_{p(sec)} = (1.414)(36 \text{ V}) = 50.9 \text{ V}$

$V_{r(rect)} = V_{p(sec)} - 1.4 \text{ V} = 50.9 \text{ V} - 1.4 \text{ V} = 49.5 \text{ V}$

Neglecting R_{surge}, $V_{r(pp)} = \left(\dfrac{1}{fR_L C}\right) V_{p(rect)} = \left[\dfrac{1}{(120 \text{ Hz})(3.3 \text{ k}\Omega)(100 \ \mu\text{F})}\right] 49.5 \text{ V} = \mathbf{1.25 \text{ V}}$

$V_{DC} = \left(1 - \dfrac{1}{2fR_L C}\right) V_{p(rect)} = V_{p(rect)} - \dfrac{V_{r(pp)}}{2} = 49.5 \text{ V} - 0.625 \text{ V} = \mathbf{48.9 \text{ V}}$

18. $V_{p(sec)} = 1.414(36 \text{ V}) = 50.9 \text{ V}$
See Figure 2-5.

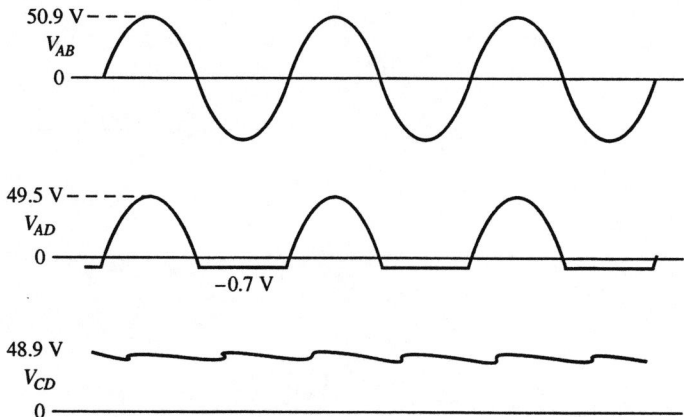

Figure 2-5

19. Load regulation $= \left(\dfrac{V_{NL} - V_{FL}}{V_{FL}}\right)100\% = \left(\dfrac{15.5 \text{ V} - 14.9 \text{ V}}{14.9 \text{ V}}\right)100\% = \mathbf{4\%}$

20. $V_{FL} = V_{NL} - (0.005)V_{NL} = 12 \text{ V} - (0.005)12 \text{ V} = \mathbf{11.94 \text{ V}}$

Section 2-4 Diode Limiting and Clamping Circuits

21. See Figure 2-6.

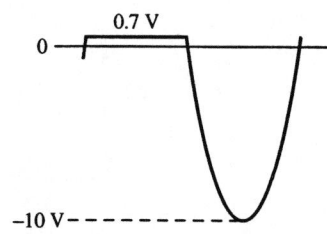

Figure 2-6

22. Apply Kirchhoff's law at the peak of the positive half cycle:

(b) $25 \text{ V} = V_R + V_R + 0.7 \text{ V}$
$2V_R = 24.3 \text{ V}$
$V_R = \dfrac{24.3 \text{ V}}{2} = 12.15 \text{ V}$
$V_{out} = V_R + 0.7 \text{ V} = 12.15 \text{ V} + 0.7 \text{ V} = 12.85 \text{ V}$
See Figure 2-7(a).

(c) $V_R = \dfrac{11.3 \text{ V}}{2} = 5.65 \text{ V}$
$V_{out} = V_R + 0.7 \text{ V} = 5.65 \text{ V} + 0.7 \text{ V} = 6.35 \text{ V}$
See Figure 2-7(b).

(d) $V_R = \dfrac{4.3 \text{ V}}{2} = 2.15 \text{ V}$

$V_{out} = V_R + 0.7 \text{ V} = 2.15 \text{ V} + 0.7 \text{ V} = 2.85 \text{ V}$

See Figure 2-7(c).

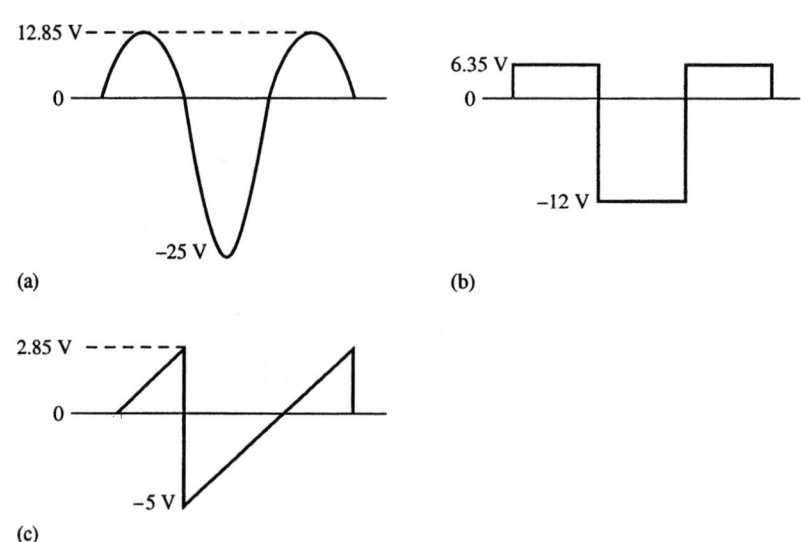

Figure 2-6

23. See Figure 2-8.

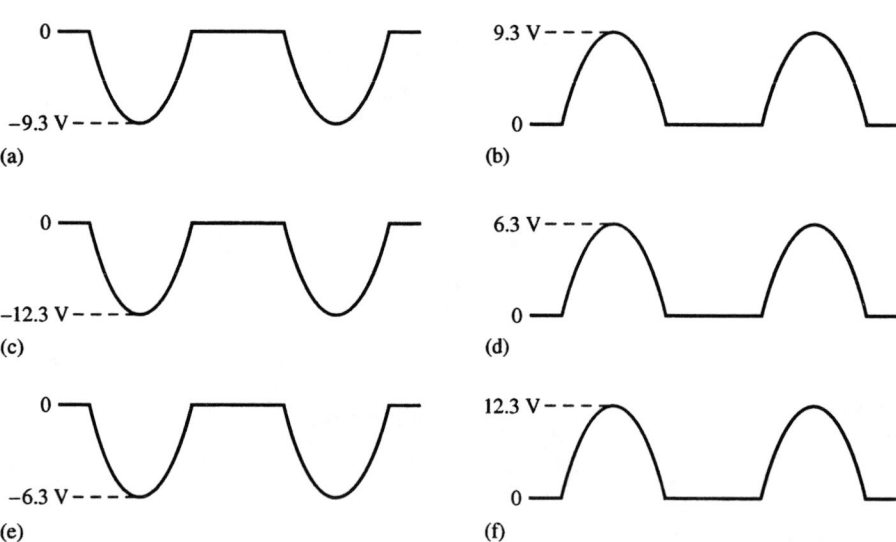

Figure 2-8

24.   See Figure 2-9.

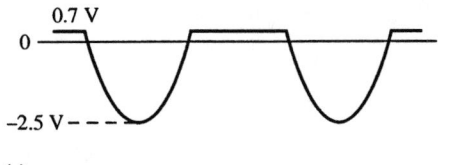

(a)

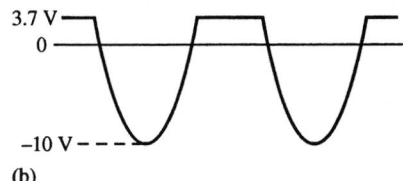

(b)

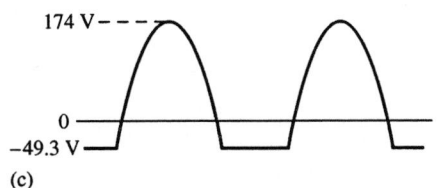

(c)

Figure 2-9

25.   See Figure 2-10.

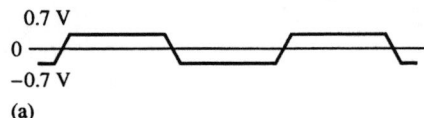

(a)

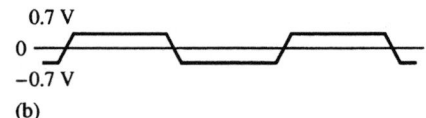

(b)

Figure 2-10

26.   See Figure 2-11.

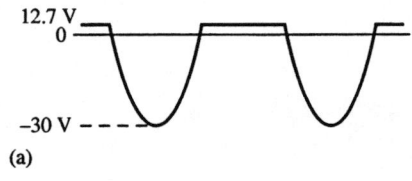

(a)

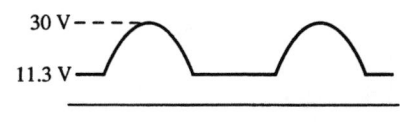

(b)

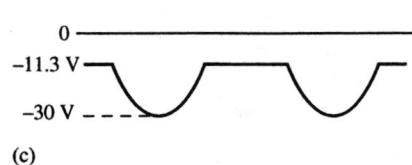

(c)

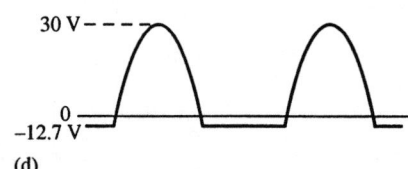

(d)

Figure 2-11

27.   (a) A sine wave with a positive peak at 0.7 V, a negative peak at –7.3 V, and a dc value of –3.3 V.
         (b) A sine wave with a positive peak at 29.3 V, a negative peak at –0.7 V, and a dc value of +14.3 V.
         (c) A square wave varying from +0.7 V to –15.3 V with a dc value of –7.3 V.
         (d) A square wave varying from +1.3 V to –0.7 V with a dc value of +0.3 V.

28.   (a) A sine wave varying from –0.7 V to +7.3 V with a dc value of +3.3 V.
         (b) A sine wave varying from –29.3 V to +7.3 V with a dc value of +14.3 V.
         (c) A square wave varying from –0.7 V to +15.3 V with a dc value of +7.3 V.
         (d) A square wave varying from –1.3 V to +0.7 V with a dc value of –0.3 V.

Chapter 2

Section 2-5 Voltage Multipliers

29. $V_{OUT} = 2V_{p(in)} = 2(1.414)(20\text{ V}) = \textbf{56.6 V}$
See Figure 2-12.

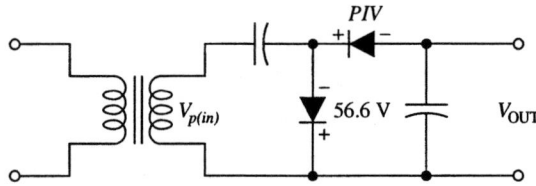

Figure 2-12

30. $V_{OUT(trip)} = 3V_{p(in)} = 3(1.414)(20\text{ V}) = \textbf{84.8 V}$
$V_{OUT(quad)} = 4V_{p(in)} = 4(1.414)(20\text{ V}) = \textbf{113 V}$
See Figure 2-13.

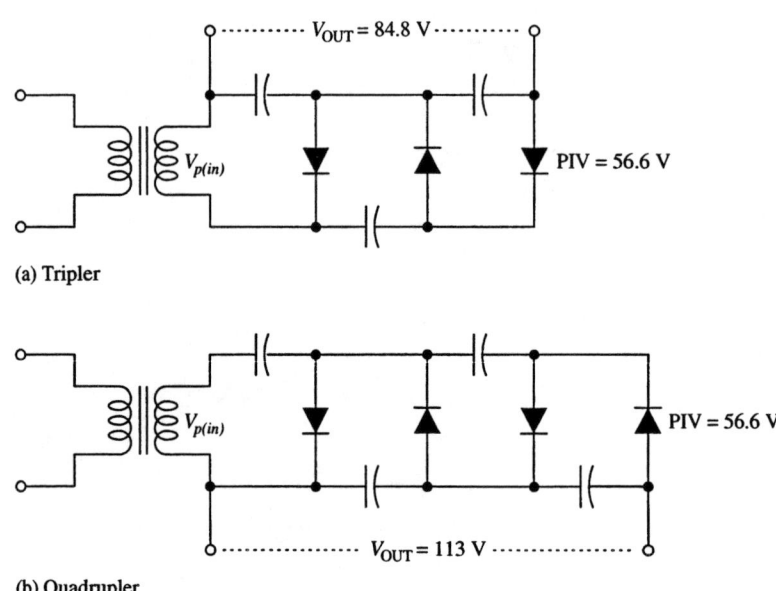

(a) Tripler

(b) Quadrupler

Figure 2-13

Section 2-6 The Diode Data Sheet

31. The PIV is specified as the peak repetitive reverse voltage = **50 V**.

32. The PIV is specified as the peak repetitive reverse voltage = **400 V**.

33. Use the specified $I_{FSM} = 800$ A.

$$R_{surge(min)} = \frac{50\text{ V}}{800\text{ A}} = \textbf{6.25 m}\Omega$$

Section 2-7 Troubleshooting

34. If a bridge rectifier diode opens, the output becomes a half-wave voltage resulting in an increased ripple at 60 Hz.

35. $$V_{avg} = \frac{2V_p}{\pi} = \frac{2(115 \text{ V})(1.414)}{\pi} \cong 104 \text{ V}$$

The output of the bridge is correct. However, the 0 V output from the filter indicates that the **surge resistor is open** or that the **capacitor is shorted**.

36. (a) Correct
(b) Incorrect. Open diode.
(c) Correct
(d) Incorrect. Open diode.

37. $V_{sec} = \dfrac{115 \text{ V}}{5} = 23 \text{ V rms}$

$V_{p(sec)} = 1.414(23 \text{ V}) = 32.5 \text{ V}$
The peak voltage for each half of the secondary is

$\dfrac{V_{p(sec)}}{2} = \dfrac{32.5 \text{ V}}{2} = 16.3 \text{ V}$

The peak inverse voltage for each diode is PIV = 2(16.3 V) + 0.7 V = 33.2 V
The peak current through each diode is

$$I_p = \frac{\dfrac{V_{p(sec)}}{2} - 0.7 \text{ V}}{R_L} = \frac{16.3 \text{ V} - 0.7 \text{ V}}{330 \ \Omega} = 47.3 \text{ mA}$$

The diode ratings exceed the actual PIV and peak current.
The circuit should not fail.

System Application Problems

38. (a) No voltage between TP1 and TP2:
Possible causes: fuse blown or power cord not plugged in.
Corrective action: check fuse and power plug. Replace fuse or insert plug.

(b) No voltage between TP3 and TP4, 110 V from TP1 to TP2:
Possible causes: open primary or shorted secondary.
Corrective action: check windings with ohmmeter. Replace transformer.

(c) 50 V between TP3 and TP4, input voltage correct:
Possible causes: partially shorted primary or wrong turns ratio.
Corrective action: check primary winding and transformer rating. Replace transformer.

(d) 25 V between TP3 and TP4, input voltage correct:
Possible causes: partially shorted secondary or wrong turns ratio.
Corrective action: check secondary winding and transformer rating. Replace transformer.

(e) Full-wave voltage with peak of 50 V from TP7 to ground:
Possible cause: Filter capacitor open.
Corrective action: check capacitor with ohmmeter. Replace capacitor.

(f) Excessive 120 Hz ripple at TP7:
Possible causes: leaky filter capacitor or excessive loading.
Corrective action: check capacitor and load. Replace capacitor or correct load condition.

(g) 60 Hz ripple at TP7:
Possible cause: open diode in bridge.
Corrective action: check diodes with ohmmeter and replace defective one.

(h) No voltage at TP7:
Possible causes: open surge resistor, blown fuse, open winding, shorted C.
Corrective action: check all and replace defective component.

39. Something must be causing a diode to open. Check all the diodes for opens this time. You will most likely find one. The PIV or the maximum surge current must have been exceeded. Excessive PIV could be caused by some shorted primary windings which would produce an excessive secondary voltage. If caused by excessive surge current, a small limiting resistor will have to be placed in series with C_1.

40. If the top diode in textbook Figure 2-87 were reversed, two forward-biased diodes would be placed in series across the secondary during the negative half-cycle which, most likely, would blow the diodes open and result in no voltage at TP8.

Advanced Problems

41.
$$V_r = \left(\frac{1}{fR_LC}\right)V_{p(in)}$$

$$C = \left(\frac{1}{fR_LV_r}\right)V_{p(in)} = \left(\frac{1}{(120\,\text{Hz})(3.3\,\text{k}\Omega)(0.5\,\text{V})}\right)35\,\text{V} = \mathbf{177}\ \mu\mathbf{F}$$

42.

$$V_{DC} = \left(1 - \frac{1}{2fR_LC}\right)V_{p(in)}$$

$$\frac{V_{DC}}{V_{p(in)}} = \left(1 - \frac{1}{2fR_LC}\right)$$

$$\frac{1}{2fR_LC} = 1 - \frac{V_{DC}}{V_{p(in)}}$$

$$\frac{1}{2fR_L\left(1 - \frac{V_{DC}}{V_{p(in)}}\right)} = C$$

$$C = \frac{1}{(240\,\text{Hz})(1.0\,\text{k}\Omega)(1 - 0.933)} = \frac{1}{(240\,\text{Hz})(1.0\,\text{k}\Omega)(0.067)} = 62.2\,\mu\text{F}$$

Then

$$V_r = \left(\frac{1}{fR_LC}\right)V_{p(in)} = \left(\frac{1}{(120\,\text{Hz})(1.0\,\text{k}\Omega)(62.2\,\mu\text{F})}\right)15\,\text{V} = \mathbf{2\,V}$$

43.   The capacitor input voltage is
$$V_{p(in)} = (1.414)(24\,\text{V}) - 1.4\,\text{V} = 32.5\,\text{V}$$

$$R_{surge} = \frac{V_{p(in)}}{I_{surge}} = \frac{32.5\,\text{V}}{50\,\text{A}} = \mathbf{651\,m\Omega}$$

The nearest standard value is 680 mΩ.

44.   See Figure 2-14.
The voltage at point A with respect to ground is
$$V_A = 1.414(9\,\text{V}) = 12.7\,\text{V}$$
Therefore,
$$V_B = 12.7\,\text{V} - 0.7\,\text{V} = 12\,\text{V}$$
$$V_r = 0.05V_B = 0.05(12\,\text{V}) = 0.6\,\text{V peak to peak}$$
$$C = \left(\frac{1}{fR_LV_r}\right)V_B = \left(\frac{1}{(120\,\text{Hz})(680\,\Omega)(0.6\,\text{V})}\right)12\,\text{V} = 245\,\mu\text{F}$$
The nearest standard value is 270 μF.
Let $R_{surge} = 1.0\,\Omega$.

$$I_{surge(max)} = \frac{12\,\text{V}}{1.0\,\Omega} = 12\,\text{A}$$

$$I_O = \frac{12\,\text{V}}{680\,\Omega} = \mathbf{17.6\,mA}$$
$$PIV = 2V_{p(out)} + 0.7\,\text{V} = \mathbf{24.7\,V}$$

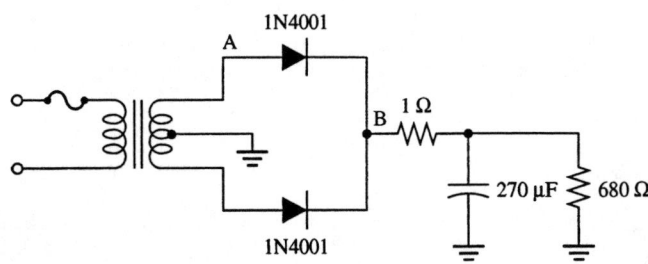

Figure 2-14

15

Chapter 2

45. See Figure 2-15.

$I_{L(max)} = 100$ mA

$$R_L = \frac{9\text{ V}}{100\text{ mA}} = 90\ \Omega$$

$V_r = 1.414(0.25\text{ V}) = 0.354\text{ V}$

$V_r = 2(0.35\text{ V}) = 0.71\text{ V}$ peak to peak

$$V_r = \left(\frac{1}{(120\text{ Hz})(90\,\Omega)C}\right)9\text{ V}$$

$$C = \frac{9\text{ V}}{(120\text{ Hz})(90\,\Omega)(0.71\text{ V})} = 1174\ \mu\text{F}$$

Use $C = 1200\ \mu$F.

Each half of the supply uses identical components. 1N4001 diodes are feasible since the average current is $(0.318)(100\text{ mA}) = 31.8$ mA.

$R_{surge} = 1.0\ \Omega$ will limit the surge current to an acceptable value.

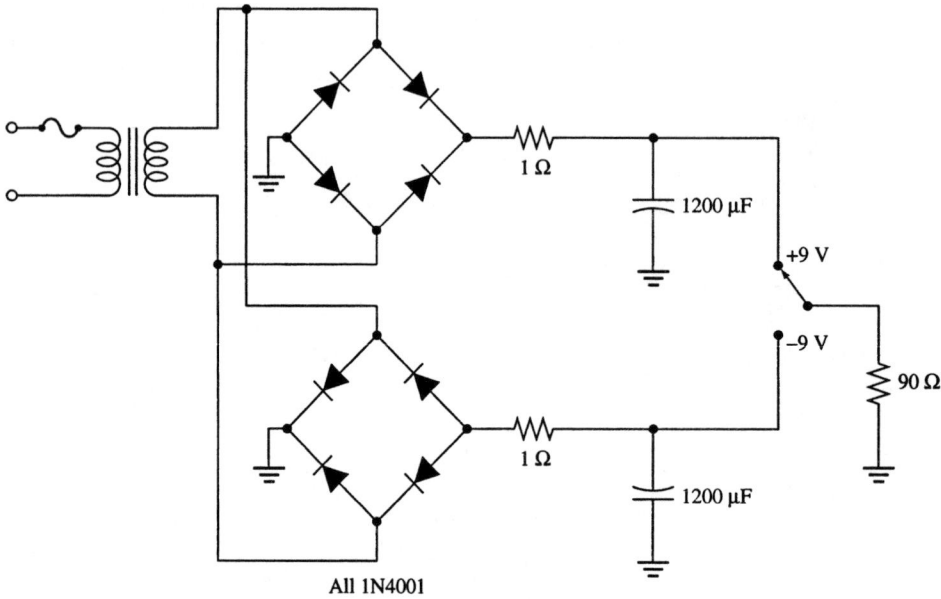

Figure 2-15

46. Both positive and negative limiting of a sinusoidal voltage is not achievable with a single dc source.

47. $V_{C1} = (1.414)(110\text{ V}) - 0.7\text{ V} = \mathbf{155\text{ V}}$
$V_{C2} = 2(1.414)(110\text{ V}) - 2(0.7\text{ V}) = \mathbf{310\text{ V}}$

16

EWB/Multisim Troubleshooting Problems

The solutions showing instrument connections for Problems 48 through 56 are available in the Solutions folder for Chapter 2 on the CD-ROM provided with the textbook. The solutions may be accessed using the password *ED5FLOYD*. The faults in the circuit files may be accessed using the password *book* (all lowercase).

48. Diode shorted

49. Diode leaky

50. Diode open

51. Bottom diode open

52. Reduced transformer turns ratio

53. Open filter capacitor

54. Diode leaky

55. D_1 open

56. Load resistor open

Chapter 3
Special-Purpose Diodes

Section 3-1 Zener Diodes

1. See Figure 3-1.

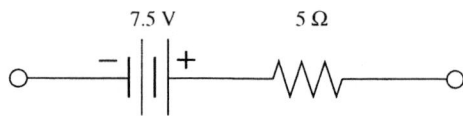

Figure 3-1

2. $I_{ZK} \cong \mathbf{3\ mA}$
$V_Z \cong \mathbf{-8.5\ V}$

3. $Z_Z = \dfrac{\Delta V_Z}{\Delta I_Z} = \dfrac{5.65\ \text{V} - 5.6\ \text{V}}{30\ \text{mA} - 20\ \text{mA}} = \dfrac{0.05\ \text{V}}{10\ \text{mA}} = \mathbf{5\ \Omega}$

4. $\Delta I_Z = 50\ \text{mA} - 25\ \text{mA} = 25\ \text{mA}$
$\Delta V_Z = \Delta I_Z Z_Z = (+25\ \text{mA})(15\ \Omega) = +0.375\ \text{V}$
$V_Z = V_{ZT} + \Delta V_Z = 4.7\ \text{V} + 0.375\ \text{V} = \mathbf{5.08\ V}$

5. $\Delta T = 70°C - 25°C = 45°C$
$V_Z = 6.8\ \text{V} + \dfrac{(6.8\ \text{V})(0.0004/°C)}{45°C} = 6.8\ \text{V} + 0.12\ \text{V} = \mathbf{6.92\ V}$

Section 3-2 Zener Diode Applications

6. $V_{\text{IN(min)}} = V_Z + I_{ZK}R = 14\ \text{V} + (1.5\ \text{mA})(560\ \Omega) = \mathbf{14.8\ V}$

7. $\Delta V_Z = (I_{ZT} - I_{ZK})Z_Z = (28.5\ \text{mA})(20\ \Omega) = 0.57\ \text{V}$
$V_{\text{OUT}} = V_{ZT} - \Delta V_Z = 14\ \text{V} - 0.57\ \text{V} = 13.43\ \text{V}$
$V_{\text{IN(min)}} = I_{ZK}R + V_{\text{OUT}} = (1.5\ \text{mA})(560\ \Omega) + 13.43\ \text{V} = \mathbf{14.3\ V}$

8. $\Delta V_Z = I_Z Z_Z = (40\ \text{mA} - 30\ \text{mA})(30\ \Omega) = 0.3\ \text{V}$
$V_Z = 12\ \text{V} + \Delta V_Z = 12\ \text{V} + 0.3\ \text{V} = 12.3\ \text{V}$
$R = \dfrac{V_{\text{IN}} - V_Z}{40\ \text{mA}} = \dfrac{18\ \text{V} - 12.3\ \text{V}}{40\ \text{mA}} = \mathbf{143\ \Omega}$

9. $V_Z \cong 12\ \text{V} + 0.3\ \text{V} = 12.3\ \text{V}$
See Figure 3-2.

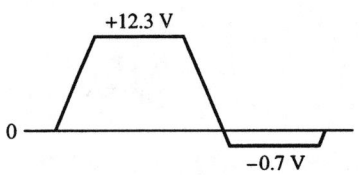

Figure 3-2

10. $V_{Z(\text{min})} = V_Z - \Delta I_Z Z_Z = 5.1\ \text{V} - (49\ \text{mA} - 1\ \text{mA})(7\ \Omega)$
$\qquad = 5.1\ \text{V} - (48\ \text{mA})(7\ \Omega) = 5.1\ \text{V} - 0.336 = 4.76\ \text{V}$
$V_R = 8\ \text{V} - 4.76\ \text{V} = 3.24\ \text{V}$
$I_T = \dfrac{V_R}{R} = \dfrac{3.24\ \text{V}}{22\ \Omega} = 147\ \text{mA}$
$I_{L(\text{max})} = 147\ \text{mA} - 1\ \text{mA} = \textbf{146 mA}$
$V_{Z(\text{max})} = 5.1\ \text{V} + (70\ \text{mA} - 49\ \text{mA})(7\ \Omega) = 5.1\ \text{V} + 0.34\ \text{V} = 5.44\ \text{V}$
$V_R = 8\ \text{V} - 5.44\ \text{V} = 2.56\ \text{V}$
$I_T = \dfrac{2.56\ \text{V}}{22\ \Omega} = 116\ \text{mA}$
$I_{L(\text{min})} = 116\ \text{mA} - 70\ \text{mA} = \textbf{46 mA}$

11. % Load regulation $= \dfrac{V_{Z(\text{max})} - V_{Z(\text{min})}}{V_{Z(\text{min})}} \times 100\% = \dfrac{5.44\ \text{V} - 4.76\ \text{V}}{4.76\ \text{V}} \times 100\% = \textbf{14.3\%}$

12. With no load and $V_{\text{IN}} = 6\ \text{V}$:
$I_Z \cong \dfrac{V_{\text{IN}} - V_Z}{R + Z_Z} = \dfrac{6\ \text{V} - 5.1\ \text{V}}{29\ \Omega} = 31\ \text{mA}$
$V_{\text{OUT}} = V_Z - \Delta I_Z Z_Z = 5.1\ \text{V} - (35\ \text{mA} - 31\ \text{mA})(7\ \Omega) = 5.1\ \text{V} - 0.028\ \text{V} = 5.07\ \text{V}$
With no load and $V_{\text{IN}} = 12\ \text{V}$:
$I_Z \cong \dfrac{V_{\text{IN}} - V_Z}{R + Z_Z} = \dfrac{12\ \text{V} - 5.1\ \text{V}}{29\ \Omega} = 238\ \text{mA}$
$V_{\text{OUT}} = V_Z + \Delta I_Z Z_Z = 5.1\ \text{V} + (238\ \text{mA} - 35\ \text{mA})(7\ \Omega) = 5.1\ \text{V} + 1.42\ \text{V} = 6.52\ \text{V}$
% Line regulation $= \dfrac{\Delta V_{\text{OUT}}}{\Delta V_{\text{IN}}} \times 100\% = \dfrac{6.52\ \text{V} - 5.07\ \text{V}}{12\ \text{V} - 6\ \text{V}} \times 100\% = \textbf{24.2\%}$

13. % Load regulation $= \dfrac{V_{\text{NL}} - V_{\text{FL}}}{V_{\text{FL}}} \times 100\% = \dfrac{8.23\ \text{V} - 7.98\ \text{V}}{7.98\ \text{V}} \times 100\% = \textbf{3.13\%}$

14. % Line regulation $= \dfrac{\Delta V_{\text{OUT}}}{\Delta V_{\text{IN}}} \times 100\% = \dfrac{0.2\ \text{V}}{10\ \text{V} - 5\ \text{V}} \times 100\% = \textbf{4\%}$

15. % Load regulation $= \dfrac{V_{\text{NL}} - V_{\text{FL}}}{V_{\text{FL}}} \times 100\% = \dfrac{3.6\ \text{V} - 3.4\ \text{V}}{3.4\ \text{V}} \times 100\% = \textbf{5.88\%}$

Chapter 3

Section 3-3 Varactor Diodes

16. At 5 V, $C = 20$ pF
    At 20 V, $C = 10$ pF
    $\Delta C = 20$ pF $- 10$ pF $= \textbf{10 pF}$ (decrease)

17. From the graph, $V_R = \textbf{3 V}$ @ 25 pF

18. $f_r = \dfrac{1}{\sqrt{2\pi L C_T}}$

    $C_T = \dfrac{1}{4\pi^2 L f_r^2} = \dfrac{1}{4\pi^2 (2\text{ mH})(1\text{ MHz})^2} = 12.7$ pF

    Since they are in series, each varactor must have a capacitance of $2C_T = \textbf{25.4 pF}$

19. Each varactor has a capacitance of 25.4 pF. Therefore, from the graph, $V_R \cong \textbf{2.5 V}$.

Section 3-4 Optical Diodes

20. Assuming $V_F = 1.2$ V,
    $I_F = \dfrac{24\text{ V} - 1.2\text{ V}}{680\ \Omega} = 33.5$ mA
    From the graph, the radiant power is approximately **80 mW**.

21. See Figure 3-3.
    $R = \dfrac{5\text{ V} - 0.7\text{ V}}{30\text{ mA}} = 143\ \Omega$
    Use nearest standard 1% value of 147 Ω or 5% value of 150 Ω.

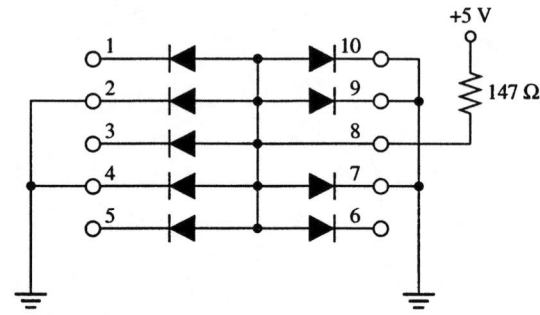

Figure 3-3

22. $I_R = \dfrac{10\text{ V}}{200\text{ k}\Omega} = \textbf{50 } \mu\textbf{A}$

23. (a) $R = \dfrac{V_S}{I} = \dfrac{3\,V}{100\,\mu A} = \textbf{30 k}\boldsymbol{\Omega}$

(b) $R = \dfrac{V_S}{I} = \dfrac{3\,V}{350\,\mu A} = \textbf{8.57 k}\boldsymbol{\Omega}$

(c) $R = \dfrac{V_S}{I} = \dfrac{3\,V}{510\,\mu A} = \textbf{5.88 k}\boldsymbol{\Omega}$

24. The microammeter reading will increase.

Section 3-5 Other Types of Diodes

25. $R = \dfrac{\Delta V}{\Delta I} = \dfrac{125\,mV - 200\,mV}{0.25\,mA - 0.15\,mA} = \dfrac{-75\,mV}{0.10\,mA} = \boldsymbol{-750\,\Omega}$

26. Tunnel diodes are used in oscillators.

27. The reflective ends cause the light to bounce back and forth, thus increasing the intensity of the light. The partially reflective end allows a portion of the reflected light to be emitted.

Section 3-6 Troubleshooting

28. (a) All voltages are correct.
(b) V_3 should be 12 V. Zener is open.
(c) V_1 should be 110 V. Fuse is open.
(d) Capacitor C_1 is open.
(e) Transformer winding open.

29. (a) With D_5 open, $V_{OUT} \cong \textbf{30 V}$
(b) With R open, $V_{OUT} = \textbf{0 V}$
(c) With C leaky, V_{OUT} has excessive **120 Hz ripple limited to 12 V**
(d) With C open, V_{OUT} is **full wave rectified voltage limited to 12 V**
(e) With D_3 open, V_{OUT} has **60 Hz ripple limited to 12 V**
(f) With D_2 open, V_{OUT} has **60 Hz ripple limited to 12 V**
(g) With T open, $V_{OUT} = \textbf{0 V}$
(h) With F open, $V_{OUT} = \textbf{0 V}$

30. The voltage reading is too low. Inspection of the circuit board reveals that the second diode from the top is connected backwards.

31. The input voltage is correct but there is 0 V at the rectifier output. Possible causes are open fuse, open transformer, or open resistor. Cannot be isolated further with given measurements.

32. The LED (D_6) will not light when any of the following faults occur: D_6 open, R_1 open, R_2 open, fuse blown, transformer winding open, D_5 shorted, or C_1 shorted.

Chapter 3

33. The photodiode D_1 will not respond when there is:
No dc voltage
R_1 open
D_1 open
A short in the threshold, counter, and display circuits.

Step 1: Check for 5.1 V dc.
Step 2: Check for a dc voltage at the D_1 cathode.

Data Sheet Problems

34. From the data sheet of textbook Figure 3-7:
  (a) @ 25°C: $P_{D(max)} =$ **1.0 W** for a 1N4738
  (b) For a 1N4751:
    @ 70°C; $P_{D(max)} = 1.0$ W $- (6.67$ mW/°C$)(20$°C$) = 1.0$ W $- 133$ mW $=$ **867 mW**
    @ 100°C; $P_{D(max)} = 1.0$ W $- (6.67$ mW/°C$)(50$°C$) = 1.0$ W $- 333$ mW $=$ **667 mW**
  (c) $I_{ZK} =$ **0.5 mA** for a 1N4738
  (d) @ 25°C: $I_{ZM} = 1$ W/27 V $=$ **37.0 mA** for a 1N4750
  (e) $\Delta Z_Z = 700$ Ω $- 7.0$ Ω $=$ **693 Ω** for a 1N4740
  (f) @ 25°C: $V_{Z(max)} = 6.8$ V $+ (4$ mV/°C$)(25$°C$) = 6.8$ V $+ 100$ mV $=$ **6.9 V** for a 1N4736
  (g) @ 75°C: $V_{Z(min)} = 20$ V $+ (15$ mV/°C$)(50$°C$) = 20$ V $+ 750$ mV $=$ **20.8 V** for a 1N4747

35. From the data sheet of textbook Figure 3-22:
  (a) $V_{R(max)} =$ **60 V** for a 1N5139
  (b) For a 1N5141:
    @ 60°C; $P_{D(max)} = 400$ mW $- (2.67$ mW/°C$)(35$°C$) = 400$ mW $- 93.5$ mW $=$ **307 mW**
  (c) For a 1N5148:
    @ 80°C; $P_{D(max)} = 2.0$ W $- (13.3$ mW/°C$)(55$°C$) = 2.0$ W $- 732$ mW $=$ **1.27 W**
  (d) $C_D \cong$ **21 pF** for a 1N5148
  (e) For maximum figure of merit a **1N5139** is best.
  (f) For $V_R = 60$ V, $C_D = 13.5$ pF/2.8 $=$ **4.82 pF** for a 1N5142.

36. From the data sheet of textbook 3-31:
  (a) 9 V cannot be applied in reverse across an MLED81.
  (b) When 5.1 V is used to forward-bias the MLED81 for $I_F = 100$ mA, $V_F \cong 1.42$ V
$$R = \frac{5.1\,\text{V} - 1.42\,\text{V}}{100\,\text{mA}} = \frac{3.68\,\text{V}}{100\,\text{mA}} = \mathbf{36.8\ \Omega}$$
  (c) At 45°C maximum power dissipation is
    100 mW $- (2.2$ mW/°C$)(20$°C$) = 100$ mW $- 44$ mW $= 56$ mW
    If $V_F = 1.5$ V and $I_F = 50$ mA, $P_D = 75$ mW. The power rating is **exceeded.**
  (d) For $I_F = 30$ mA, maximum axial radiant intensity is approximately **4.3 mW/sr.**
  (e) For $I_F = 20$ mA and $\theta = 20$°, radiant intensity is 90% or maximum or $(0.9)(20$ mW/sr$)$
    $=$ **18 mW/sr**

37. From the data sheet of textbook Figure 3-36:
  (a) With no indicent light and a 10 kΩ series resistor, the voltage across MRD821 is
    approximately equal to the **reverse bias source voltage**.
  (b) Reverse current is greatest at about **940 nm**.
  (c) At $T_A \cong 60$°C, dark current is about **40 nA**.

(d) Sensitivity is maximum for $\lambda = \mathbf{940\ nm}$.

(e) At 900 nm the sensitivity is about 80% of maximum $(0.8)(50\ \mu A/mW/cm^2)$
   $= \mathbf{40\ \mu A/mW/cm^2}$

(f) For $\lambda = 900$ nm, $\theta = 40°$ and an irradiance of 3 mW/cm^2
   $I_D = (0.8)(0.87)(50\ \mu A/mW/cm^2)(3\ mW/cm^2) = \mathbf{104\ \mu A}$

Advanced Problems

38. See Figure 3-4.

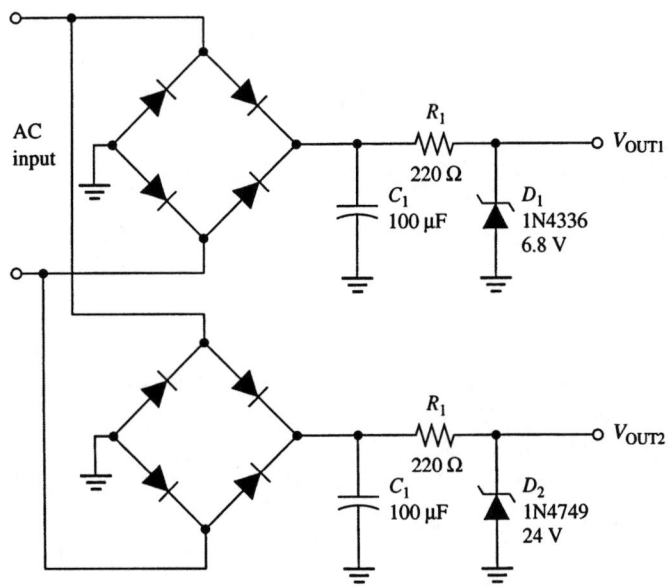

Figure 3-4

39. $V_{OUT(1)} \cong \mathbf{6.8\ V}$, $V_{OUT(2)} \cong \mathbf{24\ V}$

40. For a 1.0 kΩ load on each output:

$I_{OUT(1)} \cong \dfrac{6.8\ V}{1.0\ k\Omega} = 6.8\ mA$

$I_{OUT(2)} \cong \dfrac{24\ V}{1.0\ k\Omega} = 24\ mA$

$I_{Z1} \cong 37$ mA for V_{ZT}

$I_{Z2} \cong 10.5$ mA for V_{ZT}

$I_T = 6.8\ mA + 24\ mA + 37\ mA + 10.5\ mA = 78.3\ mA$

The fuse rating should be 100 mA or **1/8 A**.

41. See Figure 3-5.
Use a 1N4738 zener.
$I_T = 35\ mA + 31\ mA = 66\ mA$

$R = \dfrac{24\ V - 8.2\ V}{66\ mA} = 239\ \Omega$

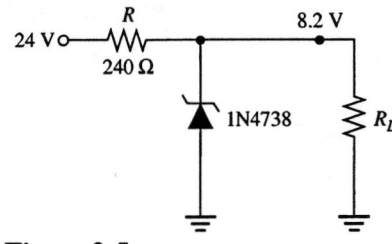

Figure 3-5

Chapter 3

42. Use a 1N5148 varactor diode.

From the graph in textbook Figure 3-22, the maximum and minimum varactor capacitances are roughly $C_{max} \cong 80$ pF @ 1 V and $C_{min} \cong 12$ pF @ 60 V

Use these capacitance values to calculate an inductance range for 350 kHz and 850 kHz:

$$L_{max} = \left(\frac{1}{2\pi f_{min} \sqrt{C_{min}}} \right)^2 = 2.92 \text{ mH}$$

$$L_{min} = \left(\frac{1}{2\pi f_{max} \sqrt{C_{max}}} \right)^2 = 2.58 \text{ mH}$$

Choose $L = 2.7$ mH and calculate required C_{min} and C_{max}:

$$C_{min} = \left(\frac{1}{2\pi f_{max} \sqrt{L}} \right)^2 = 13 \text{ pF}$$

$$C_{max} = \left(\frac{1}{2\pi f_{min} \sqrt{L}} \right)^2 = 77 \text{ pF}$$

From the graph in Figure 3-22, the reverse voltages for these capacitance values are approximately:

$V_{R(max)} \cong 50$ V for 13 pF
$V_{R(min)} \cong 1.2$ V for 77 pF
Let $V_{BIAS} = 100$ V.

$$V_{R(min)} = \left(\frac{R_3}{R_2 + R_3 + R_4 + R_5} \right) V_{BIAS}$$

$$V_{R(max)} = \left(\frac{R_3 + R_4}{R_2 + R_3 + R_4 + R_5} \right) V_{BIAS}$$

Let $R_2 + R_3 + R_4 + R_5 = 100$ kΩ.

$$R_3 = \frac{V_{R(min)}(R_2 + R_3 + R_4 + R_5)}{V_{BIAS}} = \frac{1.2 \text{ V}(100 \text{ k}\Omega)}{100 \text{ V}} = 1.2 \text{ k}\Omega$$

$$R_4 = \frac{V_{R(max)}(R_2 + R_3 + R_4 + R_5)}{V_{BIAS}} - R_3 = \frac{50 \text{ V}(100 \text{ k}\Omega)}{100 \text{ V}} - 1.2 \text{ k}\Omega = 49 \text{ k}\Omega$$

Use $R_4 = 50$ kΩ.
$R_2 + R_5 = 100$ kΩ $- 50.2$ kΩ $= 49.8$ kΩ
Let $R_5 = 1.2$ kΩ.
$R_2 = 49.8$ kΩ $- 1.2$ kΩ $= 48.6$ kΩ
Use $R_2 = 47$ kΩ.
All other component values are the same as in textbook Figure 3-24.

43. See Figure 3-6.

$$R = \frac{V_D}{I} = \frac{12\,\text{V} - 0.7\,\text{V}}{20\,\text{mA}} = 565\,\Omega$$

Use standard value of 560 Ω.

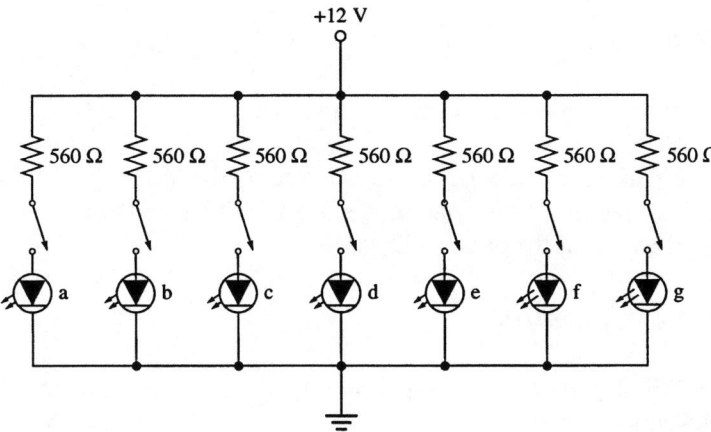

Figure 3-6

44. See Figure 3-7.

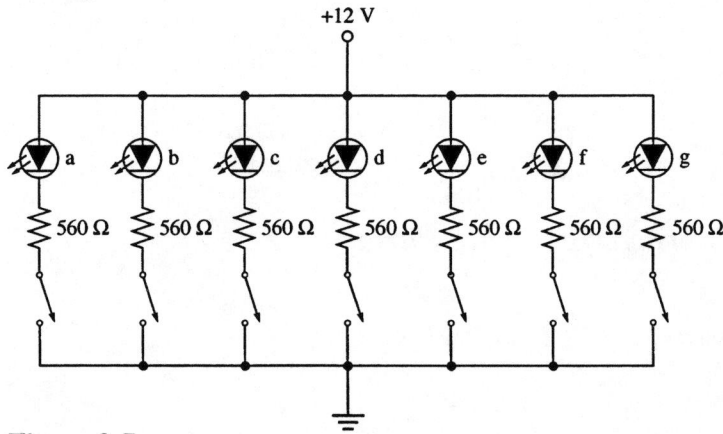

Figure 3-7

EWB/Multisim Troubleshooting Problems

The solutions showing instrument connections for Problems 45 through 48 are available in the Solutions folder for Chapter 3 on the CD-ROM provided with the textbook. The solutions may be accessed using the password *ED5FLOYD*. The faults in the circuit files may be accessed using the password *book* (all lowercase).

45. Zener diode open

46. Capacitor open

47. Zener diode shorted

48. Resistor open

Chapter 4
Bipolar Junction Transistors (BJTs)

Section 4-1 Transistor Structure

1. Majority carriers in the base region of an *npn* transistor are **holes**.

2. Because of the narrow base region, the minority carriers invading the base region find a limited number of partners for recombination and, therefore, move across the junction into the collector region rather than out of the base lead.

Section 4-2 Basic Transistor Operation

3. The base is narrow and lightly doped so that a small recombination (base) current is generated compared to the collector current.

4. $I_B = 0.02I_E = 0.02(30 \text{ mA}) = 0.6 \text{ mA}$
    $I_C = I_E - I_B = 30 \text{ mA} - 0.6 \text{ mA} = \textbf{29.4 mA}$

5. The base must be negative with respect to the collector and positive with respect to the emitter.

6. $I_C = I_E - I_B = 5.34 \text{ mA} - 475 \ \mu\text{A} = \textbf{4.87 mA}$

Section 4-3 Transistor Characteristics and Parameters

7. $\alpha_{DC} = \dfrac{I_C}{I_E} = \dfrac{8.23 \text{ mA}}{8.69 \text{ mA}} = \textbf{0.947}$

8. $\beta_{DC} = \dfrac{I_C}{I_B} = \dfrac{25 \text{ mA}}{200 \ \mu\text{A}} = \textbf{125}$

9. $I_B = I_E - I_C = 20.5 \text{ mA} - 20.3 \text{ mA} = 0.2 \text{ mA} = 200 \ \mu\text{A}$
    $\beta_{DC} = \dfrac{I_G}{I_B} = \dfrac{20.5 \text{ mA}}{200 \ \mu\text{A}} = \textbf{102.5}$

10. $I_E = I_C + I_B = 5.35 \text{ mA} + 50 \ \mu\text{A} = 5.40 \text{ mA}$
    $\alpha_{DC} = \dfrac{I_C}{I_E} = \dfrac{5.35 \text{ mA}}{5.40 \text{ mA}} = \textbf{0.99}$

11. $I_C = \alpha_{DC}I_E = 0.96(9.35 \text{ mA}) = \textbf{8.98 mA}$

12. $I_C = \dfrac{V_{R_C}}{R_C} = \dfrac{5\,\text{V}}{1.0\,\text{k}\Omega} = 5\,\text{mA}$

$\beta_{DC} = \dfrac{I_C}{I_B} = \dfrac{5\,\text{mA}}{50\,\mu\text{A}} = \mathbf{100}$

13. $\alpha_{DC} = \dfrac{\beta_{DC}}{\beta_{DC}+1} = \dfrac{100}{101} = \mathbf{0.99}$

14. $I_B = \dfrac{V_{BB}-V_{BE}}{R_B} = \dfrac{4\,\text{V}-0.7\,\text{V}}{4.7\,\text{k}\Omega} = \dfrac{3.3\,\text{V}}{4.7\,\text{k}\Omega} = \mathbf{702}\,\boldsymbol{\mu}\mathbf{A}$

$I_C = \dfrac{V_{CC}-V_{CE}}{R_C} = \dfrac{24\,\text{V}-8\,\text{V}}{470\,\Omega} = \mathbf{34}\,\mathbf{mA}$

$I_E = I_C + I_B = 34\,\text{mA} + 702\,\mu\text{A} = \mathbf{34.7}\,\mathbf{mA}$

$\beta_{DC} = \dfrac{I_C}{I_B} = \dfrac{34\,\text{mA}}{702\,\mu\text{A}} = \mathbf{48.4}$

15. (a) $V_{BE} = \mathbf{0.7}\,\mathbf{V}$

$\quad I_B = \dfrac{V_{BB}-V_{BE}}{R_B} = \dfrac{4.3\,\text{V}}{3.9\,\text{k}\Omega} = 1.1\,\text{mA}$

$\quad I_C = \beta_{DC}I_B = 50(1.1\,\text{mA}) = 55\,\text{mA}$

$\quad V_{CE} = V_{CC} - I_C R_C = 15\,\text{V} - (55\,\text{mA})(180\,\Omega) = \mathbf{5.10}\,\mathbf{V}$

$\quad V_{BC} = V_{BE} - V_{CE} = 0.7\,\text{V} - 5.10\,\text{V} = \mathbf{-4.40}\,\mathbf{V}$

(b) $V_{BE} = \mathbf{-0.7}\,\mathbf{V}$

$\quad I_B = \dfrac{V_{BB}-V_{BE}}{R_B} = \dfrac{-3\,\text{V}-(-0.7\,\text{V})}{27\,\text{k}\Omega} = \dfrac{-2.3\,\text{V}}{27\,\text{k}\Omega} = -85.2\,\mu\text{A}$

$\quad I_C = \beta_{DC}I_B = 125(-85.2\,\mu\text{A}) = -10.7\,\text{mA}$

$\quad V_{CE} = V_{CC} - I_C R_C = -8\,\text{V} - (-10.7\,\text{mA})(390\,\Omega) = \mathbf{-3.83}\,\mathbf{V}$

$\quad V_{BC} = V_{BE} - V_{CE} = 0.7\,\text{V} - (-3.83\,\text{V}) = \mathbf{3.13}\,\mathbf{V}$

16. (a) $I_{C(\text{sat})} = \dfrac{V_{CC}}{R_C} = \dfrac{15\,\text{V}}{180\,\Omega} = 83.3\,\text{mA}$

$\quad I_B = \dfrac{V_{BB}-V_{BE}}{R_B} = \dfrac{5\,\text{V}-0.7\,\text{V}}{3.9\,\text{k}\Omega} = 1.1\,\text{mA}$

$\quad I_C = \beta_{DC}I_B = 50(1.1\,\text{mA}) = 55\,\text{mA}$

$\quad I_C < I_{C(\text{sat})}$

$\quad$ Therefore, the transistor is **not saturated**.

(b) $I_{C(sat)} = \dfrac{V_{CC}}{R_C} = \dfrac{8\,V}{390\,\Omega} = 20.5\,mA$

$$I_B = \dfrac{V_{BB} - V_{BE}}{R_B} = \dfrac{3\,V - 0.7\,V}{27\,k\Omega} = 85.2\,\mu A$$

$I_C = \beta_{DC}I_B = 125(85.2\,\mu A) = 10.7\,mA$

$I_C < I_{C(sat)}$

Therefore, the transistor is **not saturated**.

17. $V_B = 2\,V$

$V_E = V_B - V_{BE} = 2\,V - 0.7\,V = 1.3\,V$

$I_E = \dfrac{V_E}{R_E} = \dfrac{1.3\,V}{1.0\,k\Omega} = \textbf{1.3 mA}$

$I_C = \alpha_{DC}I_E = (0.98)(1.3\,mA) = \textbf{1.27 mA}$

$\beta_{DC} = \dfrac{\alpha_{DC}}{1 - \alpha_{DC}} = \dfrac{0.98}{1 - 0.98} = 49$

$I_B = I_E - I_C = 1.3\,mA - 1.27\,mA = \textbf{30}\ \boldsymbol{\mu}\textbf{A}$

18. (a) $V_B = V_{BB} = \textbf{10 V}$

$V_C = V_{CC} = \textbf{20 V}$

$V_E = V_B - V_{BE} = 10\,V - 0.7\,V = \textbf{9.3 V}$

$V_{CE} = V_C - V_E = 20\,V - 9.7\,V = \textbf{10.7 V}$

$V_{BE} = \textbf{0.7 V}$

$V_{BC} = V_B - V_C = 10\,V - 20\,V = \textbf{--10 V}$

(b) $V_B = V_{BB} = \textbf{--4 V}$

$V_C = V_{CC} = \textbf{--12 V}$

$V_E = V_B - V_{BE} = -4\,V - (-0.7\,V) = \textbf{--3.3 V}$

$V_{CE} = V_C - V_E = -12\,V - (-3.3)\,V = \textbf{--8.7 V}$

$V_{BE} = \textbf{--0.7 V}$

$V_{BC} = V_B - V_C = -4\,V - (-12\,V) = \textbf{8 V}$

19. For $\beta_{DC} = 100$:

$I_E = \dfrac{V_B - V_{BE}}{R_E} = \dfrac{10\,V - 0.7\,V}{10\,k\Omega} = 930\,\mu A$

$\alpha_{DC} = \dfrac{\beta_{DC}}{1 + \beta_{DC}} = \dfrac{100}{101} = 0.990$

$I_C = \alpha_{DC}I_E = (0.990)(930\,\mu A) = 921\,\mu A$

For $\beta_{DC} = 150$:

$I_E = 930\,\mu A$

$\alpha_{DC} = \dfrac{\beta_{DC}}{1 + \beta_{DC}} = \dfrac{150}{151} = 0.993$

$I_C = \alpha_{DC}I_E = (0.993)(930\,\mu A) = 924\,\mu A$

$\Delta I_C = 924\,\mu A - 0.921\,\mu A = \textbf{3}\ \boldsymbol{\mu}\textbf{A}$

20. $P_{D(max)} = V_{CE}I_C$

$$V_{CE(max)} = \frac{P_{D(max)}}{I_C} = \frac{1.2\,\text{W}}{50\,\text{mA}} = \textbf{24 V}$$

21. $P_{D(max)} = 0.5\,\text{W} - (75°\text{C})(1\,\text{mW/°C}) = 0.5\,\text{W} - 75\,\text{mW} = \textbf{425 mW}$

Section 4-4 The Transistor as an Amplifier

22. $V_{out} = A_v V_{in} = 50(100\,\text{mV}) = \textbf{5 V}$

23. $A_v = \dfrac{V_{out}}{V_{in}} = \dfrac{10\,\text{V}}{300\,\text{mV}} = \textbf{33.3}$

24. $A_v = \dfrac{R_C}{r_e'} = \dfrac{560\,\Omega}{10\,\Omega} = 56$

$V_c = V_{out} = A_v V_{in} = 56(50\,\text{mV}) = \textbf{2.8 V}$

Section 4-5 The Transistor as a Switch

25. $I_{C(sat)} = \dfrac{V_{CC}}{R_C} = \dfrac{5\,\text{V}}{10\,\text{k}\Omega} = \textbf{500 } \boldsymbol{\mu}\textbf{A}$

$I_{B(min)} = \dfrac{I_{C(sat)}}{\beta_{DC}} = \dfrac{500\,\mu\text{A}}{150} = \textbf{3.33 } \boldsymbol{\mu}\textbf{A}$

$I_{B(min)} = \dfrac{V_{IN(min)} - 0.7\,\text{V}}{R_B}$

$R_B I_{B(min)} = V_{IN(min)} - 0.7\,\text{V}$

$V_{IN(min)} = R_B I_{B(min)} + 0.7\,\text{V} = (3.33\,\mu\text{A})(1.0\,\text{M}\Omega) + 0.7\,\text{V} = \textbf{4.03 V}$

26. $I_{C(sat)} = \dfrac{15\,\text{V}}{1.2\,\text{k}\Omega} = 12.5\,\text{mA}$

$I_{B(min)} = \dfrac{I_{C(sat)}}{\beta_{DC}} = \dfrac{12.5\,\text{mA}}{50} = 250\,\mu\text{A}$

$R_{B(min)} = \dfrac{V_{IN} - 0.7\,\text{V}}{I_{B(min)}} = \dfrac{4.3\,\text{V}}{250\,\mu\text{A}} = \textbf{17.2 k}\boldsymbol{\Omega}$

$V_{IN(cutoff)} = \textbf{0 V}$

Section 4-6 Transistor Packages and Terminal Identification

27. See Figure 4-1.

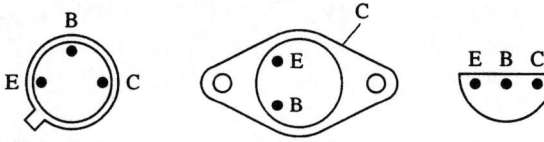

Figure 4-1

Chapter 4

28.   (a) Small-signal
(b) Power
(c) Power
(d) Small-signal
(e) RF

Section 4-7 Troubleshooting

29.   With the positive probe on the emitter and the negative probe on the base, the ohmmeter indicates an **open**, since this reverse-biases the base-emitter junction. With the positive probe on the base and the negative probe on the emitter, the ohmmeter indicates a **very low resistance**, since this forward-biases the base-collector junction.

30.   (a) Transistor's collector junction or terminal is open.
(b) Collector resistor is open.
(c) Operating properly.
(d) Transistor's base junction or terminal open (no base or collector current).

31.   (a) $I_B = \dfrac{5\,\text{V} - 0.7\,\text{V}}{68\,\text{k}\Omega} = 63.2\,\mu\text{A}$

$I_C = \dfrac{9\,\text{V} - 3.2\,\text{V}}{3.3\,\text{k}\Omega} = 1.76\,\text{mA}$

$\beta_{DC} = \dfrac{I_C}{I_B} = \dfrac{1.76\,\text{mA}}{63.2\,\mu\text{A}} = \mathbf{27.8}$

(b) $I_B = \dfrac{4.5\,\text{V} - 0.7\,\text{V}}{27\,\text{k}\Omega} = 141\,\mu\text{A}$

$I_C = \dfrac{24\,\text{V} - 16.8\,\text{V}}{470\,\Omega} = 15.3\,\text{mA}$

$\beta_{DC} = \dfrac{I_C}{I_B} = \dfrac{15.3\,\text{mA}}{141\,\mu\text{A}} = \mathbf{109}$

System Application Problems

32.   With the remote switches closed, Q_1 should be on and Q_2 should be off, keeping the relay contacts (pins 10 and 11) open. When a remote switch opens, Q_1 should turn off and Q_2 should turn on, energizing the relay and closing the contacts. If the Q_1 collector or base is open, such that Q_1 is off all the time, Q_2 will stay on all the time, so this is not the problem. Most likely, Q has failed so that it remains off all the time or R_3, or R_4, could be open. Also, the relay could be faulty.

33.   With the remote switches closed, Q_1 and Q_3 should be on and Q_2 and Q_4 should be off keeping the relay contacts (pins 10 and 11) open. When a remote switch opens, Q_1 (or Q_3) should turn off and Q_2 (or Q_4) should turn on, thus energizing the relay and closing the contacts (pins 10 and 11). If the Q_1 (or Q_3) collector or base is open, such that Q_1 (or Q_3) is off all the time, Q_2 (or Q_4) will stay on all the time. Most likely, either Q_2 (or Q_4) or its associated circuitry is faulty such that it remains on all the time. An internally open junction in Q_1 or Q_3 or an open resistor (R_1 or R_6) could cause this problem. Also, the relay may be faulty.

34.   The constant 0.1 V at pin 9 indicates that Q_6 is saturated. Most likely Q_5 has failed such that it always acts as an open switch keeping Q_6 saturated. First look for obvious problems such as a burned resistor (R_{11}) or a bad contact. Next check the Q_5 collector with pin 7 connected to pin 6. You should see approximately 0.1 V at the Q_5 collector. If Q_5 is open, you will see approximately 3.6 V at the collector.

Data Sheet Problems

35.   From the data sheet of textbook Figure 4-19:
(a) For a 2N3903, $V_{CEO(max)} = $ **40 V**
(b) For a 2N3904, $I_{C(max)} = $ **200 mA**
(c) For a 2N3903 @ 25°C, $P_{D(max)} = $ **625 mW**
(d) For a 2N3094 @ $T_C = $ 25°C, $P_{D(max)} = $ **1.5 W**
(e) For a 2N3903 with $I_C = $ 1 mA, $h_{FE(min)} = $ **35**

36.   For a 2N3904 with $T_A = $ 65°C:
$P_{D(max)} = 625$ mW $- (65$°C $- 25$°C$)(5.0$ mW/°C$)$
$= 625$ mW $- 40$°C$(5.0$ mW/°C$) = 625$ mW $- 200$ mW $= $ **425 mW**

37.   For a 2N3903 with $T_C = $ 45°C:
$P_{D(max)} = 1.5$ W $- (45$°C $- 25$°C$)(12$ mW/°C$)$
$= 1.5$ W $- 20$°C$(12$ mW/°C$) = 1.5$ W $- 240$ mW $= $ **1.26 W**

38.   For the circuits of textbook Figure 4-56:
(a) $I_B = \dfrac{3\,V - 0.7\,V}{330\,\Omega} = \dfrac{2.3\,V}{330\,\Omega} = 6.97$ mA
$h_{FE} = 15$
$I_C = 15(6.97$ mA$) = 105$ mA
$V_C = 30$ V $- (105$ mA$)(270\,\Omega) = 30$ V $- 28.2$ V $= 1.8$ V
$V_{CE} = 1.8$ V $- 0.7$ V $= 1.1$ V
$P_D = (1.1$ V$)(105$ mA$) = 112$ mW
At 50°C, $P_{D(max)} = 625$ mW $- (50$°C $- 25$°C$)(5.0$ mW/°C$) = 500$ mW
No parameter is exceeded.

(b) $V_{CEO} = 45$ V which **exceeds** $V_{CEO(max)}$.

39.   For the circuits of textbook Figure 4-57:
(a) $I_B = \dfrac{5\,V - 0.7\,V}{10\,k\Omega} = \dfrac{4.3\,V}{10\,k\Omega} = 4.30\ \mu A$
$h_{FE(max)} = 150$
$I_C = 150(4.30\ \mu A) = 64.5$ mA
$I_{C(sat)} = \dfrac{9\,V}{1.0\,k\Omega} = 9$ mA
The transistor is saturated.

(b) $I_B = \dfrac{3\,V - 0.7\,V}{100\,k\Omega} = \dfrac{2.3\,V}{100\,k\Omega} = 23\ \mu A$

$h_{FE(max)} = 300$

$I_C = 300(23\ \mu A) = 6.90\ mA$

$I_{C(sat)} = \dfrac{12\,V}{560\,\Omega} = 21.4\ mA$

The transistor is not saturated.

40.　$I_{B(min)} = \dfrac{I_C}{h_{FE(max)}} = \dfrac{10\,mA}{150} = \mathbf{66.7\ \mu A}$

$I_{B(max)} = \dfrac{I_C}{h_{FE(min)}} = \dfrac{10\,mA}{50} = \mathbf{200\ \mu A}$

41.　For the circuits of textbook Figure 4-58:

(a) $I_B = \dfrac{8\,V - 0.7\,V}{68\,k\Omega} = \dfrac{7.3\,V}{68\,k\Omega} = 107\ \mu A$

$h_{FE} = 150$

$I_C = 150(107\ \mu A) = 16.1\ mA$

$V_C = 15\,V - (16.1\,mA)(680\,\Omega) = 15\,V - 10.95\,V = 4.05\,V$

$V_{CE} = 4.05\,V - 0.7\,V = 3.35\,V$

$P_D = (3.35\,V)(16.1\,mA) = 53.9\ mW$

At 40°C, $P_{D(max)} = 360\,mW - (40°C - 25°C)(2.06\,mW/°C) = 329\ mW$

No parameter is exceeded.

(b) $I_B = \dfrac{5\,V - 0.7\,V}{4.7\,k\Omega} = \dfrac{4.3\,V}{4.7\,k\Omega} = 915\ \mu A$

$h_{FE} = 300$

$I_C = 300(915\ \mu A) = 274\ mA$

$I_{C(sat)} \cong \dfrac{35\,V - 0.3\,V}{470\,\Omega} = 73.8\ mA$

The transistor is in hard saturation. Assuming $V_{CE(sat)} = 0.3\,V$,

$P_D = (0.3\,V)(73.8\,mA) = 22.1\ mW$

No parameter is exceeded.

Advanced Problems

42.　$\beta_{DC} = \dfrac{\alpha_{DC}}{1 - \alpha_{DC}}$

$\beta_{DC} - \beta_{DC}\alpha_{DC} = \alpha_{DC}$

$\beta_{DC} = \alpha_{DC}(1 + \beta_{DC})$

$\alpha_{DC} = \dfrac{\beta_{DC}}{(1 + \beta_{DC})}$

43. $I_C = 150(500\ \mu A) = \textbf{75 mA}$

$V_{CE} = 15\ V - (180\ \Omega)(75\ mA) - 0.7\ V = \textbf{0.8 V}$

Since $V_{CE(sat)} = 0.3\ V\ @\ I_C = 50\ mA$, the transistor comes out of saturation, although marginally.

44. From the data sheet, $\beta_{DC(min)} = 15$ (for $I_C = 100\ mA$)

$I_{B(max)} = \dfrac{150\ mA}{15} = 10\ mA$

$R_{B(min)} = \dfrac{3\ V - 0.7\ V}{10\ mA} = \dfrac{2.3\ V}{10\ mA} = 230\ \Omega$

Use the standard value of $240\ \Omega$ for R_B.

To avoid saturation, the load resistance cannot exceed about

$\dfrac{9\ V - 1\ V}{150\ mA} = 53.3\ \Omega$

See Figure 4-2.

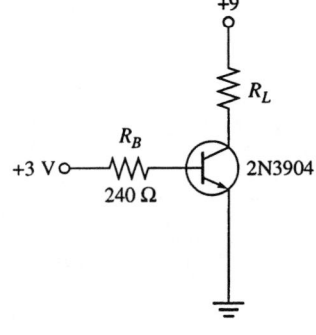

Figure 4-2

45. Since $I_B = 10\ mA$ for $I_C = 150\ mA$,

$R_{B(min)} = \dfrac{9\ V - 0.7\ V}{10\ mA} = \dfrac{8.3\ V}{10\ mA} = 830\ \Omega$

Use $910\ \Omega$. The load cannot exceed $53.3\ \Omega$.

See Figure 4-3.

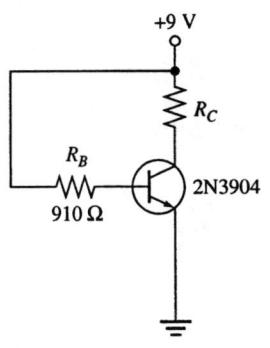

Figure 4-3

46. $R_{C(min)} = A_v r_e' = 50(8\ \Omega) = 400\ \Omega$ (Use $430\ \Omega$)

$I_C = \dfrac{12\ V - 5\ V}{430\ \Omega} = 16.3\ mA$

Assuming $h_{FE} = 100$,

$I_B = \dfrac{16.3\ mA}{100} = 163\ \mu A$

$R_{B(max)} = \dfrac{4\ V - 0.7\ V}{163\ \mu A} = 20.3\ k\Omega$ (Use $18\ k\Omega$)

See Figure 4-4.

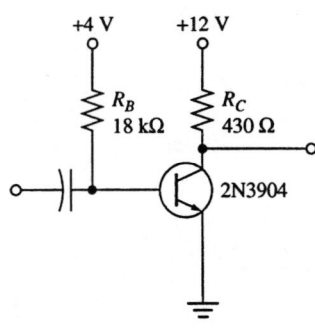

Figure 4-4

Chapter 4

EWB/Multisim Troubleshooting Problems

The solutions showing instrument connections for Problems 47 through 54 are available in the Solutions folder for Chapter 4 on the CD-ROM provided with the textbook. The solutions may be accessed using the password *ED5FLOYD*. The faults in the circuit files may be accessed using the password *book* (all lowercase).

47.　　R_B shorted

48.　　R_C open

49.　　Collector-emitter shorted

50.　　Collector-emitter open

51.　　R_E leaky

52.　　Collector-emitter shorted

53.　　R_B open

54.　　R_C open

Chapter 5
Transistor Bias Circuits

Section 5-1 The DC Operating Point

1.   The transistor is biased too close to **saturation**.

2. $I_C = \beta_{DC}I_B = 75(150\ \mu A) = 11.3$ mA
      $V_{CE} = V_{CC} - I_C R_C = 18\ V - (11.3\ mA)(1.0\ k\Omega) = 18\ V - 11.3\ V = 6.75$ V
      Q-point: $V_{CEQ} = \mathbf{6.75\ V},\ I_{CQ} = \mathbf{11.3\ mA}$

3. $I_{C(sat)} \cong \dfrac{V_{CC}}{R_C} = \dfrac{18\ V}{1.0\ k\Omega} = \mathbf{18\ mA}$

4. $V_{CE(cutoff)} = \mathbf{18\ V}$

5.   Horizontal intercept (cutoff):
      $V_{CE} = V_{CC} = \mathbf{20\ V}$
      Vertical intercept (saturation):

      $I_{C(sat)} = \dfrac{V_{CC}}{R_C} = \dfrac{20\ V}{10\ k\Omega}\ \mathbf{2\ mA}$

6. $I_B = \dfrac{V_{BB} - 0.7\ V}{R_B}$

      $V_{BB} = I_B R_B + 0.7\ V = (20\ \mu A)(1.0\ M\Omega) + 0.7\ V = \mathbf{20.7\ V}$
      $I_C = \beta_{DC}I_B = 50(20\ \mu A) = \mathbf{1\ mA}$
      $V_{CE} = V_{CC} - I_C R_C = 20\ V - (1\ mA)(10\ k\Omega) = \mathbf{10\ V}$

7.   See Figure 5-1.
      $V_{CE} = V_{CC} - I_C R_C$
      $R_C = \dfrac{V_{CC} - V_{CE}}{I_C} = \dfrac{10\ V - 4\ V}{5\ mA} = \mathbf{1.2\ k\Omega}$

      $I_B = \dfrac{I_C}{\beta_{DC}} = \dfrac{5\ mA}{100} = 0.05$ mA

      $R_B = \dfrac{10\ V - 0.7\ V}{0.05\ mA} = \mathbf{186\ k\Omega}$
      $P_{D(min)} = V_{CE}I_C = (4\ V)(5\ mA) = \mathbf{20\ mW}$

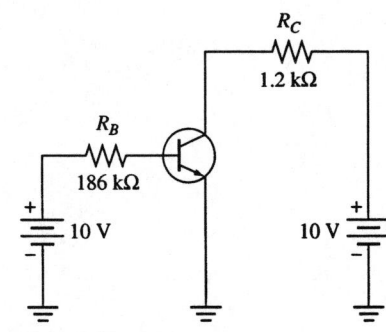

Figure 5-1

35

Chapter 5

8. $I_B = \dfrac{V_{BB} - V_{BE}}{R_B} = \dfrac{1.5\,\text{V} - 0.7\,\text{V}}{10\,\text{k}\Omega} = 80\,\mu\text{A}$

$I_{C(sat)} = \dfrac{V_{CC}}{R_C} = \dfrac{8\,\text{V}}{390\,\Omega} = 20.5\,\text{mA}$

$I_C = \beta_{DC}I_B = 75(80\,\mu\text{A}) = 6\,\text{mA}$

The transistor is biased in the linear region because
$0 < I_C < I_{C(sat)}$.

Section 5-2   Voltage-Divider Bias

9. $\beta_{DC(min)}R_E = 10R_2$

$\beta_{DC(min)} = \dfrac{10R_2}{R_E} = \dfrac{47\,\text{k}\Omega}{680\,\Omega} = \mathbf{69.1}$

10. $I_{C(sat)} = \dfrac{V_{CC}}{R_C + R_E} = \dfrac{15\,\text{V}}{2.18\,\text{k}\Omega} = 6.88\,\text{mA}$

$V_{E(sat)} = I_{C(sat)}R_E = (6.88\,\text{mA})(680\,\Omega) = 4.68\,\text{V}$

$V_B = V_{E(sat)} + 0.7\,\text{V} = 4.68\,\text{V} + 0.7\,\text{V} = 5.38\,\text{V}$

$\left(\dfrac{R_2 \parallel \beta_{DC}R_E}{R_1 + R_2 \parallel \beta_{DC}R_E}\right)15\,\text{V} = 5.38\,\text{V}$

$\left(R_2 \parallel \beta_{DC}R_E\right)(15\,\text{V}) = (5.38\,\text{V})\left(R_1 + R_2 \parallel \beta_{DC}R_E\right)$

$\left(R_2 \parallel \beta_{DC}R_E\right)(15\,\text{V}) - \left(R_2 \parallel \beta_{DC}R_E\right)(5.38\,\text{V}) = R_1(5.38\,\text{V})$

$\left(R_2 \parallel \beta_{DC}R_E\right)(15\,\text{V} - 5.38\,\text{V}) = (22\,\text{k}\Omega)(5.38\,\text{V})$

$R_2 \parallel \beta_{DC}R_E = \dfrac{(22\,\text{k}\Omega)(5.38\,\text{V})}{15\,\text{V} - 5.38\,\text{V}} = 12.3\,\text{k}\Omega$

$\dfrac{1}{R_2} + \dfrac{1}{\beta_{DC}R_E} = \dfrac{1}{12.3\,\text{k}\Omega}$

$\dfrac{1}{R_2} + \dfrac{1}{102\,\text{k}\Omega} = \dfrac{1}{12.3\,\text{k}\Omega}$

$\dfrac{1}{R_2} = 71.5\,\mu\text{S}$

$R_2 = \mathbf{14\,k\Omega}$

11. $V_B = \left(\dfrac{R_2}{R_1 + R_2}\right)V_{CC} = \left(\dfrac{2\,\text{k}\Omega}{24\,\text{k}\Omega}\right)15\,\text{V} = 1.25\,\text{V}$

$V_E = 1.25\,\text{V} - 0.7\,\text{V} = 0.55\,\text{V}$

$I_E = \dfrac{V_E}{R_E} = \dfrac{0.55\,\text{V}}{680\,\Omega} = 809\,\mu\text{A}$

$I_C \cong \mathbf{809\,\mu A}$

$V_{CE} = V_{CC} - I_C R_C - V_E = 15\,\text{V} - (809\,\mu\text{A})(1.5\,\text{k}\Omega + 680\,\Omega) = \mathbf{13.2\,V}$

12. $V_B = \left(\dfrac{R_2\|\beta_{DC}R_E}{R_1 + R_2\|\beta_{DC}R_E}\right)V_{CC} = \left(\dfrac{15\,k\Omega\|(110)(1.0\,k\Omega)}{47\,k\Omega + 15\,k\Omega\|(110)(1.0\,k\Omega)}\right)9\,V = \textbf{1.97 V}$

$V_E = V_B - 0.7\,V = 1.97\,V - 0.7\,V = \textbf{1.27 V}$

$I_C \cong I_E = \dfrac{V_E}{R_E} = \dfrac{1.27\,V}{1.0\,k\Omega} = 1.27\,mA$

$V_C = V_{CC} - I_C R_C = 9\,V - (1.27\,mA)(2.2\,k\Omega) = \textbf{6.21 V}$

13. See Figure 5-2.

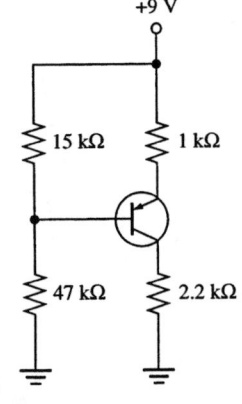

Figure 5-2

14. (a) $R_{IN(base)} = \beta_{DC}R_E = 50(560\,\Omega) = 28\,k\Omega$

$V_B = \left(\dfrac{5.6\,k\Omega \| 28\,k\Omega}{33\,k\Omega + 5.6\,k\Omega \| 28\,k\Omega}\right)(-12\,V) = \left(\dfrac{4.67\,k\Omega}{37.7\,k\Omega}\right)(-12\,V) = \textbf{-1.49 V}$

(b) $R_{IN(base)} = 50(1120\,\Omega) = 56\,k\Omega$

$V_B = \left(\dfrac{5.6\,k\Omega \| 5.6\,k\Omega}{33\,k\Omega + 56\,k\Omega \| 5.6\,k\Omega}\right)(-12\,V) = \left(\dfrac{5.09\,k\Omega}{38.1\,k\Omega}\right)(-12\,V) = \textbf{-1.6 V}$

15. (a) $V_{EQ} = V_B + 0.7\,V = -1.49\,V + 0.7\,V = -0.79\,V$

$I_{CQ} \cong I_E = \dfrac{V_E}{R_E} = \dfrac{-0.79\,V}{560\,\Omega} = \textbf{-1.41 mA}$

$V_{CQ} = V_{CC} - I_C R_C = -12\,V - (-1.41\,mA)(1.8\,k\Omega) = -9.46\,V$

$V_{CEQ} = V_{CQ} - V_{EQ} = -9.46\,V - (-0.79\,V) = \textbf{-8.67 V}$

(b) $P_{D(min)} = I_{CQ}V_{CEQ} = (-1.41\,mA)(-8.67\,V) = \textbf{12.2 mW}$

Section 5-3 Other Bias Methods

16. $V_{BB} = V_{CC};\ V_E = 0\,V$

$I_B = \dfrac{V_{CC} - 0.7\,V}{R_B} = \dfrac{12\,V - 0.7\,V}{22\,k\Omega} = \dfrac{11.3\,V}{22\,k\Omega} = \textbf{514 }\mu\textbf{A}$

$I_C = \beta_{DC}I_B = 90(514\ \mu A) = \textbf{46.3 mA}$

$V_{CE} = V_{CC} - I_C R_C = 12\,V - (46.3\,mA)(100\,\Omega) = \textbf{7.37 V}$

17. $I_{CQ} = 180(514\ \mu A) = \textbf{92.5 mA}$

$V_{CEQ} = 12\,V - (92.5\,mA)(100\,\Omega) = \textbf{2.75 V}$

18. I_C changes in the circuit with a common V_{CC} and V_{BB} supply because a change in V_{CC} causes I_B to change which, in turn, changes I_C.

19. $I_B = \dfrac{V_{BB} - V_{BE}}{R_B} = \dfrac{9\text{ V} - 0.7\text{ V}}{15\text{ k}\Omega} = 553\ \mu\text{A}$

$I_{C(\text{sat})} = \dfrac{V_{CC}}{R_C} = \dfrac{9\text{ V}}{100\ \Omega} = 90\text{ mA}$

For $\beta_{DC} = 50$:

$I_C = \beta_{DC}I_B = 50(553\ \mu\text{A}) = \mathbf{27.7\text{ mA}}$

$V_{CE} = V_{CC} - I_CR_C = 9\text{ V} - (27.67\text{ mA})(100\ \Omega) = \mathbf{6.23\text{ V}}$

For $\beta_{DC} = 125$:

$I_C = \beta_{DC}I_B = 125(553\ \mu\text{A}) = \mathbf{69.2\text{ mA}}$

$V_{CE} = V_{CC} - I_CR_C = 9\text{ V} - (69.2\text{ mA})(100\ \Omega) = \mathbf{2.08\text{ V}}$

Since $I_C < I_{C(\text{sat})}$ for the range of β_{DC}, the circuit remains **biased in the linear region**.

20. $I_{C(\text{sat})} = \dfrac{V_{CC}}{R_C} = \dfrac{9\text{ V}}{100\ \Omega} = 90\text{ mA}$

At 0°C:

$\beta_{DC} = 110 - 110(0.5) = 55$

$I_B = \dfrac{V_{CC} - V_{BE}}{R_B} = \dfrac{9\text{ V} - 0.7\text{ V}}{15\text{ k}\Omega} = 553\ \mu\text{A}$

$I_C = \beta_{DC}I_B = 55(553\ \mu\text{A}) = 30.4\text{ mA}$

$V_{CE} = V_{CC} - I_CR_C = 9\text{ V} - (30.4\text{ mA})(100\ \Omega) = 5.96\text{ V}$

At 70°C:

$\beta_{DC} = 110 + 110(0.75) = 193$

$I_B = 553\ \mu\text{A}$

$I_C = \beta_{DC}I_B = 193(553\ \mu\text{A}) = 107\text{ mA}$

$I_C > I_{C(\text{sat})}$, therefore the transistor is in saturation at 70°C.

$\Delta I_C = I_{C(\text{sat})} - I_{C(0°)} = 90\text{ mA} - 30.4\text{ mA} = \mathbf{59.6\text{ mA}}$

$\Delta V_{CE} \cong V_{CE(0°)} - V_{CE(\text{sat})} = 5.96\text{ V} - 0\text{ V} = \mathbf{5.96\text{ V}}$

21. Assuming $V_B \cong 0\text{ V}$,

$V_E \cong V_B - V_{BE} = 0\text{ V} - 0.7\text{ V} = -0.7\text{ V}$

$I_E \cong \dfrac{V_E - V_{EE}}{R_E + R_B/\beta_{DC}} = \dfrac{-0.7\text{ V} - (-5\text{ V})}{2.2\text{ k}\Omega + 22\text{ k}\Omega/100} = \dfrac{4.3\text{ V}}{2.42\text{ k}\Omega} = 1.78\text{ mA}$

$I_C \cong I_E$

$I_B = \dfrac{1.78\text{ mA}}{100} = 17.8\ \mu\text{A}$

$V_B = (17.8\ \mu\text{A})(22\text{ k}\Omega) = \mathbf{-391\text{ mV}}$

$V_E = -391\text{ mV} - 0.7\text{ V} = \mathbf{-1.10\text{ V}}$

$V_C = V_{CC} - I_CR_C = 5\text{ V} - (1.78\text{ mA})(1.0\text{ k}\Omega) = \mathbf{3.22\text{ V}}$

22. Assume that at saturation, $V_{CE} \cong 0\text{ V}$.

Since $V_E = -1.10\text{ V}$ and $V_{C(\text{sat})} \cong V_{E(\text{sat})}$

$I_{C(\text{sat})} = \dfrac{V_{CC} - V_{C(\text{sat})}}{R_C} = \dfrac{5\text{ V} - (-1.10\text{ V})}{1.0\text{ k}\Omega} = 6.1\text{ mA}$

$R_{E(\text{min})} \cong \dfrac{V_{RE}}{I_{C(\text{sat})}} = \dfrac{3.9\text{ V}}{6.1\text{ mA}} = \mathbf{639\ \Omega}$

23. At 100° C:

$V_{BE} = 0.7 \text{ V} - (2.5 \text{ mV/°C})(75°\text{C}) = 0.513 \text{ V}$

$I_E = \dfrac{V_{EE} - V_{BE}}{R_E} = \dfrac{5 \text{ V} - 0.513 \text{ V}}{2.2 \text{ k}\Omega} = 2.04 \text{ mA}$

At 25°C:

$I_E = \dfrac{5 \text{ V} - 0.7 \text{ V}}{2.2 \text{ k}\Omega} = \dfrac{4.3 \text{ V}}{2.2 \text{ k}\Omega} = 1.95 \text{ mA}$

$\Delta I_E = 2.04 \text{ mA} - 1.95 \text{ mA} = \mathbf{0.09 \text{ mA}}$

24. A change in β_{DC} does not affect the circuit when $R_E \gg R_B/\beta_{DC}$. Since

$I_E = \dfrac{V_{EE} - V_{BE}}{R_E + R_B / \beta_{DC}}$

In the equation, if R_B/β_{DC} is much smaller than R_E, the effect of β_{DC} is negligible.

25. Assume $\beta_{DC} = 100$.

$I_C \cong I_E = \dfrac{V_{EE} - V_E}{R_E} = \dfrac{10 \text{ V} - 0.7 \text{ V}}{470 \ \Omega + 10 \text{ k}\Omega/100} = \mathbf{16.3 \text{ mA}}$

$V_{CE} = V_{EE} - V_{CC} - I_C(R_C + R_E) = 20 \text{ V} - 13.1 \text{ V} = \mathbf{-6.95 \text{ V}}$

26. $V_B = \mathbf{0.7 \text{ V}}$

$I_C = \dfrac{V_{CC} - V_{BE}}{R_C + R_B / \beta_{DC}} = \dfrac{3 \text{ V} - 0.7 \text{ V}}{1.8 \text{ k}\Omega + 33 \text{ k}\Omega/90} = \mathbf{1.06 \text{ mA}}$

$V_C = V_{CC} - I_C R_C = 3 \text{ V} - (1.06 \text{ mA})(1.8 \text{ k}\Omega) = \mathbf{1.09 \text{ V}}$

27. $I_C = 1.06 \text{ mA}$ from Problem 26.

$I_C = 1.06 \text{ mA} - (0.25)(1.06 \text{ mA}) = 0.795 \text{ mA}$

$I_C = \dfrac{V_{CC} - V_{BE}}{R_C + R_B / \beta_{DC}}$

$R_C = \dfrac{V_{CC} - V_{BE} - I_C R_B / \beta_{DC}}{I_C} = \dfrac{3 \text{ V} - 0.7 \text{ V} - (0.795 \text{ mA})(33 \text{ k}\Omega)/90}{0.795 \text{ mA}} = \mathbf{2.53 \text{ k}\Omega}$

28. $I_C = 0.795 \text{ mA}$ from Problem 27.

$V_{CE} = V_{CC} - I_C R_C = 3 \text{ V} - (0.795 \text{ mA})(2.63 \text{ k}\Omega) = 0.989 \text{ V}$

$P_{D(min)} = V_{CE} I_C = (0.989 \text{ V})(0.795 \text{ mA}) = \mathbf{786 \ \mu\text{W}}$

29. See Figure 5-3.

$I_C = \dfrac{V_{CC} - V_{BE}}{R_C + R_B / \beta_{DC}} = \dfrac{12 \text{ V} - 0.7 \text{ V}}{1.2 \text{ k}\Omega + 47 \text{ k}\Omega/200} = \mathbf{7.87 \text{ mA}}$

$V_C = V_{CC} - I_C R_C = 12 \text{ V} - (7.87 \text{ mA})(1.2 \text{ k}\Omega) = \mathbf{2.56 \text{ V}}$

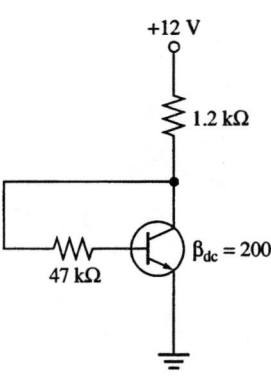

Figure 5-3

Chapter 5

Section 5-4 Troubleshooting

30. $V_1 = 0.7$ V, $\qquad V_2 = 0$ V

$$I_B = \frac{8\,V - 0.7\,V}{33\,k\Omega} - \frac{0.7\,V}{10\,k\Omega} = 221\ \mu A - 70\ \mu A = 151\ \mu A$$

$$I_C = 200(151\ \mu A) = 30.2\text{ mA}$$

$$I_{C(sat)} = \frac{8\,V}{2.2\,k\Omega} = 3.64\text{ mA, so } V_C \cong V_E = 0\text{ V}$$

If the problem is corrected,

$$V_1 = \left(\frac{10\,k\Omega}{10\,k\Omega + 33\,k\Omega}\right)8\,V = \mathbf{1.86\ V}$$

$$V_2 = V_E = 1.86\,V - 0.7\,V = \mathbf{1.16\ V}$$

$$I_E = \frac{1.16\,V}{1.0\,k\Omega} = 1.16\text{ mA}$$

$$V_3 = V_C = 8\,V - (1.16\text{ mA})(2.2\,k\Omega) = \mathbf{5.45\ V}$$

31. (a) Open collector
(b) No problems
(c) Transistor shorted from collector-to-emitter
(d) Open emitter

32. For $\beta_{DC} = 35$:

$$V_B = \left(\frac{4.5\,k\Omega}{14.5\,k\Omega}\right)(-10\,V) = -3.1\text{ V}$$

For $\beta_{DC} = 100$:

$$V_B = \left(\frac{5.17\,k\Omega}{15.17\,k\Omega}\right)(-10\,V) = -3.4\text{ V}$$

The measured base voltage at point 4 is within the correct range.

$$V_E = -3.1\,V + 0.7\,V = -2.4\text{ V}$$

$$I_C \cong I_E = \frac{-2.4\,V}{680\,\Omega} = -3.53\text{ mA}$$

$$V_C = -10\,V - (-3.53\text{ mA})(1.0\,k\Omega) = -6.47\text{ V}$$

Allowing for some variation in V_{BE} and for resistor tolerances, the measured collector and emitter voltages are correct.

33. (a) The 680 Ω resistor is open:

Meter 1: **10 V**

Meter 2: **floating**

Meter 3: $V_B = \left(\dfrac{5.6\,k\Omega}{15.6\,k\Omega}\right)(-10\,V) = \mathbf{-3.59\ V}$

Meter 4: **10 V**

(b) The 5.6 kΩ resistor is open.

$$I_B = \frac{9.3\ V}{10\ k\Omega + 35(680\ \Omega)} = 275\ \mu A$$

$$I_C = 35(275\ \mu A) = 9.6\ mA$$

$$I_{C(sat)} = \frac{10\ V}{1680\ \Omega} = 5.95\ mA$$

The transistor is saturated.
Meter 1: **10 V**
Meter 2: (5.95 mA)(680 Ω) = **4.05 V**
Meter 3: 4.05 V + 0.7 V = **4.75 V**
Meter 4: 10 V − (5.95 mA)(1.0 kΩ) = **4.05 V**

(c) The 10 kΩ resistor is open. The transistor is off.
Meter 1: **10 V**
Meter 2: **0 V**
Meter 3: **0 V**
Meter 4: **10 V**

(d) The 1.0 kΩ resistor is open. Collector current is zero.
Meter 1: **10 V**

Meter 3: $\left(\dfrac{5.6\ k\Omega \parallel 680\ \Omega}{10\ k\Omega + 5.6\ k\Omega \parallel 680\ \Omega}\right)(10\ V) + 0.7\ V = 0.57\ V + 0.7\ V = \mathbf{1.27\ V}$

Meter 2: 1.27 V − 0.7 V = **0.57 V**
Meter 4: **floating**

(e) A short from emitter to ground.
Meter 1: **10 V**
Meter 2: **0 V**
Meter 3: **0.7 V**

$$I_B \cong \frac{(10\ V - 0.7\ V)}{10\ k\Omega} = \frac{9.3\ V}{10\ k\Omega} = 0.93\ mA$$

$$I_{C(min)} = 35(0.93\ mA) = 32.6\ mA$$

$$I_{C(sat)} = \frac{10\ V}{1.0\ k\Omega} = 10\ mA$$

The transistor is saturated.
Meter 4: ≅ **0 V**

(f) An open base-emitter junction. The transistor is off.
Meter 1: **10 V**
Meter 2: **0 V**

Meter 3: $\left(\dfrac{5.6\ k\Omega}{15.6\ k\Omega}\right)(10\ V) = \mathbf{3.59\ V}$

Meter 4: **10 V**

Chapter 5

System Application Problems

34. With R_1 shorted:
$V_B = \textbf{0 V}$, $V_E = \textbf{0 V}$, $V_C = V_{CC} = \textbf{9.1 V}$

35. Faults that will cause the transistor of textbook Figure 5-30 to go into cutoff:
R_1 **open**, R_2 **shorted**, base lead or BE junction **open**.

36. $R_{IN(base)} = 70(470\ \Omega) = 32.9\ \text{k}\Omega$

$R_{IN} = 2.7\ \text{k}\Omega \parallel 32.9\ \text{k}\Omega = 2.50\ \text{k}\Omega$

$$V_B = \left(\frac{2.50\ \text{k}\Omega}{2.50\ \text{k}\Omega + 5.6\ \text{k}\Omega}\right)5.1\ \text{V} = \left(\frac{2.50\ \text{k}\Omega}{8.10\ \text{k}\Omega}\right)5.1\ \text{V} = 1.57\ \text{V}$$

$V_E = 1.57\ \text{V} - 0.7\ \text{V} = \textbf{0.872 V}$

$$\text{So, } I_C \cong I_E = \frac{0.872\ \text{V}}{470\ \Omega} = \textbf{1.86 mA}$$

$V_C = 5.1\ \text{V} - (1.86\ \text{mA})(1.0\ \text{k}\Omega) = \textbf{3.24 V}$

37. The following measurements would indicate an open CB junction:
$V_C = V_{CC} = \textbf{+9.1 V}$
V_B **normal**
$V_E \cong \textbf{0 V}$

Data Sheet Problems

38. For $T = 45°C$ and $R_2 = 2.7\ \text{k}\Omega$

$R_{IN(base)} = 2.7\ \text{k}\Omega \parallel (30)(470\ \Omega) = 2.7\ \text{k}\Omega \parallel 14.1\ \text{k}\Omega = 2.27\ \text{k}\Omega$ min

$R_{IN(base)} = 2.7\ \text{k}\Omega \parallel (300)(470\ \Omega) = 2.7\ \text{k}\Omega \parallel 141\ \text{k}\Omega = 2.65\ \text{k}\Omega$ max

$$V_{B(min)} = \left(\frac{2.27\ \text{k}\Omega}{2.27\ \text{k}\Omega + 5.6\ \text{k}\Omega}\right)9.1\ \text{V} = \left(\frac{2.27\ \text{k}\Omega}{7.87}\right)9.1\ \text{V} = \textbf{2.62 V}$$

$V_{E(min)} = 2.62\ \text{V} - 0.7\ \text{V} = \textbf{1.92 V}$

$$\text{So, } I_C \cong I_E = \frac{1.92\ \text{V}}{470\ \Omega} = 4.09\ \text{mA}$$

$V_{C(max)} = 9.1\ \text{V} - (4.09\ \text{mA})(1.0\ \text{k}\Omega) = \textbf{5.01 V}$

$$V_{B(max)} = \left(\frac{2.65\ \text{k}\Omega}{2.65\ \text{k}\Omega + 5.6\ \text{k}\Omega}\right)9.1\ \text{V} = \left(\frac{2.65\ \text{k}\Omega}{8.25\ \text{k}\Omega}\right)9.1\ \text{V} = \textbf{2.92 V}$$

$V_{E(max)} = 2.92\ \text{V} - 0.7\ \text{V} = \textbf{2.22 V}$

$$\text{So, } I_C \cong I_E = \frac{2.22\ \text{V}}{470\ \Omega} = 4.73\ \text{mA}$$

$V_{C(min)} = 9.1\ \text{V} - (4.73\ \text{mA})(1.0\ \text{k}\Omega) = \textbf{4.37 V}$

For $T = 55°C$ and $R_2 = 1.24\,k\Omega$:

$R_{IN(base)} = 1.24\,k\Omega \parallel (30)(470\,\Omega) = 1.24\,k\Omega \parallel 14.1\,k\Omega = 1.14\,k\Omega$ min

$R_{IN(base)} = 1.24\,k\Omega \parallel (300)(470\,\Omega) = 1.24\,k\Omega \parallel 141\,k\Omega = 1.23\,k\Omega$ max

$V_{B(min)} = \left(\dfrac{1.14\,k\Omega}{1.14\,k\Omega + 5.6\,k\Omega}\right)9.1\,V = \left(\dfrac{1.14\,k\Omega}{6.74\,k\Omega}\right)9.1\,V = \mathbf{1.54\ V}$

$V_{E(min)} = 1.54\,V - 0.7\,V = \mathbf{0.839\ V}$

So, $I_C \cong I_E = \dfrac{0.839\,V}{470\,\Omega} = 1.78\,mA$

$V_{C(max)} = 9.1\,V - (1.78\,mA)(1.0\,k\Omega) = \mathbf{7.32\ V}$

$V_{B(max)} = \left(\dfrac{1.23\,k\Omega}{1.23\,k\Omega + 5.6\,k\Omega}\right)9.1\,V = \left(\dfrac{1.23\,k\Omega}{6.83\,k\Omega}\right)9.1\,V = \mathbf{1.64\ V}$

$V_{E(max)} = 1.64\,V - 0.7\,V = \mathbf{0.938\ V}$

So, $I_C \cong I_E = \dfrac{0.938\,V}{470\,\Omega} = 2.0\,mA$

$V_{C(min)} = 9.1\,V - (2.0\,mA)(1.0\,k\Omega) = \mathbf{7.10\ V}$

39. At $T = 45°C$ for minimum β_{DC}:
$P_{D(max)} = (5.01\,V - 1.92\,V)(4.09\,mA) = (3.09\,V)(4.09\,mA) = 12.6\,mW$
At $T = 55°C$ for minimum β_{DC}:
$P_{D(max)} = (7.32\,V - 0.839\,V)(1.78\,mA) = (6.48\,V)(1.78\,mA) = 11.5\,mW$
For maximum beta values, the results are comparable and nowhere near the maximum.
$P_{D(max)} = 625\,mW - (5.0\,m/°C)(30°C) = 475\,mW$
No ratings are exceeded.

40. For the data sheet of Figure 5-51 in the textbook:
(a) For a 2N2222A, $I_{C(max)} = \mathbf{800\ mA}$ continuous
(b) For a 2N2118, $V_{BE(max)} = \mathbf{5.0\ V}$ for reverse breakdown or $V_{BE(max)} = \mathbf{2.6\ V}$ for saturation

41. For a 2N2222 @ $T = 100°C$:
$P_{D(max)} = 0.8\,W - (4.57\,mW/°C)(100°C - 25°C) = 0.8\,W - 343\,mW = \mathbf{457\ mW}$

42. If I_C changes from 1 mA to 500 mA in a 2N2219, the percentage change in β_{DC} is
$\Delta\beta_{DC} = \left(\dfrac{30 - 50}{50}\right)100\% = \mathbf{-40\%}$

Advanced Problems

43. See Figure 5-4.
$R_C = \dfrac{V_{CC} - V_{CEQ}}{I_{CQ}} = \dfrac{15\,V - 5\,V}{5\,mA} = 2\,k\Omega$
Assume $\beta_{DC} = 100$.
$I_{BQ} = \dfrac{I_{CQ}}{\beta_{DC}} = \dfrac{5\,mA}{100} = 50\,\mu A$
$R_B = \dfrac{V_{CC} - V_{BE}}{I_{BQ}} = \dfrac{15\,V - 0.7\,V}{50\,\mu A} = 286\,k\Omega$

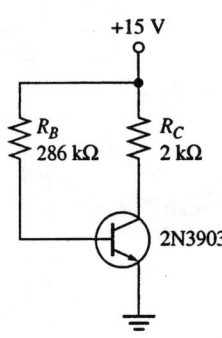

Figure 5-4

Chapter 5

44. See Figure 5-5.
Assume $\beta_{DC} = 200$.

$$I_{BQ} = \frac{I_{CQ}}{\beta_{DC}} = \frac{10\,mA}{200} = 50\,\mu A$$

Let $R_B = 1.0\,k\Omega$

$$R_E = \frac{12\,V - (50\,\mu A)(1.0\,k\Omega) - 0.7\,V}{10\,mA} = \frac{11.3\,V}{10\,mA} = 1.13\,k\Omega$$

$$R_C = \frac{12\,V - (-12\,V + 11.3\,V + 4\,V)}{10\,mA} = \frac{8.7\,V}{10\,mA} = = 870\,\Omega$$

870 Ω and 1.13 kΩ are not standard values. $R_C = 820\,\Omega$ and
$R_E = 1.2\,k\Omega$ give $I_{CQ} \cong 9.38\,mA$, $V_{CEQ} \cong 5.05\,mA$.

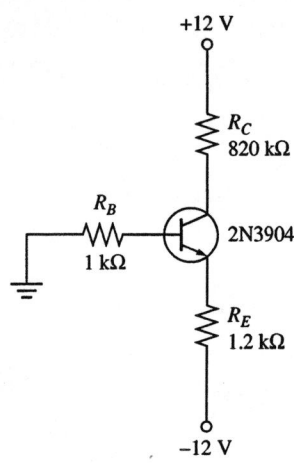

Figure 5-5

45. See Figure 5-6.
$\beta_{DC(min)} \cong 70$. Let $R_E = 1.0\,k\Omega$.
$V_E = I_E R_E = 1.5\,mA(1.0\,k\Omega) = 1.5\,V$
$V_B = 1.5\,V + 0.7\,V = 2.2\,V$

$$R_C = \frac{V_{CC} - V_{CEQ} - V_E}{I_{CQ}} = \frac{9\,V - 1.5\,V - 3\,V}{1.5\,mA} = 3\,k\Omega$$

$$R_1 + R_2 = \frac{V_{CC}}{I_{CC(max)} - I_{CQ}} = \frac{9\,V}{5\,mA - 1.5\,mA} = 2.57\,k\Omega\ min$$

Asssuming $\beta_{DC} R_E >> R_2$,

$$\frac{R_1}{R_2} = \frac{6.8\,V}{2.2\,V} = 3.09$$

$R_1 = 3.09 R_2$
$R_1 + R_2 = R_2 + 3.09 R_2 = 2.57\,k\Omega$
$4.09 R_2 = 2.57\,k\Omega$

$$R_2 = \frac{2.57\,k\Omega}{4.09} = 628\,\Omega$$

So, $R_2 \cong 620$ and $R_2 = 1.92\,k\Omega \cong 2\,k\Omega$.
From this,
$R_{IN(base)} = 70(1.0\,k\Omega) = 70\,k\Omega >> R_2$

so, $V_B = \left(\frac{620\,\Omega}{2.62\,k\Omega}\right) 9V = 2.13\,V$

$V_E = 2.13\,V - 0.7\,V = 1.43\,V$

$$I_{CQ} \cong I_E = \frac{1.43\,V}{1.0\,k\Omega} = 1.43\,mA$$

$V_{CEQ} = 9\,V - (1.43\,mA)(1.0\,k\Omega + 3\,k\Omega) = 3.28\,V$

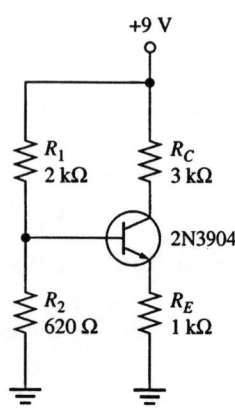

Figure 5-6

46. See Figure 5-7.

$\beta_{DC} \cong 75$.

$I_{BQ} = \dfrac{10\,\text{mA}}{75} = 133\ \mu\text{A}$

$R_C = \dfrac{V_{CC} - V_{CE}}{I_{CQ}} = \dfrac{5\,\text{V} - 1.5\,\text{V}}{10\,\text{mA}} = 350\ \Omega$ (use 360 Ω)

$R_B = \dfrac{V_{CE} - 0.7\,\text{V}}{I_{BQ}} = \dfrac{1.55\,\text{V} - 0.7\,\text{V}}{133\ \mu\text{A}} = 6\ \text{k}\Omega$ (use 6.2 kΩ)

$I_{CQ} = \dfrac{5\,\text{V} - 0.7\,\text{V}}{360\ \Omega + 6.2\ \text{k}\Omega/75} = 9.71\,\text{mA}$

$V_{CEQ} = V_C = 5\,\text{V} - (9.71\,\text{mA})(360\ \Omega) = 1.50\,\text{V}$

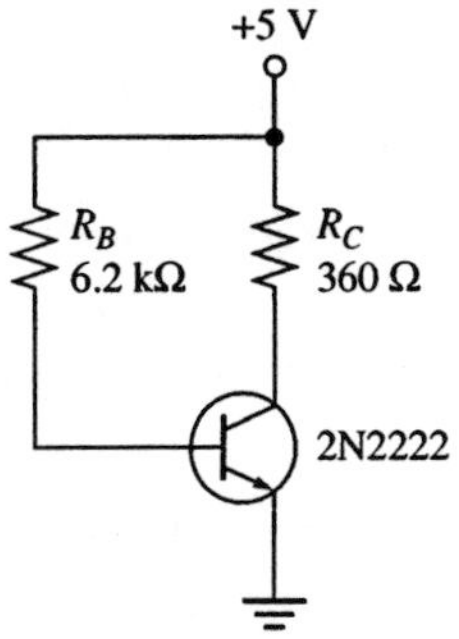

Figure 5-7

47. The 2N3904 in textbook Figure 5-49 **can be replaced** with a 2N2222 and maintain the same voltage range from 45°C to 55°C because the voltage-divider circuit is essentially β independent and the β_{DC} parameters of the two transistors are comparable.

48. For the 2N2222 using the data sheet of Figure 5-51 and Figure 5-52 at $I_C = 150$ mA and $V_{CE} = 1.0$ V:

At $T = -55$°C, $h_{FE(min)} = (0.45)(50) = \mathbf{22.5}$

At $T = 25$°C, $h_{FE(min)} = (0.63)(50) = \mathbf{31.5}$

At $T = 175$°C, $h_{FE(min)} = (0.53)(50) = \mathbf{26.6}$

49. If the ADC loading of the temperature conversion circuit changes from 100 kΩ to 10 kΩ, the Q-point will have a reduced V_{CEQ} because the current through R_C will consist of the same I_C and a larger I_L. I_{CQ} is unaffected in the sense that the transistor collector current is the same, although the collector resistance current is larger. The transistor saturates sooner so that lower temperatures do not register as well, if at all.

50. It is not feasible to operate the circuit from a 5.1 V dc supply and maintain the same range of output voltages because the output voltage at 54°C is 7.06 V.

EWB/Multisim Troubleshooting Problems

The solutions showing instrument connections for Problems 51 through 56 are available in the Solutions folder for Chapter 5 on the CD-ROM provided with the textbook. The solutions may be accessed using the password *ED5FLOYD*. The faults in the circuit files may be accessed using the password *book* (all lowercase).

51. R_C open

52. R_B open

53. R_2 open

54. Collector-emitter shorted

55. R_C shorted

56. Base-emitter open

Chapter 6
BJT Amplifiers

Section 6-1 Amplifier Operation

1.   Approximately **1 mA**

2.   From the graph of Figure 6-4, the highest value of dc collector current is about **6 mA**.

Section 6-2 Transistor AC Equivalent Circuits

3. $r'_e = \dfrac{25\,\text{mV}}{I_E} = \dfrac{25\,\text{mV}}{3\,\text{mA}} = \textbf{8.33}\ \boldsymbol{\Omega}$

4. $\beta_{ac} = h_{fe} = \textbf{200}$

5. $I_C = \beta_{DC}I_B = 130(10\ \mu A) = 1.3\ \text{mA}$

$I_E = \dfrac{I_C}{\alpha_{DC}} = \dfrac{1.3\,\text{mA}}{0.99} = 1.31\ \text{mA}$

$r'_e = \dfrac{25\,\text{mV}}{I_E} = \dfrac{25\,\text{mV}}{1.31\,\text{mA}} = \textbf{19}\ \boldsymbol{\Omega}$

6. $\beta_{DC} = \dfrac{I_C}{I_B} = \dfrac{2\,\text{mA}}{15\ \mu A} = \textbf{133}$

$\beta_{ac} = \dfrac{\Delta I_C}{\Delta I_B} = \dfrac{0.35\,\text{mA}}{3\ \mu A} = \textbf{117}$

Section 6-3 The Common-Emitter Amplifier

7.   See Figure 6-1.

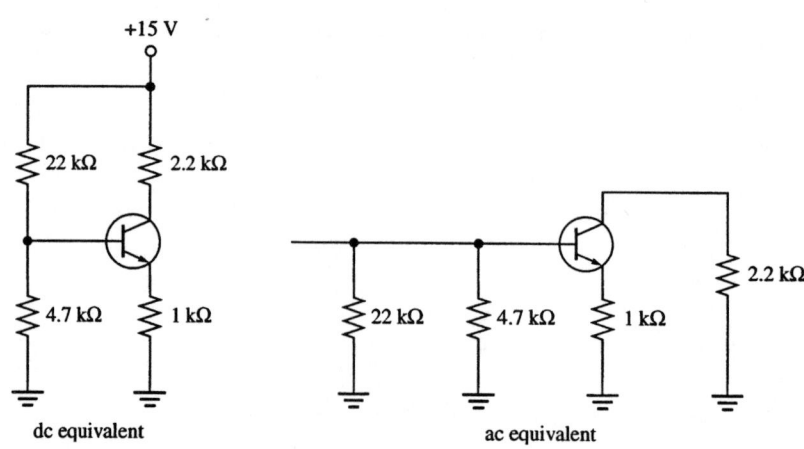

dc equivalent   ac equivalent

Figure 6-1

46

8.   (a) $V_B = \left(\dfrac{4.7\,k\Omega}{4.7\,k\Omega + 22\,k\Omega}\right)15\,V = 2.64\,V$

      $V_E = 2.64\,V - 0.7\,V = 1.94\,V$

      $I_E = \dfrac{1.94\,V}{1.0\,k\Omega} = 1.94\,mA$

      $r'_e \cong \dfrac{25\,mV}{I_E} = \dfrac{25\,mV}{1.94\,mA} = 12.9\,\Omega$

      $R_{in(base)} = \beta_{ac}\left(r'_e + R_E\right) = 100(1012.9\,\Omega) \cong \mathbf{101\,k\Omega}$

   (b) $R_{in} = R_{in(base)} \parallel R_1 \parallel R_2 = 101\,k\Omega \parallel 22\,k\Omega \parallel 4.7\,k\Omega = \mathbf{3.73\,k\Omega}$

   (c) $A_v = \dfrac{R_C}{R_E + r'_e} = \dfrac{2.2\,k\Omega}{12.02\,\Omega} = \mathbf{2.17}$

9.   (a) $R_{in(base)} = \beta_{ac}r'_e = 100(12.9\,\Omega) = \mathbf{1.29\,k\Omega}$

   (b) $R_{in} = 1.29\,k\Omega \parallel 22\,k\Omega \parallel 4.7\,k\Omega = \mathbf{968\,\Omega}$

   (c) $A_v = \dfrac{R_C}{r'_e} = \dfrac{2.2\,k\Omega}{12.9\,\Omega} = \mathbf{171}$

10.   (a) $R_{in(base)} = \beta_{ac}r'_e = 100(12.9\,\Omega) = \mathbf{1.29\,k\Omega}$

   (b) $R_{in} = 1.29\,k\Omega \parallel 22\,k\Omega \parallel 4.7\,k\Omega = \mathbf{968\,\Omega}$

   (c) $A_v = \dfrac{R_c}{r'_e} = \dfrac{R_C \parallel R_L}{r'_e} = \dfrac{2.2\,k\Omega \parallel 10\,k\Omega}{12.9\,\Omega} = \mathbf{140}$

11.   (a) $V_B = \left(\dfrac{R_2 \parallel \beta_{DC}R_E}{R_1 + R_2 \parallel \beta_{DC}R_E}\right)V_{CC} = \left(\dfrac{12\,k\Omega \parallel 75(1.0\,k\Omega)}{47\,k\Omega + 12\,k\Omega \parallel 75(1.0\,k\Omega)}\right)18\,V = \mathbf{3.25\,V}$

   (b) $V_E = V_B - 0.7\,V = \mathbf{2.55\,V}$

   (c) $I_E = \dfrac{V_E}{R_E} = \dfrac{2.55\,V}{1.0\,k\Omega} = \mathbf{2.55\,mA}$

   (d) $I_C \cong I_E = \mathbf{2.55\,mA}$

   (e) $V_C = V_{CC} - I_C R_C = 18\,V - (2.55\,mA)(3.3\,k\Omega) = \mathbf{9.59\,V}$

   (f) $V_{CE} = V_C - V_E = 9.59\,V - 2.55\,V = \mathbf{7.04\,V}$

12.   From Problem 11, $I_E = 2.55\,mA$

   (a) $R_{in(base)} = \beta_{ac}r'_e \cong \beta_{ac}\left(\dfrac{25\,mV}{I_E}\right) = 70\left(\dfrac{25\,mV}{2.55\,mA}\right) = \mathbf{686\,\Omega}$

   (b) $R_{in} = R_1 \parallel R_2 \parallel R_{in(base)} = 47\,k\Omega \parallel 12\,k\Omega \parallel 686\,\Omega = \mathbf{640\,\Omega}$

   (c) $A_v = \dfrac{R_C \parallel R_L}{r'_e} = \dfrac{3.3\,k\Omega \parallel 10\,k\Omega}{9.8\,\Omega} = \mathbf{253}$

   (d) $A_i = \beta_{ac} = \mathbf{70}$

   (e) $A_p = A_v A_i = (253)(70) = \mathbf{17,710}$

Chapter 6

13.
$$V_b = \left(\frac{R_{in}}{R_{in} + R_s}\right)V_{in} = \left(\frac{640\,\Omega}{640\,\Omega + 600\,\Omega}\right)12\,\mu V$$

Attenuation of the input network is

$$\left(\frac{R_{in}}{R_{in} + R_s}\right) = \left(\frac{640\,\Omega}{640\,\Omega + 600\,\Omega}\right) = 0.516$$

$$A_v' = 0.516A_v = 0.516(253) = \mathbf{131}$$

$$\theta = \mathbf{180°}$$

14.
$$V_B = \left(\frac{R_2 \parallel \beta_{DC}R_E}{R_1 + R_2 \parallel \beta_{DC}R_E}\right)V_{CC} = \left(\frac{3.3\,k\Omega \parallel 150(100\,\Omega)}{12\,k\Omega + 3.3\,k\Omega \parallel 150(100\,\Omega)}\right)8\,V = 1.47\,V$$

$$I_E = \frac{V_B - 0.7\,V}{R_E} = \frac{1.47\,V - 0.7\,V}{100\,\Omega} = 7.7\,mA$$

$$r_e' = \frac{25\,mV}{I_E} = \frac{25\,mV}{7.7\,mA} = 3.25\,\Omega$$

$$A_{v(min)} = \frac{R_C}{R_E + r_e'} = \frac{330\,\Omega}{100\,\Omega + 3.25\,\Omega} = \mathbf{3.2}$$

$$A_{v(max)} = \frac{R_C}{r_e'} = \frac{330\,\Omega}{3.25\,\Omega} = \mathbf{102}$$

15. Maximum gain is at $R_e = 0\,\Omega$.

$$R_{IN(base)} = \beta_{DC}R_E = 150(100\,\Omega) = 15\,k\Omega$$

$$V_B = \left(\frac{R_2 \parallel R_{IN(base)}}{R_1 + R_2 \parallel R_{IN(base)}}\right)V_{CC} = \left(\frac{3.3\,k\Omega \parallel 15\,k\Omega}{12\,k\Omega + 3.3\,k\Omega \parallel 15\,k\Omega}\right)8\,V = 1.47\,V$$

$$I_E = \frac{V_B - V_{BE}}{R_E} = \frac{1.47\,V - 0.7\,V}{100\,\Omega} = 7.7\,mA$$

$$r_e' \cong \frac{25\,mV}{7.7\,mA} = 3.25\,\Omega$$

$$A_{v(max)} = \frac{R_C \parallel R_L}{r_e'} = \frac{330\,\Omega \parallel 600\,\Omega}{3.25\,\Omega} = \mathbf{65.5}$$

Minimum gain is at $R_e = 100\,\Omega$.

$$A_{v(min)} = \frac{R_C \parallel R_L}{R_E + r_e'} = \frac{212.9\,\Omega}{103.25\,\Omega} = \mathbf{2.06}$$

16. $R_{in} = R_1 \parallel R_2 \parallel \beta_{ac} r'_e = 3.3\,\text{k}\Omega \parallel 12\,\text{k}\Omega \parallel 150(3.25\,\Omega) = 410\,\Omega$

Attenuation of the input network is

$$\frac{R_{in}}{R_{in}+R_s} = \frac{410\,\Omega}{410\,\Omega + 300\,\Omega} = 0.5777$$

$$A_v = \frac{R_c}{r'_e} = \frac{330\,\Omega \parallel 1.0\,\text{k}\Omega}{3.25\,\Omega} = 76.3$$

$$A'_v = 0.5777 A_v = 0.5777(76.3) = \mathbf{44}$$

17. See Figure 6-2.

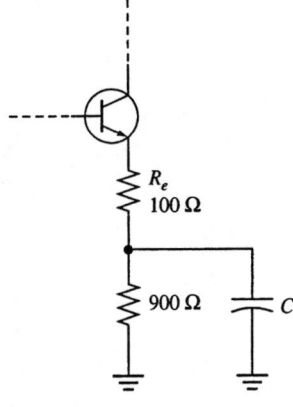

$$r'_e \cong \frac{25\,\text{mV}}{2.55\,\text{mA}} = 9.8\,\Omega$$

$R_e \geq 10 r'_e$

Set $R_e = 100\,\Omega$.

The gain is reduced to

$$A_v = \frac{R_C}{R_e + r'_e} = \frac{3.3\,\text{k}\Omega}{109.8\,\Omega} = 30.1$$

Figure 6-2

Section 6-4 The Common-Collector Amplifier

18. $V_B = \left(\frac{R_2}{R_1+R_2}\right)V_{CC} = \left(\frac{4.7\,\text{k}\Omega}{14.7\,\text{k}\Omega}\right)5.5\,\text{V} = 1.76\,\text{V}$

$$I_E = \frac{V_B - 0.7\,\text{V}}{R_E} = \frac{1.76\,\text{V} - 0.7\,\text{V}}{1.0\,\text{k}\Omega} = 1.06\,\text{mA}$$

$$r'_e \cong \frac{25\,\text{mV}}{1.06\,\text{mA}} = 23.6\,\Omega$$

$$A_v = \frac{R_E}{R_E + r'_e} = \frac{1.0\,\text{k}\Omega}{1.0\,\text{k}\Omega + 23.6\,\Omega} = \mathbf{0.977}$$

19. $R_{in} = R_1 \parallel R_2 \parallel \beta_{ac}(r'_e + R_E) \cong R_1 \parallel R_2 \parallel \beta_{ac}R_E = 10\,\text{k}\Omega \parallel 4.7\,\text{k}\Omega \parallel 100\,\text{k}\Omega = \mathbf{3.1\,k\Omega}$

$$V_{OUT} = V_B - 0.7\,\text{V} = \left(\frac{R_2}{R_1+R_2}\right)V_{CC} - 0.7\,\text{V} = \left(\frac{4.7\,\text{k}\Omega}{14.7\,\text{k}\Omega}\right)5.5\,\text{V} - 0.7\,\text{V} = \mathbf{1.06\,V}$$

20. The voltage gain is **reduced** because $A_v = \dfrac{R_e}{R_e + r'_e}$.

21. $V_B = \left(\dfrac{R_2}{R_1 + R_2}\right)V_{CC} = \left(\dfrac{4.7\,\text{k}\Omega}{14.7\,\text{k}\Omega}\right)5.5\,\text{V} = 1.76\,\text{V}$

$I_E = \dfrac{V_B - V_{BE}}{R_E} = \dfrac{1.76\,\text{V} - 0.7\,\text{V}}{1.0\,\text{k}\Omega} = 1.06\,\text{mA}$

$r_e' \cong \dfrac{25\,\text{mV}}{I_E} = \dfrac{25\,\text{mV}}{1.06\,\text{mA}} = 23.6\,\Omega$

$A_v = \dfrac{R_E \parallel R_L}{r_e' + R_E \parallel R_L}$

$A_v\left(r_e' + R_E \parallel R_L\right) = R_E \parallel R_L$

$R_E \parallel R_L - A_v\left(R_E \parallel R_L\right) = A_v r_e'$

$\left(R_E \parallel R_L\right)\left(1 - A_v\right) = A_v r_e'$

$\left(R_E \parallel R_L\right) = \dfrac{A_v r_e'}{\left(1 - A_v\right)} = \dfrac{0.9(23.6\,\Omega)}{1 - 0.9} = 212.4\,\Omega$

$R_L R_E = 212.4 R_L + 212.4 R_E$

$R_L R_E - 212.4 R_L = 212.4 R_E$

$R_L = \dfrac{212.4 R_E}{R_E - 212.4} = \dfrac{(212.4\,\Omega)(1000\,\Omega)}{1000\,\Omega - 212.4\,\Omega} = \mathbf{270\,\Omega}$

22. (a) $V_{C1} = \mathbf{10\,V}$

$V_{B1} = \left(\dfrac{R_2}{R_1 + R_2}\right)V_{CC} = \left(\dfrac{22\,\text{k}\Omega}{55\,\text{k}\Omega}\right)10\,\text{V} = \mathbf{4\,V}$

$V_{E1} = V_{B1} - 0.7\,\text{V} = 4\,\text{V} - 0.7\,\text{V} = \mathbf{3.3\,V}$

$V_{C2} = \mathbf{10\,V}$

$V_{B2} = V_{E1} = \mathbf{3.3\,V}$

$V_{E2} = V_{B2} - 0.7\,\text{V} = 3.3\,\text{V} - 0.7\,\text{V} = \mathbf{2.6\,V}$

(b) $\beta_{DC}' = \beta_{DC1}\beta_{DC2} = (150)(100) = \mathbf{15{,}000}$

(c) $I_{E1} = \dfrac{V_{E1}}{\beta_{DC2}R_E} = \dfrac{3.3\,\text{V}}{(100(1.5\,\text{k}\Omega))} = \mathbf{22\,\mu A}$

$r_{e1}' \cong \dfrac{25\,\text{mV}}{I_{E1}} = \dfrac{25\,\text{mV}}{22\,\mu A} = \mathbf{1.14\,k\Omega}$

$I_{E2} = \dfrac{V_{E2}}{R_E} = \dfrac{2.6\,\text{V}}{1.5\,\text{k}\Omega} = 1.73\,\text{mA}$

$r_{e2}' \cong \dfrac{25\,\text{mV}}{I_{E2}} = \dfrac{25\,\text{mV}}{1.73\,\text{mV}} = \mathbf{14.5\,\Omega}$

(d) $R_{in} = R_1 \parallel R_2 \parallel R_{in(base1)}$

$R_{in(base1)} = \beta_{ac1}\beta_{ac2}R_E = (150)(100)(1.5\,\text{k}\Omega) = 22.5\,\text{M}\Omega$

$R_{in} = 33\,\text{k}\Omega \parallel 22\,\text{k}\Omega \parallel 22.5\,\text{M}\Omega = \mathbf{13.2\,k\Omega}$

23. $R_{in(base)} = \beta_{ac1}\beta_{ac2}R_E = (150)(100)(1.5\,k\Omega) = 22.5\,M\Omega$

$R_{in} = R_2 \parallel R_1 \parallel R_{in(base)} = 22\,k\Omega \parallel 33\,k\Omega \parallel 22.5\,M\Omega = 13.2\,k\Omega$

$I_{in} = \dfrac{V_{in}}{R_{in}} = \dfrac{1\,V}{13.2\,k\Omega} = 75.8\,\mu A$

$I_{in(base1)} = \dfrac{V_{in}}{R_{in(base1)}} = \dfrac{1\,V}{22.5\,M\Omega} = 44.4\,nA$

$I_e \cong \beta_{ac1}\beta_{ac2}I_{in(base1)} = (150)(100)(44.4\,nA) = 667\,\mu A$

$A_i' = \dfrac{I_e}{I_{in}} = \dfrac{667\,\mu A}{75.8\,\mu A} = \mathbf{8.8}$

Section 6-5 The Common-Base Amplifier

24. The main disadvantage of a common-base amplifier is **low input impedance**. Another disadvantage is **unity current gain**.

25. $V_E = \left(\dfrac{R_2}{R_1+R_2}\right)V_{CC} - V_{BE} = \left(\dfrac{10\,k\Omega}{32\,k\Omega}\right)24\,V - 0.7\,V = 6.8\,V$

$I_E = \dfrac{6.8\,V}{620\,\Omega} = 10.97\,mA$

$R_{in(emitter)} = r_e' \cong \dfrac{25\,mV}{I_E} = \dfrac{25\,mA}{10.97\,mA} = \mathbf{2.28\,\Omega}$

$A_v = \dfrac{R_C}{r_e'} = \dfrac{1.2\,k\Omega}{2.28\,\Omega} = \mathbf{526}$

$A_i \cong \mathbf{1}$

$A_p = A_iA_v \cong \mathbf{526}$

26. (a) Common-base   (b) Common-emitter   (c) Common-collector

Section 6-6 Multistage Amplifiers

27. $A_v' = A_{v1}A_{v2} = (20)(20) = \mathbf{400}$

28. $A_{v(dB)}' = 10\,dB + 10\,dB + 10\,dB = \mathbf{30\,dB}$

$20\log A_v' = 30\,dB$

$\log A_v' = \dfrac{30}{20} = 1.5$

$A_v' = \mathbf{31.6}$

Chapter 6

29.   (a) $V_E\left(\dfrac{R_2}{R_1 + R_2}\right)V_{CC} - V_{BE} = \left(\dfrac{8.2\,\text{k}\Omega}{33\,\text{k}\Omega + 8.2\,\text{k}\Omega}\right)15\,\text{V} - 0.7\,\text{V} = 2.29\,\text{V}$

$$I_E = \frac{V_E}{R_E} = \frac{2.29\,\text{V}}{1.0\,\text{k}\Omega} = 2.29\,\text{mA}$$

$$r'_e \cong \frac{25\,\text{mV}}{I_E} = \frac{25\,\text{mV}}{2.29\,\text{mA}} = 10.9\,\Omega$$

$$R_{in(2)} = R_5 \parallel R_4 \parallel \beta_{ac}r'_e = 8.2\,\text{k}\Omega \parallel 33\,\text{k}\Omega \parallel 175(10.9\,\Omega) = 1.48\,\text{k}\Omega$$

$$A_{v1} = \frac{R_C \parallel R_{in(2)}}{r'_e} = \frac{3.3\,\text{k}\Omega \parallel 1.48\,\text{k}\Omega}{10.9\,\Omega} = 93.6$$

$$A_{v2} = \frac{R_C}{r'_e} = \frac{3.3\,\text{k}\Omega}{10.9\,\Omega} = 302$$

(b) $A'_v = A_{v1}A_{v2} = (93.6)(302) = \mathbf{28{,}267}$

(c) $A_{v1(dB)} = 20\log(93.6) = \mathbf{39.4\ dB}$
$A_{v2(dB)} = 20\log(302) = \mathbf{49.6\ dB}$
$A'_{v(dB)}\ 20\log(28{,}267) = \mathbf{89.0\ dB}$

30.   (a) $A_{v1} = \dfrac{R_C \parallel R_{in(2)}}{r'_e} = \dfrac{3.3\,\text{k}\Omega \parallel 1.48\,\text{k}\Omega}{10.9\,\Omega} = \mathbf{93.6}$

$$A_{v2} = \frac{R_C \parallel R_L}{r'_e} = \frac{3.3\,\text{k}\Omega \parallel 18\,\text{k}\Omega}{10.9\,\Omega} = \mathbf{255}$$

(b) $R_{in(1)} = R_1 \parallel R_2 \parallel r'_e = 33\,\text{k}\Omega \parallel 8.2\,\text{k}\Omega \parallel 175(10.9\,\Omega) = 1.48\,\text{k}\Omega$
Attenuation of the input network is

$$\frac{R_{in(1)}}{R_{in(1)} + R_s} = \frac{1.48\,\text{k}\Omega}{1.48\,\text{k}\Omega + 75\,\Omega} = 0.95$$

$$A'_v = (0.95)A_{v1}A_{v2} = (0.95)(93.6)(255) = \mathbf{22{,}675}$$

(c) $A_{v1(dB)} = 20\log(93.6) = \mathbf{39.4\ dB}$
$A_{v2(dB)} = 20\log(255) = \mathbf{48.1\ dB}$
$A'_{v(dB)} = 20\log(22{,}675) = \mathbf{87.1\ dB}$

31. $V_{B1} = \left(\dfrac{R_2}{R_1 + R_2}\right)V_{CC} = \left(\dfrac{22\,\text{k}\Omega}{122\,\text{k}\Omega}\right)12\,\text{V} = \mathbf{2.16\ V}$

$V_{E1} = V_{B1} - 0.7\,\text{V} = \mathbf{1.46\ V}$

$I_{C1} \cong I_{E1} = \dfrac{V_{E1}}{R_4} = \dfrac{1.46\,\text{V}}{4.7\,\text{k}\Omega} = 0.311\,\text{mA}$

$V_{C1} = V_{CC} - I_{C1}R_3 = 12\,\text{V} - (0.311\,\text{mA})(22\,\text{k}\Omega) = \mathbf{5.16\ V}$
$V_{B2} = V_{C1} = \mathbf{5.16\ V}$
$V_{E2} = V_{B2} - 0.7\,\text{V} = 5.16\,\text{V} - 0.7\,\text{V} = \mathbf{4.46\ V}$

$$I_{C2} \cong I_{E2} = \frac{V_{E2}}{R_6} = \frac{4.46\,\text{V}}{10\,\text{k}\Omega} = 0.446\,\text{mA}$$

$$V_{C2} = V_{CC} - I_{C2}R_5 = 12\,\text{V} - (0.446\,\text{mA})(10\,\text{k}\Omega) = \textbf{7.54 V}$$

$$r'_{e2} \cong \frac{25\,\text{mV}}{I_{E2}} = \frac{25\,\text{mV}}{0.446\,\text{mA}} = 56\,\Omega$$

$$R_{in(2)} = \beta_{ac}r'_{e2} = (125)(56\,\Omega) = 7\,\text{k}\Omega$$

$$r'_{e1} \cong \frac{25\,\text{mV}}{I_{E1}} = \frac{25\,\text{mV}}{0.311\,\text{mA}} = 80.4\,\Omega$$

$$A_{v1} = \frac{R_3 \parallel R_{in(2)}}{r'_{e1}} = \frac{22\,\text{k}\Omega \parallel 7\,\text{k}\Omega}{80.4\,\text{k}\Omega} = \textbf{66}$$

$$A_{v2} = \frac{R_5}{r'_{e2}} = \frac{10\,\text{k}\Omega}{56\,\Omega} = \textbf{179}$$

$$A'_v = A_{v1}A_{v2} = (66)(179) = \textbf{11,814}$$

32.   (a) $20\log(12) = \textbf{21.6 dB}$
  (b) $20\log(50) = \textbf{34.0 dB}$
  (c) $20\log(100) = \textbf{40.0 dB}$
  (d) $20\log(2500) = \textbf{68.0 dB}$

33.   (a) $20\log\left(\frac{V_2}{V_1}\right) = 3\,\text{dB}$ (b) $20\log\left(\frac{V_2}{V_1}\right) = 6\,\text{dB}$ (c) $20\log\left(\frac{V_2}{V_1}\right) = 10\,\text{dB}$

$\log\left(\frac{V_2}{V_1}\right) = \frac{3}{20} = 0.15$ $\log\left(\frac{V_2}{V_1}\right) = \frac{6.}{20} = 0.3$ $\log\left(\frac{V_2}{V_1}\right) = \frac{10}{20} = 0.5$

$\frac{V_2}{V_1} = \textbf{1.41}$ $\frac{V_2}{V_1} = \textbf{2}$ $\frac{V_2}{V_1} = \textbf{3.16}$

(d) $20\log\left(\frac{V_2}{V_1}\right) = 20\,\text{dB}$ (b) $20\log\left(\frac{V_2}{V_1}\right) = 40\,\text{dB}$

$\log\left(\frac{V_2}{V_1}\right) = \frac{20}{20} = 1$ $\log\left(\frac{V_2}{V_1}\right) = \frac{40}{20} = 2$

$\frac{V_2}{V_1} = \textbf{10}$ $\frac{V_2}{V_1} = \textbf{100}$

Chapter 6

Section 6-7 Troubleshooting

34.
$$V_E = \left(\frac{R_1}{R_1 + R_2}\right)10\text{ V} - 0.7\text{ V} = \left(\frac{10\text{ k}\Omega}{57\text{ k}\Omega}\right)10\text{ V} - 0.7\text{ V} = 1.05\text{ V}$$

$$I_E = \frac{V_E}{R_4} = \frac{1.05\text{ V}}{1.0\text{ k}\Omega} = 1.05\text{ mA}$$

$$V_C = 10\text{ V} - (1.05\text{ mA})(4.7\text{ k}\Omega) = 5.07\text{ V}$$

$$V_{CE} = 5.07\text{ V} - 1.05\text{ V} = 4.02\text{ V}$$

$$r'_{CE} \cong \frac{V_{CE}}{I_E} = \frac{4.02\text{ V}}{1.05\text{ mA}} = 3.83\text{ k}\Omega$$

With C_2 shorted:

$$R_{IN(2)} = R_6 \,\|\, \beta_{DC}R_8 = 10\text{ k}\Omega \,\|\, 125(1.0\text{ k}\Omega) = 9.26\text{ k}\Omega$$

Looking from the collector of Q_1:

$$\left(r'_{CE} + R_4\right) \,\|\, R_{IN(2)} = (3.83\text{ k}\Omega + 1.0\text{ k}\Omega) \,\|\, 9.26\text{ k}\Omega = 3.17\text{ k}\Omega$$

$$V_{C1} = \left(\frac{3.17\text{ k}\Omega}{3.17\text{ k}\Omega + 4.7\text{ k}\Omega}\right)10\text{ V} = \mathbf{4.03\text{ V}}$$

35. Q_1 is in **cutoff**. $I_C = 0$ A, so $V_{C2} = \mathbf{10\text{ V}}$.

36.
   (a) Reduced gain
   (b) No output signal
   (c) Reduced gain
   (d) Bias levels of first stage will change. I_C will increase and Q_1 will go into saturation.
   (e) No signal at the Q_1 collector
   (f) Signal at the Q_2 base. No output signal.

37. $r'_e = 10.9\ \Omega$ $R_{in} = 1.48\text{ k}\Omega$
        $A_{v1} = 93.6$ $A_{v2} = 302$

Test Point	DC Volts	AC Volts (rms)
Input	0 V	25 μA
Q_1 base	2.99 V	20.8 μV
Q_1 emitter	2.29 V	0 V
Q_1 collector	7.44 V	1.95 mV
Q_2 base	2.99 V	1.95 mV
Q_2 emitter	2.29 V	0 V
Q_2 collector	7.44 V	589 mV
Output	0 V	589 mV

System Application Problems

38. For the block diagram of textbook Figure 6-40 with no output from the power amplifier or preamplifier and only one faulty block, the power amplifier must be ok because the fault must be one that affects the preamplifier's output prior to the power amplifier. Check the input to the preamplifier.

39. For the circuit of textbook Figure 6-53, the dc and ac operating parameters are

$$V_{B1} = \left(\frac{15\,k\Omega}{83\,k\Omega}\right)9\,V = (0.181)9\,V = 1.63\,V$$

$$V_E = 1.63\,V - 0.7\,V = 0.93\,V$$

$$I_{E1} = 927\,\mu A$$

$$r_e' = \frac{25\,mV}{927\,\mu A} = 27\,\Omega$$

$$A_{v(1)} = \frac{2.2\,k\Omega}{27\,\Omega} = 81.5\ unloaded$$

$$V_{B2} = \left(\frac{22\,k\Omega \,\|\, (200)(1.22\,k\Omega)}{100\,k\Omega + 22\,k\Omega \,\|\, (200)(1.22\,k\Omega)}\right)9\,V = 0.81\,V$$

$$I_{E2} = \frac{0.81\,V}{1.22\,k\Omega} = 665\,\mu A$$

$$r_e' = \frac{25\,mV}{665\,\mu A} = 37.6\,\Omega$$

$$A_{v(2)} = \frac{4.7\,k\Omega}{220\,\Omega + 37.6\,\Omega} = 18.2\ unloaded$$

$$Z_{in(2)} = 100\,k\Omega \,\|\, 22\,k\Omega \,\|\, (200)(288\,\Omega) = 13.7\,k\Omega$$

So, the loaded gain of Q_1 is equal to

$$\frac{13.7\,k\Omega}{13.7\,k\Omega + 2.2\,k\Omega} = 0.862\ \text{of the unloaded gain}$$

(a) With C_2 open, the input circuit is developed in Figure 6-3. From this,

$$A_v = \frac{R_C}{R_4 \,\|\, \left(r_e' + (R_1 \,\|\, R_2)/\beta_{ac}\right)}$$

$$= \frac{2.2\,k\Omega}{1.0\,k\Omega \,\|\, \left(27\,\Omega + (68\,k\Omega \,\|\, 15\,k\Omega)/200\right)} = 27.1\ unloaded$$

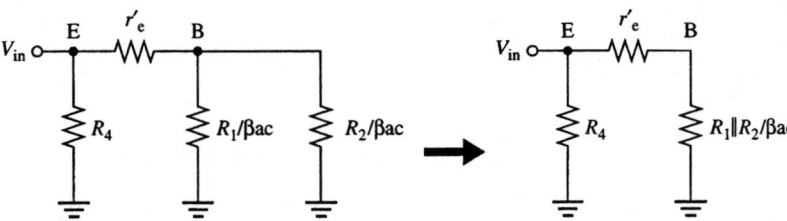

Figure 6-3

Chapter 6

The loading factor is unchanged and stage 2 is unaffected so the overall ac gain is
$$A'_v = (0.862)(27.1)(18.2) = 425$$
$$V_{out(2)} = 2 \text{ mV}(425) = \textbf{850 mV rms}$$
$$V_{C(2)} = 9 \text{ V} - (4.7 \text{ k}\Omega)(665 \text{ } \mu\text{A}) = \textbf{5.87 V dc}$$

(b) If C_1 is open, no input is applied so
$$V_{out(2)} = \textbf{0 V}$$
$$V_{C(2)} = \textbf{5.87 V}$$

(c) If C_3 is open, no signal is coupled to Q_2.
$$V_{out(2)} = \textbf{0 V}$$
$$V_{C(2)} = \textbf{5.87 V}$$

(d) If C_4 is open, the gain of stage 2 changes to
$$A_v = \frac{R_7}{r'_{e(2)} + R_8 + R_9} = \frac{4.7 \text{ k}\Omega}{37.6 \text{ }\Omega + 220 \text{ }\Omega + 1.0 \text{ k}\Omega} = 3.74$$
$$V_{out(2)} = (2 \text{ mV})(27.1)(3.74) = \textbf{203 mV rms}$$
$$V_{C(2)} = \textbf{5.87 V}$$

(e) If the Q_1 collector is internally open, no signal reaches the base of Q_2.
$$V_{out} = \textbf{0 V}$$
$$V_{C(2)} = \textbf{5.87 V}$$

(f) If the Q_2 emitter is shorted to ground, the transistor saturates.
$$V_{out} = \textbf{0 V}$$
$$V_{C(2)} = \textbf{0 V}$$

40.
$$V_{B2} = \left(\frac{220 \text{ k}\Omega \parallel (200)(1.22 \text{ k}\Omega)}{100 \text{ k}\Omega + 220 \text{ k}\Omega \parallel (200)(1.22 \text{ k}\Omega)} \right) 9 \text{ V} = 4.83 \text{ V}$$
$$V_E = 4.83 \text{ V} - 0.7 \text{ V} = 4.13 \text{ V}$$
$$I_E = \frac{4.13 \text{ V}}{1.22 \text{ k}\Omega} = 3.38 \text{ mA}$$
$$r'_e = \frac{25 \text{ mV}}{3.38 \text{ mA}} = 7.39 \text{ }\Omega$$
$$V_{C(2)} = 9 \text{ V} - (4.7 \text{ k}\Omega)(3.38 \text{ mA}) = -6.9 \text{ V}$$
The transistor is saturated, so $V_{out} = \textbf{0 V}$.
$$V_{C(2)} = \left(\frac{1.22 \text{ k}\Omega}{5.92 \text{ k}\Omega} \right) 9 \text{ V} = \textbf{1.85 V}$$

41. (a) Q_1 is in **cutoff**.
(b) $V_{C1} = \textbf{9 V}$
(c) V_{C2} is unchanged and at **5.87 V**

Data Sheet Problems

42. From the data sheet in textbook Appendix C:
    (a) for a 2N3947, $\beta_{ac(min)} = h_{fe(min)} = \mathbf{100}$
    (b) For a 2N3947, $r'_{e(min)}$ cannot be determined since $h_{re(min)}$ is not given.
    (c) For a 2N3947, $r'_{c(min)}$ cannot be determined since $h_{re(min)}$ is not given.

43. From the 2N3947 data sheet in Appendix C:
    (a) For a 2N3947, $\beta_{ac(max)} = \mathbf{700}$

    (b) For a 2N3947, $r'_{e(max)} = \dfrac{h_{re}}{h_{oe}} = \dfrac{20 \times 10^{-4}}{50 \ \mu S} = \mathbf{40 \ \Omega}$

    (c) For a 2N3947, $r'_{c(max)} = \dfrac{h_{re}+1}{h_{oe}} = \dfrac{20 \times 10^{-4}+1}{50 \ \mu S} = \mathbf{20 \ k\Omega}$

44. For maximum current gain, a **2N3947** should be used.

45. In the circuit of textbook Figure 6-53, a leaky coupling capacitor would affect the biasing of the transistors, attenuate the ac signal, and decrease the frequency response.

46. See Figure 6-4.

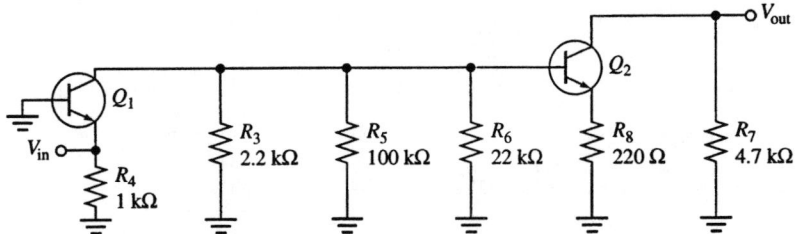

AC equivalent circuit

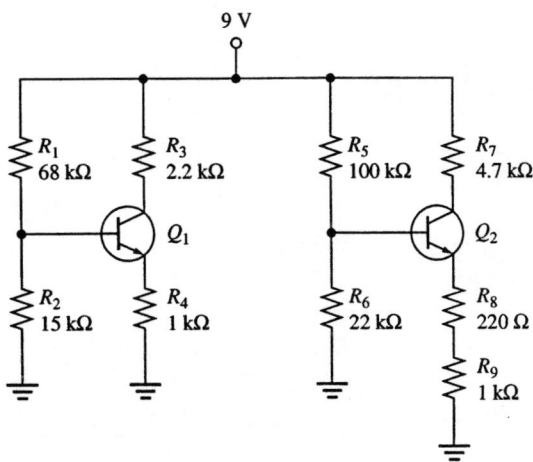

DC equivalent circuit

Figure 6-4

Chapter 6

47. See Figure 6-5.

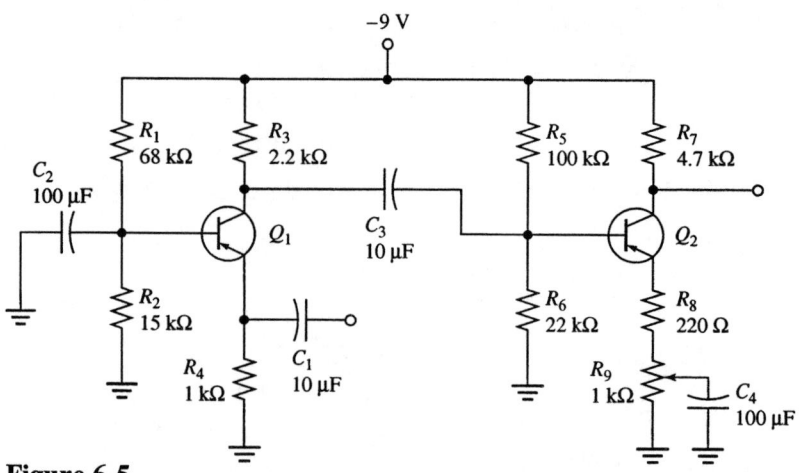

Figure 6-5

48. $R_C > (100)(330 \ \Omega) = 33 \ k\Omega$
To prevent cutoff, V_C must be no greater than
$12 \ V - (100)(1.414)(25 \ mV) = 8.46 \ V$
In addition, V_C must fall no lower than $8.46 \ V - 3.54 \ V = 4.93 \ V$ to prevent saturation.
$R_C = 100(R_E + r'_e)$

$r'_e = \dfrac{25 \ mV}{I_E}$

$12 \ V - I_C R_C = 8.46 \ V$

$I_C R_C = 3.54 \ V$

$I_C(100(R_E + r'_e)) = 3.54 \ V$

$I_C \left(100 \left(330 \ \Omega + \dfrac{25 \ mV}{I_C} \right) \right) \cong 3.54 \ V$

$(33 \ k\Omega)I_C + 2.5 \ V = 3.54 \ V$

$I_C = 31.4 \ \mu A$

$r'_e \cong \dfrac{25 \ mV}{31.4 \ \mu A} = 797 \ \Omega$

$R_C = 100(330 \ \Omega + 797 \ \Omega) = 113 \ k\Omega$
Let $R_C = 120 \ k\Omega$.
$V_C = 12 \ V - (31.4 \ \mu A)(120 \ k\Omega) = 8.23 \ V$
$V_{C(sat)} = 8.23 \ V - 3.54 \ V = 4.69 \ V$

$\dfrac{R_{E(tot)}}{R_C} = \dfrac{4.69 \ V}{7.31 \ V}$

$R_{E(tot)} = (0.642)(120 \ k\Omega) = 77 \ k\Omega$. Let $R_E = 68 \ k\Omega$.

$V_E = (31.4 \ \mu A)(68 \ k\Omega) = 2.14 \ V$

$V_B = 2.14 \ V + 0.7 \ V = 2.84 \ V$

$\dfrac{R_2}{R_1} = \dfrac{2.84 \ V}{9.16 \ V} = 0.310$

$R_2 = 0.310 R_1$. If $R_1 = 20 \ k\Omega$, $R_2 = 6.2 \ k\Omega$.
The amplifier circuit is shown in Figure 6-6.

The amplifier circuit is shown in Figure 6-6.

From the design:

$$V_B = \left(\frac{6.2\,\text{k}\Omega}{26.2\,\text{k}\Omega}\right)12\,\text{V} = 2.84\,\text{V}$$

$$V_E = 2.14\,\text{V}$$

$$I_C \cong I_E = \frac{2.14\,\text{V}}{68.3\,\text{k}\Omega} = 31.3\,\mu\text{A}$$

$$r'_e = \frac{25\,\text{mV}}{31.3\,\mu\text{A}} = 798\,\Omega$$

$$A_v = \frac{120\,\text{k}\Omega}{795\,\Omega + 330\,\Omega} = 106\ \text{or}\ 40.5\ \text{dB}$$

$$V_C = 12\,\text{V} - (31.3\,\mu\text{A})(120\,\text{k}\Omega) = 8.24\,\text{V}$$

The design is a close fit.

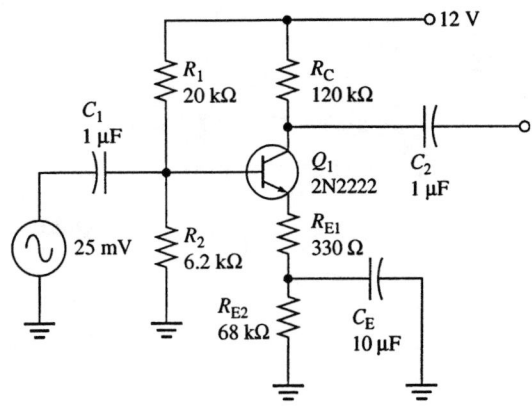

Figure 6-6

49.   See Figure 6-7.

$R_{in} = 120\,\text{k}\Omega \parallel 120\,\text{k}\Omega \parallel (100)(5.1\,\text{k}\Omega) = 53.6\,\text{k}\Omega$ minimum

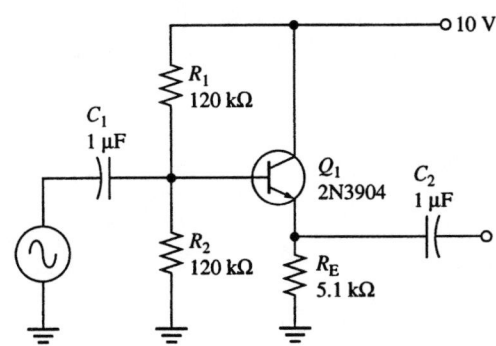

Figure 6-7

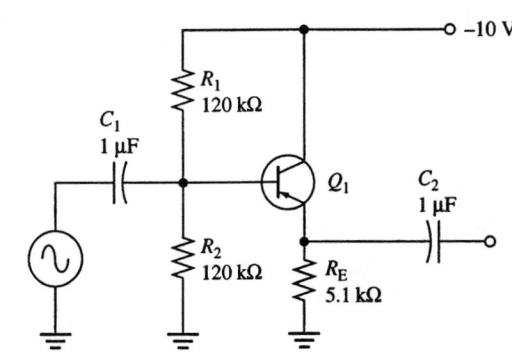

Figure 6-8

50.   See Figure 6-8.

51.   See Figure 6-9.

$$I_C = \frac{6\,\text{V} - 0.7\,\text{V}}{510\,\Omega + 2\,\text{k}\Omega/100} = 10\,\text{mA}$$

$$r'_e = \frac{25\,\text{mV}}{10\,\text{mA}} = 2.5\,\Omega$$

$$A_v = \frac{180\,\Omega}{2.5\,\Omega} = 72.4$$

This is reasonably close ($\approx$3.3% off) and can be made closer by putting a 7.5 Ω resistor in series with the 180 Ω collector resistor.

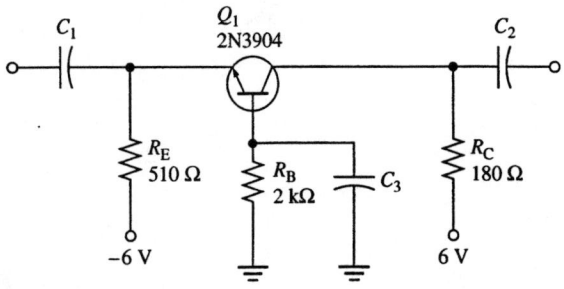

Figure 6-9

Chapter 6

52.   The cutoff frequency of C_3 is

$$\frac{1}{2\pi(10\ \mu F)\left(22\ k\Omega + (100\ k\Omega \parallel 22\ k\Omega \parallel (200)(220\ \Omega + 33\ \Omega))\right)} = 0.45\ \text{Hz}$$

The cutoff frequency of C_2 is

$$\frac{1}{2\pi(10\ \mu F)(1.0\ k\Omega \parallel 27\ \Omega)} = 606\ \text{Hz}$$

C_2 must be increased to

$$\frac{1}{2\pi(10\ \text{Hz})(1.0\ k\Omega \parallel 27\ \Omega)} = \mathbf{606\ \mu F}\ \text{(nearest standard value is 680 } \mu F\text{)}$$

53. $I_C \cong I_E$

$$A_v = \frac{R_C}{r_e'} \cong \frac{R_C}{25\ \text{mV}/I_E} \cong \frac{R_C}{25\ \text{mV}/I_C} = \frac{R_C I_C}{25\ \text{mV}} = \frac{V_{R_C}}{25\ \text{mV}} = 40V_{R_C}$$

EWB/Multisim Troubleshooting Problems

The solutions showing instrument connections for Problems 54 through 59 are available in the Solutions folder for Chapter 6 on the CD-ROM provided with the textbook. The solutions may be accessed using the password *ED5FLOYD*. The faults in the circuit files may be accessed using the password *book* (all lowercase).

54. C_2 open

55. C_2 shorted

56. R_E leaky

57. C_1 open

58. C_2 open

59. C_3 open

Chapter 7
Field-Effect Transistors (FETs)

Section 7-1 The JFET

1. (a) A greater V_{GS} **narrows** the depletion region.
   (b) The channel resistance **increases** with increased V_{GS}.

2. The gate-to-source voltage of an *n*-channel JFET must be zero or negative in order to maintain the required reverse-bias condition.

3. See Figure 7-1.

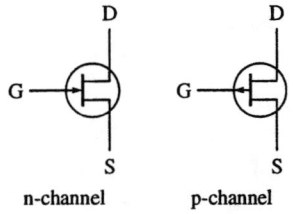

n-channel   p-channel

Figure 7-1

4. See Figure 7-2.

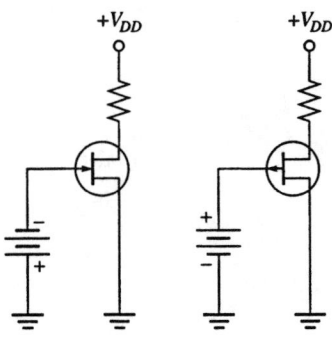

Figure 7-2

Section 7-2 JFET Characteristics and Parameters

5. $V_{DS} = V_P = $ **5 V** at point where I_D becomes constant.

6. $V_{GS(off)} = -V_P = $ **–6 V**
   The device is **on**, because $V_{GS} = -2$ V.

7. By definition, $I_D = I_{DSS}$ when $V_{GS} = 0$ V for values of $V_{DS} > V_P$.
   Therefore, $I_D = $ **10 mA**.

8. Since $V_{GS} > V_{GS(off)}$, the JFET is off and $I_D = $ **0 A**.

Chapter 7

9. $V_P = -V_{GS(off)} = -(-4 \text{ V}) = 4 \text{ V}$

The voltmeter reads V_{DS}. As V_{DD} is increased, V_{DS} also increases. The point at which I_D reaches a constant value is $V_{DS} = V_P = \mathbf{4\ V}$.

10. $I_D = I_{DSS}\left(1 - \dfrac{V_{GS}}{V_{GS(off)}}\right)^2$

$I_D = 5 \text{ mA}\left(1 - \dfrac{0 \text{ V}}{-8 \text{ V}}\right)^2 = 5 \text{ mA}$

$I_D = 5 \text{ mA}\left(1 - \dfrac{-1 \text{ V}}{-8 \text{ V}}\right)^2 = 3.83 \text{ mA}$

$I_D = 5 \text{ mA}\left(1 - \dfrac{-2 \text{ V}}{-8 \text{ V}}\right)^2 = 2.81 \text{ mA}$

$I_D = 5 \text{ mA}\left(1 - \dfrac{-3 \text{ V}}{-8 \text{ V}}\right)^2 = 1.95 \text{ mA}$

$I_D = 5 \text{ mA}\left(1 - \dfrac{-4 \text{ V}}{-8 \text{ V}}\right)^2 = 1.25 \text{ mA}$

$I_D = 5 \text{ mA}\left(1 - \dfrac{-5 \text{ V}}{-8 \text{ V}}\right)^2 = 0.703 \text{ mA}$

$I_D = 5 \text{ mA}\left(1 - \dfrac{-6 \text{ V}}{-8 \text{ V}}\right)^2 = 0.313 \text{ mA}$

$I_D = 5 \text{ mA}\left(1 - \dfrac{-7 \text{ V}}{-8 \text{ V}}\right)^2 = 0.078 \text{ mA}$

$I_D = 5 \text{ mA}\left(1 - \dfrac{-8 \text{ V}}{-8 \text{ V}}\right)^2 = 0 \text{ mA}$

See Figure 7-3.

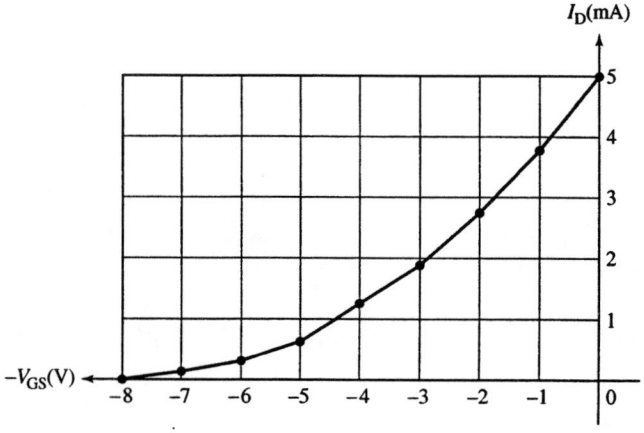

Figure 7-3

11.

$$I_D = I_{DSS}\left(1 - \frac{V_{GS}}{V_{GS(off)}}\right)^2$$

$$1 - \frac{V_{GS}}{V_{GS(off)}} = \sqrt{\frac{I_D}{I_{DSS}}}$$

$$\frac{V_{GS}}{V_{GS(off)}} = 1 - \sqrt{\frac{I_D}{I_{DSS}}}$$

$$V_{GS} = V_{GS(off)}\left(1 - \sqrt{\frac{I_D}{I_{DSS}}}\right)$$

$$V_{GS} = -8\text{ V}\left(1 - \sqrt{\frac{2.25\text{ mA}}{5\text{ mA}}}\right) = -8\text{ V}(0.329) = \mathbf{-2.63\text{ V}}$$

12.

$$g_m = g_{m0}\left(1 - \frac{V_{GS}}{V_{GS(off)}}\right) = 3200\ \mu S\left(1 - \frac{-4\text{ V}}{-8\text{ V}}\right) = \mathbf{1600\ \mu S}$$

13.

$$g_m = g_{m0}\left(1 - \frac{V_{GS}}{V_{GS(off)}}\right) = 2000\ \mu S\left(1 - \frac{-2\text{ V}}{-7\text{ V}}\right) = \mathbf{1429\ \mu S}$$

$$y_{fs} = g_m = \mathbf{1429\ \mu S}$$

14.

$$R_{IN} = \frac{V_{GS}}{I_{GSS}} = \frac{10\text{ V}}{5\text{ nA}} = \mathbf{2000\text{ M}\Omega}$$

15.

$$V_{GS} = 0\text{ V: } I_D = I_{DSS}\left(1 - \frac{V_{GS}}{V_{GS(off)}}\right)^2 = 8\text{ mA}(1 - 0)^2 = \mathbf{8\text{ mA}}$$

$$V_{GS} = -1\text{ V: } I_D = 8\text{ mA}\left(1 - \frac{-1\text{ V}}{-5\text{ V}}\right)^2 = 8\text{ mA}(1 - 0.2)^2 = 8\text{ mA}(0.8)^2 = \mathbf{5.12\text{ mA}}$$

$$V_{GS} = -2\text{ V: } I_D = 8\text{ mA}\left(1 - \frac{-2\text{ V}}{-5\text{ V}}\right)^2 = 8\text{ mA}(1 - 0.4)^2 = 8\text{ mA}(0.6)^2 = \mathbf{2.88\text{ mA}}$$

$$V_{GS} = -3\text{ V: } I_D = 8\text{ mA}\left(1 - \frac{-3\text{ V}}{-5\text{ V}}\right)^2 = 8\text{ mA}(1 - 0.6)^2 = 8\text{ mA}(0.4)^2 = \mathbf{1.28\text{ mA}}$$

$$V_{GS} = -4\text{ V: } I_D = 8\text{ mA}\left(1 - \frac{-4\text{ V}}{-5\text{ V}}\right)^2 = 8\text{ mA}(1 - 0.8)^2 = 8\text{ mA}(0.2)^2 = \mathbf{0.320\text{ mA}}$$

$$V_{GS} = -5\text{ V: } I_D = 8\text{ mA}\left(1 - \frac{-5\text{ V}}{-5\text{ V}}\right)^2 = 8\text{ mA}(1 - 1)^2 = 8\text{ mA}(0)^2 = \mathbf{0\text{ mA}}$$

Section 7-3 JFET Biasing

16. $V_{GS} = -I_D R_S = -(12\text{ mA})(100\ \Omega) = -1.2\text{ V}$

Chapter 7

17. $R_S = \left|\dfrac{V_{GS}}{I_D}\right| = \left|\dfrac{-4\,V}{5\,mA}\right| = \textbf{800 }\boldsymbol{\Omega}$

18. $R_S = \left|\dfrac{V_{GS}}{I_D}\right| = \left|\dfrac{-3\,V}{2.5\,mA}\right| = \textbf{1.2 k}\boldsymbol{\Omega}$

19. (a) $I_D = I_{DSS} = \textbf{20 mA}$
   (b) $I_D = \textbf{0 A}$
   (c) I_D **increases**

20. (a) $V_S = (1\,mA)(1.0\,k\Omega) = 1\,V$ (b) $V_S = (5\,mA)(100\,\Omega) = 0.5\,V$
   $V_D = 12\,V - (1\,mA)(4.7\,k\Omega) = 7.3\,V$ $V_D = 9\,V - (5\,mA)(470\,\Omega) = 6.65\,V$
   $V_G = 0\,V$ $V_G = 0\,V$
   $V_{GS} = V_G - V_S = 0\,V - 1\,V = \textbf{--1 V}$ $V_{GS} = V_G - V_S = 0\,V - 0.5\,V = \textbf{--0.5 V}$
   $V_{DS} = 7.3\,V - 1\,V = \textbf{6.3 V}$ $V_{DS} = 6.65\,V - 0.5\,V = \textbf{6.15 V}$

   (c) $V_S = (-3\,mA)(470\,\Omega) = -1.41\,V$
   $V_D = -15\,V - (3\,mA)(2.2\,k\Omega) = -8.4\,V$
   $V_G = 0\,V$
   $V_{GS} = V_G - V_S = 0\,V - (-1.41\,V) = \textbf{1.41 V}$
   $V_{DS} = -8.4\,V - (-1.41\,V) = \textbf{--6.99 V}$

21. From the graph, $V_{GS} \cong -2\,V$ at $I_D = 9.5\,mA$.
   $R_S = \left|\dfrac{V_{GS}}{I_D}\right| = \left|\dfrac{-2\,V}{9.5\,mA}\right| = \textbf{211 }\boldsymbol{\Omega}$

22. $I_D = \dfrac{I_{DSS}}{2} = \dfrac{14\,mA}{2} = \textbf{7 mA}$

   $V_{GS} = \dfrac{V_{GS(off)}}{3.414} = \dfrac{-10\,V}{3.414} = \textbf{--2.93 V}$
   Since $V_G = 0\,V$, $V_S = V_G$.

   $R_S = \left|\dfrac{V_{GS}}{I_D}\right| = \dfrac{2.93\,V}{7\,mA} = \textbf{419 }\boldsymbol{\Omega}$ (The nearest standard value is 430 Ω.)

   $R_D = \dfrac{V_{DD} - V_D}{I_D} = \dfrac{24\,V - 12\,V}{7\,mA} = \textbf{1.7 k}\boldsymbol{\Omega}$ (The nearest standard value is 1.8 kΩ.)
   Select $R_G = 1.0\,M\Omega$. See Figure 7-4.

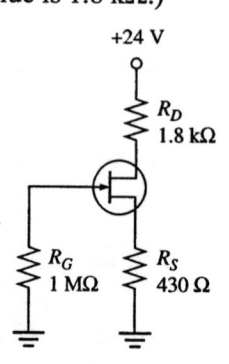

Figure 7-4

64

23. $R_{IN(total)} = R_G \parallel R_{IN}$

$$R_{IN} = \left| \frac{V_{GS}}{I_{GSS}} \right| = \left| \frac{-10\,V}{20\,nA} \right| = 500\,M\Omega$$

$R_{IN(total)} = 10\,M\Omega \parallel 500\,M\Omega = \mathbf{9.8\,M\Omega}$

24. For $I_D = 0$
$V_{GS} = -I_D R_S = (0)(330\,\Omega) = 0\,V$
For $I_D = I_{DSS} = 5\,mA$
$V_{GS} = -I_D R_S = -(5\,mA)(330\,\Omega) = -1.65\,V$
From the graph in Figure 7-61 in the textbook, the Q-point is
$V_{GS} \cong \mathbf{-0.95\,V}$ and $I_D \cong \mathbf{2.9\,mA}$

25. For $I_D = 0$,
$V_{GS} = 0\,V$
For $I_D = I_{DSS} = 10\,mA$,
$V_{GS} = -I_D R_S = (10\,mA)(390\,\Omega) = 3.9\,V$
From the graph in Figure 7-62 in the textbook, the Q-point is
$V_{GS} \cong \mathbf{2.1\,V}$ and $I_D \cong \mathbf{5.3\,mA}$

26. Since $V_{R_D} = 9\,V - 5\,V = 4\,V$

$$I_D = \frac{V_{R_D}}{R_D} = \frac{4\,V}{4.7\,k\Omega} = 0.85\,mA$$

$V_S = I_D R_S = (0.85\,mA)(3.3\,k\Omega) = 2.81\,V$

$$V_G = \left(\frac{R_2}{R_1 + R_2} \right) V_{DD} = \left(\frac{2.2\,M\Omega}{12.2\,M\Omega} \right) 9\,V = 1.62\,V$$

$V_{GS} = V_G - V_S = 1.62\,V - 2.81\,V = -1.19\,V$
Q-point: $I_D = \mathbf{0.85\,mA}$, $V_{GS} = \mathbf{-1.19\,V}$

27. For $I_D = 0$

$$V_{GS} = V_G = \left(\frac{R_2}{R_1 + R_2} \right) V_{DD} = \left(\frac{2.2\,M\Omega}{5.5\,M\Omega} \right) 12\,V = 4.8\,V$$

For $V_{GS} = 0\,V$, $V_S = 4.8\,V$

$$I_D = \frac{V_S}{R_S} = \frac{|V_G - V_{GS}|}{R_S} = \frac{4.8\,V}{3.3\,k\Omega} = 1.45\,mA$$

The Q-point is taken from the graph in Figure 7-64 in the textbook.
$I_D \cong \mathbf{1.9\,mA}$, $V_{GS} = \mathbf{-1.5\,V}$

Section 7-4 The MOSFET

28. See Figure 7-5.

n-channel D-MOSFET   p-channel D-MOSFET   n-channel E-MOSFET   p-channel E-MOSFET

Figure 7-5

Chapter 7

29. An *n*-channel D-MOSFET with a positive V_{GS} is operating in the **enhancement mode.**

30. An E-MOSFET has no physical channel or depletion mode. A D-MOSFET has a physical channel and can be operated in either depletion or enhancement modes.

31. MOSFETs have a very high input resistance because the gate is insulated from the channel by an SiO_2 layer.

Section 7-5 MOSFET Characteristics and Parameters

32. (a) *n* channel

(b) $I_D = I_{DSS}\left(1 - \dfrac{V_{GS}}{V_{GS(off)}}\right)^2$ $\qquad I_D = 8\,\text{mA}\left(1 - \dfrac{-5\,\text{V}}{-5\,\text{V}}\right)^2 = \textbf{0 mA}$

$I_D = 8\,\text{mA}\left(1 - \dfrac{-4\,\text{V}}{-5\,\text{V}}\right)^2 = \textbf{0.32 mA}$ $\qquad I_D = 8\,\text{mA}\left(1 - \dfrac{-3\,\text{V}}{-5\,\text{V}}\right)^2 = \textbf{1.28 mA}$

$I_D = 8\,\text{mA}\left(1 - \dfrac{-2\,\text{V}}{-5\,\text{V}}\right)^2 = \textbf{2.88 mA}$ $\qquad I_D = 8\,\text{mA}\left(1 - \dfrac{-1\,\text{V}}{-5\,\text{V}}\right)^2 = \textbf{5.12 mA}$

$I_D = 8\,\text{mA}\left(1 - \dfrac{0\,\text{V}}{-5\,\text{V}}\right)^2 = \textbf{8 mA}$ $\qquad I_D = 8\,\text{mA}\left(1 - \dfrac{1\,\text{V}}{-5\,\text{V}}\right)^2 = \textbf{11.5 mA}$

$I_D = 8\,\text{mA}\left(1 - \dfrac{2\,\text{V}}{-5\,\text{V}}\right)^2 = \textbf{15.7 mA}$ $\qquad I_D = 8\,\text{mA}\left(1 - \dfrac{3\,\text{V}}{-5\,\text{V}}\right)^2 = \textbf{20.5 mA}$

$I_D = 8\,\text{mA}\left(1 - \dfrac{4\,\text{V}}{-5\,\text{V}}\right)^2 = \textbf{25.9 mA}$ $\qquad I_D = 8\,\text{mA}\left(1 - \dfrac{5\,\text{V}}{-5\,\text{V}}\right)^2 = \textbf{32 mA}$

(c) See Figure 7-6.

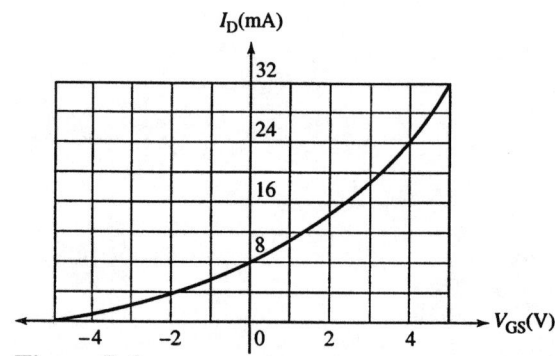

Figure 7-6

33. $I_D = I_{DSS}\left(1 - \dfrac{V_{GS}}{V_{GS(off)}}\right)^2$

$I_{DSS} = \dfrac{I_D}{\left(1 - \dfrac{V_{GS}}{V_{GS(off)}}\right)^2} = \dfrac{3\,\text{mA}}{\left(1 - \dfrac{-2\,\text{V}}{-10\,\text{V}}\right)^2} = \textbf{4.69 mA}$

34. $K = \dfrac{I_{D(on)}}{(V_{GS} - V_{GS(th)})^2} = \dfrac{10\,\text{mA}}{(-12\,\text{V} + 3\,\text{V})^2} = 0.12\,\text{mA/V}^2$

$I_D = K(V_{GS} - V_{GS(off)})^2 = (0.12\,\text{mA/V}^2)(-6\,\text{V} + 3\,\text{V})^2 = \textbf{1.08 mA}$

Section 7-6 MOSFET Biasing

35. (a) Depletion
(b) Enhancement
(c) Zero bias
(d) Depletion

36. (a) $V_{GS} = \left(\dfrac{10\,\text{M}\Omega}{14.7\,\text{M}\Omega}\right)10\,\text{V} = \textbf{6.8 V}$ This MOSFET is **on**.

(b) $V_{GS} = \left(\dfrac{1.0\,\text{M}\Omega}{11\,\text{M}\Omega}\right)(-25\,\text{V}) = \textbf{-2.27 V}$ This MOSFET is **off**.

37. Since $V_{GS} = 0$ V for each circuit, $I_D = I_{DSS} = 8$ mA.
(a) $V_{DS} = V_{DD} - I_D R_D = 12\,\text{V} - (8\,\text{mA})(1.0\,\text{k}\Omega) = \textbf{4 V}$
(b) $V_{DS} = V_{DD} - I_D R_D = 15\,\text{V} - (8\,\text{mA})(1.2\,\text{k}\Omega) = \textbf{5.4 V}$
(c) $V_{DS} = V_{DD} - I_D R_D = -9\,\text{V} - (-8\,\text{mA})(560\,\Omega) = \textbf{-4.52 V}$

38. (a) $I_{D(on)} = 3$ mA @ 4 V, $V_{GS(th)} = 2$ V

$V_{GS} = \left(\dfrac{R_2}{R_1 + R_2}\right)V_{DD} = \left(\dfrac{4.7\,\text{M}\Omega}{14.7\,\text{M}\Omega}\right)10\,\text{V} = \textbf{3.2 V}$

$K = \dfrac{I_{D(on)}}{(V_{GS} - V_{GS(th)})^2} = \dfrac{3\,\text{mA}}{(4\,\text{V} - 2\,\text{V})^2} = \dfrac{3\,\text{mA}}{(2\,\text{V})^2} = 0.75\,\text{mA/V}^2$

$I_D = K(V_{GS} - V_{GS(th)})^2 = (0.75\,\text{mA/V}^2)(3.2\,\text{V} - 2\,\text{V})^2 = 1.08\,\text{mA}$

$V_{DS} = V_{DD} - I_D R_D = 10\,\text{V} - (1.08\,\text{mA})(1.0\,\text{k}\Omega) = 10\,\text{V} - 1.08\,\text{V} = \textbf{8.92 V}$

(b) $I_{D(on)} = 2$ mA @ 4 V, $V_{GS(th)} = 1.5$ V

$V_{GS} = \left(\dfrac{R_2}{R_1 + R_2}\right)V_{DD} = \left(\dfrac{10\,\text{M}\Omega}{20\,\text{M}\Omega}\right)5\,\text{V} = \textbf{2.5 V}$

$K = \dfrac{I_{D(on)}}{(V_{GS} - V_{GS(th)})^2} = \dfrac{2\,\text{mA}}{(3\,\text{V} - 1.5\,\text{V})^2} = \dfrac{2\,\text{mA}}{(1.5\,\text{V})^2} = 0.89\,\text{mA/V}^2$

$I_D = K(V_{GS} - V_{GS(th)})^2 = (0.89\,\text{mA/V}^2)(2.5\,\text{V} - 1.5\,\text{V})^2 = 0.89\,\text{mA}$

$V_{DS} = V_{DD} - I_D R_D = 5\,\text{V} - (0.89\,\text{mA})(1.5\,\text{k}\Omega) = 5\,\text{V} - 1.34\,\text{V} = \textbf{3.66 V}$

39.   (a) $V_{DS} = V_{GS} = \textbf{5 V}$

$$I_D = \frac{V_{DD} - V_{DS}}{R_D} = \frac{12\,V - 5\,V}{2.2\,k\Omega} = \textbf{3.18 mA}$$

        (b) $V_{DS} = V_{GS} = \textbf{3.2 V}$

$$I_D = \frac{V_{DD} - V_{DS}}{R_D} = \frac{8\,V - 3.2\,V}{4.7\,k\Omega} = \textbf{1.02 mA}$$

40. $V_{DS} = V_{DD} - I_D R_D = 15\,V - (1\,mA)(8.2\,k\Omega) = 6.8\,V$
        $V_{GS} = V_{DS} - I_G R_G = 6.8\,V - (50\,pA)(22\,M\Omega) = \textbf{6.799 V}$

Section 7-7 Troubleshooting

41.   When I_D goes to zero, the possible faults are:
        R_D or R_S open, JFET drain-to-source open, no supply voltage, or ground connection open.

42.   If I_D goes to 16 mA, the possible faults are:
        The JFET is shorted from drain-to-source or V_{DD} has increased.

43.   If V_{DD} is changed to −20 V, I_D will change very little or none because the device is operating in the constant-current region of the characteristic curve.

44.   The device is off. The gate bias voltage must be less than $V_{GS(th)}$. The gate could be shorted or partially shorted to ground.

45.   The device is saturated, so there is very little voltage from drain-to-source. This indicates that V_{GS} is too high. The 1.0 MΩ bias resistor is probably **open**.

System Application Problems

46.   With the 100 μF capacitor open, power supply noise or ripple *could* affect the sensor outputs, producing false readings and alarms.

47.   From the graph in textbook Figure 7-53:
        For pH = 5, $V_{OUT} = \textbf{300 mV}$
        For pH = 9, $V_{OUT} = \textbf{−400 mV}$

48.   A possible problem is that the voltmeter has an input resistance of 1 MΩ instead of 10 MΩ and is loading the sensor output.

49. $V_{OUT} \cong 15\,V - (2.9\,mA)(1\,k\Omega)\ 15\,V - 2.9\,V = \textbf{12.1 V}$

Data Sheet Problems

50.   The 2N5457 is an *n*-channel JFET.

51. From the data sheet in textbook Figure 7-14:
    (a)   For a 2N5457, $V_{\text{GS(off)}} = $ **–0.5 V** minimum
    (b)   For a 2N5457, $V_{\text{DS(max)}} = $ **25 V**
    (c)   For a 2N5458 @ 25°C, $P_{\text{D(max)}} = $ **310 mW**
    (d)   For a 2N5459, $V_{\text{GS(rev)}} = $ **–25 V** maximum

52. $P_{\text{D(max)}} = 310 \text{ mW} - (2.82 \text{ mW/°C})(65°C - 25°C) = 310 \text{ mW} - 113 \text{ mW} = \textbf{197 mW}$

53. $g_{m0\text{(min)}} = y_{fs} = \textbf{2000 } \boldsymbol{\mu}\textbf{S}$

54. Typical $I_D = I_{\text{DSS}} = \textbf{9 mA}$

55. From the data sheet in textbook Figure 7-41:
Minimum $V_{\text{GS(th)}} = \textbf{1 V}$

56. For a 2N7008 with $V_{\text{GS}} = 10$ V, $I_D = \textbf{500 mA}$

57. From the data sheet graph in textbook Figure 7-52:
At $V_{\text{GS}} = +3$ V, $I_D \cong \textbf{13 mA}$
At $V_{\text{GS}} = -2$ V, $I_D \cong \textbf{0.4 mA}$

58. $y_{fs} = 1500 \ \mu\text{S}$ at $f = 1$ kHz and at $f = 1$ MHz for both the 2N3796 and 2N3797.
There is **no change** in y_{fs} over the frequency range.

59. For a 2N3796, $V_{\text{GS(off)}} = \textbf{–3.0 V}$ typical

Advanced Problems

60. For the circuit of textbook Figure 7-71:

$$I_D = I_{\text{DSS}}\left(1 - \frac{V_{\text{GS}}}{V_{\text{GS(off)}}}\right)^2 \text{ where } V_{\text{GS}} = I_D R_S$$

From the 2N5457 data sheet:
$I_{\text{DSS(min)}} = 1.0$ mA and $V_{\text{GS(off)}} = -0.5$ V minimum
$I_D = 66.3 \ \mu\text{A}$
$V_{\text{GS}} = -(66.3 \ \mu\text{A})(5.6 \text{ k}\Omega) = \textbf{–0.371 V}$
$V_{\text{DS}} = 12 \text{ V} - (66.3 \ \mu\text{A})(10 \text{ k}\Omega + 5.6 \text{ k}\Omega) = \textbf{11.0 V}$

61. For the circuit of textbook Figure 7-72:

$$V_C = \left(\frac{3.3 \text{ k}\Omega}{13.3 \text{ k}\Omega}\right)9 \text{ V} = (0.248)(9 \text{ V}) = 2.23 \text{ V}$$

From the equation,

$$I_D = I_{\text{DSS}}\left(\frac{V_{\text{GS}}}{1 - V_{\text{GS(off)}}}\right)^2 \text{ where } V_{\text{GS}} = V_G - I_D R_S$$

I_D is maximum for $I_{\text{DSS(max)}}$ and $V_{\text{GS(off)}}$ max, so that
$I_{\text{DSS}} = 16$ mA and $V_{\text{GS(off)}} = -8.0$ V
$I_D = \textbf{3.58 mA}$
$V_{\text{GS}} = 2.23 \text{ V} - (3.58 \text{ mA})(1.8 \text{ k}\Omega) = 2.23 \text{ V} - 6.45 \text{ V} = \textbf{–4.21 V}$

Chapter 7

62. From the 2N5457 data sheet:

$I_{DSS(min)} = 1.0$ mA and $V_{GS(off)} = -0.5$ minimum

$I_{D(min)} = \textbf{66.3 } \boldsymbol{\mu}\textbf{A}$

$V_{DS(max)} = 12$ V $- (66.3 \ \mu A)(15.6 \ k\Omega) = \textbf{11.0 V}$

and

$I_{DSS(max)} = 5.0$ mA and $V_{GS(off)} = -6.0$ maximum

$I_{D(max)} = \textbf{677 } \boldsymbol{\mu}\textbf{A}$

$V_{DS(min)} = 12$ V $- (677 \ \mu A)(15.6 \ k\Omega) = \textbf{1.4 V}$

63. $V_{pH} = +300$ mV

$I_D = (2.9 \ \text{mA})(1 + 0.3 \ \text{V}/5.0 \ \text{V})^2 = (2.9 \ \text{mA})(1.06)^2 = 3.26$ mA

$V_{DS} = 15$ V $- (3.26 \ \text{mA})(2.76 \ k\Omega) = 15$ V $- 8.99$ V $= \textbf{+6.01 V}$

64. $1 \ \text{mA} = I_{DSS}\left(1 - \dfrac{(1\,\text{mA})R_S}{V_{GS(off)}}\right)^2$

$1 \ \text{mA} = 2.9 \ \text{mA}\left(1 - \dfrac{(1\,\text{mA})R_S}{-0.5 \ \text{V}}\right)^2$

$0.345 = \left(1 - \dfrac{(1\,\text{mA})R_S}{-0.5 \ \text{V}}\right)^2$

$0.587 = 1 - \dfrac{(1\,\text{mA})R_S}{-0.5 \ \text{V}}$

$0.413 = \dfrac{(1\,\text{mA})R_S}{-0.5 \ \text{V}}$

$R_S = 2.06 \ k\Omega$

Use $R_S = \textbf{2.2 } \boldsymbol{k\Omega}$.

Then $I_D = 963 \ \mu A$

$V_{GS} = V_S = (963 \ \mu A)(2.2 \ k\Omega) = 2.19$ V

So, $V_D = 2.19$ V $+ 4.5$ V $= 6.62$ V

$R_D = \dfrac{9 \ \text{V} - 6.62 \ \text{V}}{963 \mu A} = 2.47 \ k\Omega$

Use $R_D = \textbf{2.4 } \boldsymbol{k\Omega}$.

So, $V_{DS} = 9$ V $- (963 \ \mu A)(4.6 \ k\Omega) = 4.57$ V

65. Let $I_D = 20$ mA.

$$R_D = \frac{4\text{ V}}{20\text{ mA}} = \mathbf{200\ \Omega}$$

Let $V_S = 2$ V.

$$R_S = \frac{2\text{ V}}{20\text{ mA}} = \mathbf{100\ \Omega}$$

For the 2N7008:

$$K = \frac{I_{D(on)}}{(V_{GS(on)} - V_{GS(th)})^2} = \frac{500\text{ mA}}{(10\text{ V} - 1\text{ V})^2} = 6.17\text{ mA/V}^2$$

Let $I_D = 20$ mA.

$$(V_{GS} - 1\text{ V})^2 = \frac{20\text{ V}}{6.17\text{ mA/V}^2} = 3.24$$

$V_{GS} - 1\text{ V} = 1.8$ V

$V_{GS} = 2.8$ V

$V_G = V_S + 2.8\text{ V} = 4.8$ V

For the voltage divider:

$$\frac{R_1}{R_2} = \frac{7.2\text{ V}}{4.8\text{ V}} = 1.5$$

Let $R_2 = \mathbf{10\ k\Omega}$.

$R_1 = (1.5)(10\text{ k}\Omega) = \mathbf{15\ k\Omega}$

EWB/Multisim Troubleshooting Problems

The solutions showing instrument connections for Problems 66 through 74 are available in the Solutions folder for Chapter 7 on the CD-ROM provided with the textbook. The solutions may be accessed using the password *ED5FLOYD*. The faults in the circuit files may be accessed using the password *book* (all lowercase).

66. R_S shorted

67. R_D shorted

68. R_G shorted

69. R_1 open

70. Drain-source open

71. R_D open

72. R_2 shorted

73. Drain-source shorted

74. R_1 shorted

Chapter 8
FET Amplifiers

Section 8-1 FET Amplification

1. (a) $I_D = g_m V_{gs} = (6000\ \mu S)(10\ mV) = \textbf{60}\ \boldsymbol{\mu}\textbf{A}$
    (b) $I_D = g_m V_{gs} = (6000\ \mu S)(150\ mV) = \textbf{900}\ \boldsymbol{\mu}\textbf{A}$
    (c) $I_D = g_m V_{gs} = (6000\ \mu S)(0.6\ V) = \textbf{3.6 mA}$
    (d) $I_D = g_m V_{gs} = (6000\ \mu S)(1\ V) = \textbf{6 mA}$

2. $A_v = g_m R_d$

    $R_d = \dfrac{A_v}{g_m} = \dfrac{20}{3500\ \mu S} = \textbf{5.71 k}\boldsymbol{\Omega}$

3. $A_v = \left(\dfrac{R_D r'_{ds}}{R_D + r'_{ds}} \right) g_m = \left(\dfrac{(4.7\ k\Omega)(12\ k\Omega)}{16.7\ k\Omega} \right) 4.2\ mS = \textbf{14.2}$

4. $R_d = R_D \parallel r'_{ds} = 4.7\ k\Omega \parallel 12\ k\Omega = 3.38\ k\Omega$

    $A_v = \dfrac{g_m R_d}{1 + g_m R_s} = \dfrac{(4.2\ mS)(3.38\ k\Omega)}{1 + (4.2\ mS)(1.0\ k\Omega)} = \textbf{2.73}$

Section 8-2 Common-Source Amplifiers

5. (a) *N*-channel D-MOSFET with zero-bias.
       $V_{GS} = \textbf{0 V}$.
    (b) *P*-channel JFET with self-bias.
       $V_{GS} = -I_D R_S = (-3\ mA)(330\ \Omega) = \textbf{--0.99 V}$
       N-channel E-MOSFET with voltage-divider bias.

    (c) $V_{GS} = \left(\dfrac{R_2}{R_1 + R_2} \right) V_{DD} = \left(\dfrac{4.7\ k\Omega}{14.7\ k\Omega} \right) 12\ V = \textbf{3.84 V}$

6. (a) $V_G = \textbf{0 V}, \quad V_S = \textbf{0 V}$
       $V_D = V_{DD} - I_D R_D = 15\ V - (8\ mA)(1.0\ k\Omega) = \textbf{7 V}$

    (b) $V_G = \textbf{0 V}$
       $V_S = -I_D R_D = -(3\ mA)(330\ \Omega) = \textbf{--0.99 V}$
       $V_D = V_{DD} - I_D R_D = -10\ V - (-3\ mA)(1.5\ k\Omega) = \textbf{--5.5 V}$

    (c) $V_G = \left(\dfrac{R_2}{R_1 + R_2} \right) V_{DD} = \left(\dfrac{4.7\ k\Omega}{14.7\ k\Omega} \right) 12\ V = \textbf{3.84 V}$
       $V_S = \textbf{0 V}$
       $V_D = V_{DD} - I_D R_D = 12\ V - (6\ mA)(1.0\ k\Omega) = \textbf{6 V}$

7.   (a) *n*-channel D-MOSFET
      (b) *n*-channel JFET
      (c) *p*-channel E-MOSFET

8.   From the curve in Figure 8-18(a) in the textbook:
      $I_{d(pp)} \cong 3.9 \text{ mA} - 1.3 \text{ mA} = \textbf{2.6 mA}$

9.   From the curve in Figure 8-18(b) in the textbook:
      $I_{d(pp)} \cong 6 \text{ mA} - 2 \text{ mA} = \textbf{4 mA}$
      From the curve in Figure 8-18(c) in the textbook:
      $I_{d(pp)} \cong 4.5 \text{ mA} - 1.3 \text{ mA} = \textbf{3.2 mA}$

10. $V_D = V_{DD} - I_D R_D = 12 \text{ V} - (2.83 \text{ mA})(1.5 \text{ k}\Omega) = \textbf{7.76 V}$
      $V_S = I_D R_S = (2.83 \text{ mA})(1.0 \text{ k}\Omega) = \textbf{2.83 V}$
      $V_{DS} = V_D - V_S = 7.76 \text{ V} - 2.83 \text{ V} = \textbf{4.93 V}$
      $V_{GS} = V_G - V_S = 0 \text{ V} - 2.83 \text{ V} = \textbf{--2.83 V}$

11. $A_v = g_m R_d = g_m\left(R_D \parallel R_L\right) = 5000 \text{ } \mu S(1.5 \text{ k}\Omega \parallel 10 \text{ k}\Omega) = 6.52$
      $V_{pp(out)} = (2.828)(50 \text{ mV})(6.52) = \textbf{920 mV}$

12. $A_v = g_m R_d$
      $R_d = 1.5 \text{ k}\Omega \parallel 1.5 \text{ k}\Omega = 750 \text{ }\Omega$
      $A_v = (5000 \text{ } \mu S)(750 \text{ }\Omega) = 3.75$
      $V_{out} = A_v V_{in} = (3.75)(50 \text{ mV}) = \textbf{188 mV rms}$

13.   (a) $A_v = g_m R_d = g_m\left(R_D \parallel R_L\right) = 3.8 \text{ mS}(1.2 \text{ k}\Omega \parallel 22 \text{ k}\Omega) = 3.8 \text{ mS}(1138 \text{ }\Omega) = \textbf{4.32}$
      (b) $A_v = g_m R_d = g_m\left(R_D \parallel R_L\right) = 5.5 \text{ mS}(2.2 \text{ k}\Omega \parallel 10 \text{ k}\Omega) = 5.5 \text{ mS}(1.8 \text{ k}\Omega) = \textbf{9.92}$

14.   See Figure 8-1.

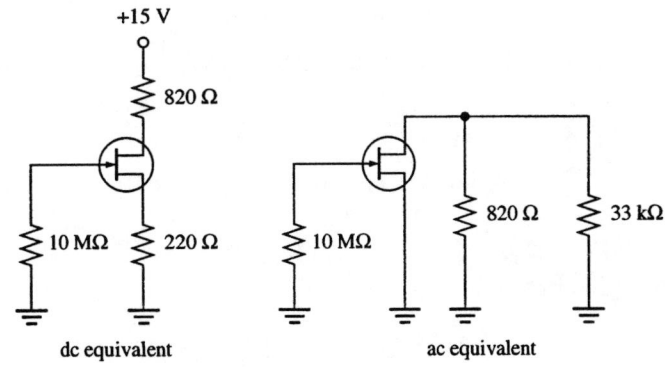

+15 V

820 Ω

10 MΩ   220 Ω   10 MΩ   820 Ω   33 kΩ

dc equivalent   ac equivalent

Figure 8-1

15. $I_D = \dfrac{I_{DSS}}{2} = \dfrac{15 \text{ mA}}{2} = \textbf{7.5 mA}$

16. $V_{GS} = (7.5 \text{ mA})(220 \text{ }\Omega) = 1.65 \text{ V}$

$$g_{m0} = \frac{2I_{DSS}}{\left|V_{GS(off)}\right|} = \frac{2(15 \text{ mA})}{4 \text{ V}} = 7.5 \text{ mS}$$

$g_m = (7.5 \text{ mS})(1 - 1.65 \text{ V}/4 \text{ V}) = 4.41 \text{ mS}$

$$A_v = \frac{g_m R_d}{1 + g_m R_S} = \frac{(4.41 \text{ mS})(820 \text{ }\Omega \parallel 3.3 \text{ k}\Omega)}{1 + (4.41 \text{ mS})(220 \text{ }\Omega)} = \frac{(4.41 \text{ mS})(657 \text{ }\Omega)}{1 + 0.97} = \textbf{1.47}$$

17. $A_v = g_m R_d = (4.41 \text{ mS})(820 \text{ }\Omega \parallel 3.3 \text{ k}\Omega \parallel 4.7 \text{ k}\Omega) = (4.41 \text{ mS})(576 \text{ }\Omega) = \textbf{2.54}$

18. $I_D = \dfrac{I_{DSS}}{2} = \dfrac{9 \text{ mA}}{2} = \textbf{4.5 mA}$

$V_{GS} = -I_D R_S = -(4.5 \text{ mA})(330 \text{ }\Omega) = \textbf{-1.49 V}$

$V_{DS} = V_{DD} - I_D(R_D + R_S) = 9 \text{ V} - (4.5 \text{ mA})(1.33 \text{ k}\Omega) = \textbf{3 V}$

19. $A_v = g_m R_d = g_m(R_D \parallel R_L) = 3700 \text{ }\mu\text{S}(1.0 \text{ k}\Omega \parallel 10 \text{ k}\Omega) = 3700 \text{ }\mu\text{S}(909 \text{ }\Omega) = 3.36$

$V_{out} = A_v V_{in} = (3.36)(10 \text{ mV}) = \textbf{33.6 mV rms}$

20. $V_{GS} = \left(\dfrac{R_2}{R_1 + R_2}\right)V_{DD} = \left(\dfrac{6.8 \text{ k}\Omega}{24.8 \text{ k}\Omega}\right)20 \text{ V} = \textbf{5.48 V}$

$$K = \frac{I_{D(on)}}{(V_{GS} - V_{GS(th)})^2} = \frac{18 \text{ mA}}{(10 \text{ V} - 2.5 \text{ V})^2} = 0.32 \text{ mA/V}^2$$

$I_D = K(V_{GS} - V_{GS(th)})^2 = 0.32 \text{ mA/V}^2(5.48 \text{ V} - 2.5 \text{ V})^2 = \textbf{2.84 mA}$

$V_{DS} = V_{DD} - I_D R_D = 20 \text{ V} - (2.84 \text{ mA})(1.0 \text{ k}\Omega) = \textbf{17.2 V}$

21. $R_{IN} = \left|\dfrac{V_{GS}}{I_{GSS}}\right| = \left|\dfrac{-15 \text{ V}}{25 \text{ nA}}\right| = 600 \text{ M}\Omega$

$R_{in} = 10 \text{ M}\Omega \parallel 600 \text{ M}\Omega = \textbf{9.84 M}\Omega$

22. $A_v = g_m R_d = 48 \text{ mS}(1.0 \text{ k}\Omega \parallel 10 \text{ M}\Omega) \cong 4.8$

$V_{out} = A_v V_{in} = 4.8(10 \text{ mV}) = \textbf{48 mV rms}$

$I_D = I_{DSS} = 15 \text{ mA}$

$V_D = 24 \text{ V} - (15 \text{ mA})(1.0 \text{ k}\Omega) = \textbf{9 V}$

See Figure 8-2.

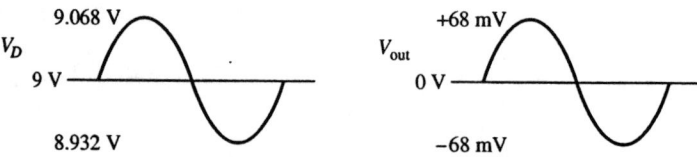

Figure 8-2

23.

$$V_{GS} = \left(\frac{R_2}{R_1 + R_2}\right) V_{DD} = \left(\frac{47\,k\Omega}{94\,k\Omega}\right) 18\,V = \mathbf{9\,V}$$

$$K = \frac{I_{D(on)}}{(V_{GS} - V_{GS(th)})^2} = \frac{8\,mA}{(12\,V - 4\,V)^2} = 0.125\,mA/V^2$$

$$I_{D(on)} = K(V_{GS} - V_{GS(th)})^2 = 0.125\,mA/V^2(9\,V - 4\,V)^2 = \mathbf{3.13\,mA}$$

$$V_{DS} = V_{DD} - I_D R_D = 18\,V - (3.125\,mA)(1.5\,k\Omega) = \mathbf{13.3\,V}$$

$$A_v = g_m R_D = 4500\,\mu S(1.5\,k\Omega) = 6.75$$

$$V_{ds} = A_v V_{in} = 6.75(100\,mV) = \mathbf{675\,mV\ rms}$$

Section 8-3 Common-Drain Amplifiers

24. $R_s = 1.2\,k\Omega \,\|\, 10\,M\Omega \cong 1.2\,k\Omega$

$$A_v = \frac{g_m R_s}{1 + g_m R_s} = \frac{(5500\,\mu S)(1.2\,k\Omega)}{1 + (5500\,\mu S)(1.2\,k\Omega)} = \mathbf{0.868}$$

$$R_{IN} = \left|\frac{V_{GS}}{I_{GSS}}\right| = \left|\frac{-15\,V}{50\,pA}\right| = 3 \times 10^{11}\,\Omega$$

$$R_{in} = 10\,M\Omega \,\|\, 3 \times 10^{11}\,\Omega \cong \mathbf{10\,M\Omega}$$

25. $R_s = 1.2\,k\Omega \,\|\, 10\,M\Omega \cong 10\,M\Omega$

$$A_v = \frac{g_m R_s}{1 + g_m R_s} = \frac{(3000\,\mu S)(10\,M\Omega)}{1 + (3000\,\mu S)(10\,M\Omega)} = \mathbf{0.783}$$

$$R_{IN} = \left|\frac{V_{GS}}{I_{GSS}}\right| = \left|\frac{-15\,V}{50\,pA}\right| = 3 \times 10^{11}\,\Omega$$

$$R_{in} = 10\,M\Omega \,\|\, 3 \times 10^{11}\,\Omega \cong \mathbf{10\,M\Omega}$$

26. (a) $R_s = 4.7\,k\Omega \,\|\, 47\,k\Omega = 4.27\,k\Omega$

$$A_v = \frac{g_m R_s}{1 + g_m R_s} = \frac{(3000\,\mu S)(4.27\,k\Omega)}{1 + (3000\,\mu S)(4.27\,k\Omega)} = \mathbf{0.928}$$

(b) $R_s = 1.0\,k\Omega \,\|\, 100\,\Omega = 90.9\,\Omega$

$$A_v = \frac{g_m R_s}{1 + g_m R_s} = \frac{(4300\,\mu S)(90.9\,\Omega)}{1 + (4300\,\mu S)(90.9\,\Omega)} = \mathbf{0.281}$$

27. (a) $R_s = 4.7\,k\Omega \,\|\, 10\,k\Omega = 3.2\,k\Omega$

$$A_v = \frac{g_m R_s}{1 + g_m R_s} = \frac{(3000\,\mu S)(3.2\,k\Omega)}{1 + (3000\,\mu S)(3.2\,k\Omega)} = \mathbf{0.906}$$

(b) $R_s = 100\,\Omega \,\|\, 10\,k\Omega = 99\,\Omega$

$$A_v = \frac{g_m R_s}{1 + g_m R_s} = \frac{(4300\,\mu S)(99\,\Omega)}{1 + (4300\,\mu S)(99\,\Omega)} = \mathbf{0.299}$$

Chapter 8

Section 8-4 Common-Gate Amplifiers

28. $A_v = g_m R_d = 4000\mu\text{S}(1.5 \text{ k}\Omega) = \textbf{6.0}$

29. $R_{in(source)} = \dfrac{1}{g_m} = \dfrac{1}{4000\ \mu\text{S}} = \textbf{250 }\boldsymbol{\Omega}$

30. $A_v = g_m R_d = 3500\mu\text{S}(10 \text{ k}\Omega) = \textbf{35}$

$R_{in} = R_\text{S} \parallel \left(\dfrac{1}{g_m}\right) = 2.2 \text{ k}\Omega \parallel \left(\dfrac{1}{3500\ \mu\text{S}}\right) = \textbf{253 }\boldsymbol{\Omega}$

Section 8-5 Troubleshooting

31. (a) $V_{\text{D1}} = V_{\text{DD}}$; No signal at Q_1 drain; No output signal
(b) $V_{\text{D1}} \cong 0$ V (floating); No signal at Q_1 drain; No output signal
(c) $V_{\text{GS1}} = 0$ V; $V_\text{S} = 0$ V; V_{D1} less than normal; Clipped output signal
(d) Correct signal at Q_1 drain; No signal at Q_2 gate; No output signal
(e) $V_{\text{D2}} = V_{\text{DD}}$; Correct signal at Q_2 gate; No Q_2 drain signal or output signal

32. (a) $V_{out} = 0$ V if C_1 is open.

(b) $A_{v1} = g_m R_d = 5000\ \mu\text{S}(1.5 \text{ k}\Omega) = 7.5$
$A_{v2} = \dfrac{g_m R_d}{1 + g_m R_s} = \dfrac{7.5}{1 + (5000\ \mu\text{S})(470\ \Omega)} = 2.24$
$A_v = A_{v1} A_{v2} = (7.5)(2.24) = 16.8$
$V_{out} = A_v V_{in} = (16.8)(10 \text{ mV}) = 168 \text{ mV}$

(c) No effect on V_{out} unless V_D is so low that clipping occurs.

(d) No V_{out} because there is no signal at the Q_2 gate.

System Application Problems

33. The 10 μF capacitor between the drain of Q_1 and the gate of Q_2 is open.

34. At test point 2: 250 mV is correct
At test point 3: 800 mV is approximately correct
At test point 4: 530 mV is too low
At test point 5: 2.12 V is too low but consistent with TP4
Most likely, the coupling capacitor between stage 1 and stage 2 is leaky. Replace.

35. $V_{\text{D2}} = 12 \text{ V} - (5.10 \text{ mA})(1.5 \text{ k}\Omega) = \textbf{4.35 V}$
$V_{d1} = (100 \text{ mV})(2200\ \mu\text{S})(1.5 \text{ k}\Omega) = 330 \text{ mV}$
$V_{d2} = (330 \text{ mV})(2600\ \mu\text{S})(1.5 \text{ k}\Omega) = \textbf{1.29 V rms}$

Data Sheet Problems

36. The 2N3796 FET is an *n-channel D-MOSFET*.

37. (a) For a 2N3796, the typical $V_{GS(off)}$ = **–3.0 V**
(b) For a 2N3797, $V_{DS(max)}$ = **20 V**
(c) At T_A = 25°C, $P_{D(max)}$ = **200 mW**
(d) For a 2N3797, $V_{GS(max)}$ = **±10 V**

38. P_D = 200 mW – (1.14 mW/°C)(55°C – 25°C) = **166 mW**

39. For a 2N3796 with f = 1 kHz, g_{m0} = **900 μS** minimum

40. At V_{GS} = 3.5 V and V_{DS} = 10 V,
$I_{D(min)}$ = **9.0 mA**, $I_{D(typ)}$ = **14 mA**, $I_{D(max)}$ = **18 mA**

41. For a zero-biased 2N3796, $I_{D(typ)}$ = **1.5 mA**

42. $A_{v(max)}$ = (1800 μS)(2.2 kΩ) = **3.96**

Advanced Problems

43. $R_{d(min)}$ = 1.0 k$\Omega \parallel$ 4 kΩ = 800 Ω
$A_{v(min)}$ = (2.5 mS)(800 Ω) = **2.0**
$R_{d(max)}$ = 1.0 k$\Omega \parallel$ 10 kΩ = 909 Ω
$A_{v(min)}$ = (7.5 mS)(909 Ω) = **6.82**

44. $I_{DSS(typ)}$ = 2.9 mA
$$R_D + R_S = \frac{12\,V}{2.9\,mA} = 414\,k\Omega$$
$$\frac{1}{g_m} = \frac{1}{2300\,\mu S} = 435\,\Omega$$
If R_S = 0 Ω, then $R_D \cong$ 4 kΩ (3.9 kΩ standard)
A_v = (2300 μS)(3.9 kΩ) = **8.97**
V_{DS} = 24 V – (2.9 mA)(3.9 kΩ) = 24 V – 11.3 V = **12.7 V**
The circuit is a common-source zero-biased amplifier with a drain resistor of 3.9 kΩ.

45. To maintain V_{DS} = 12 V for the range of I_{DSS} values:
For $I_{DSS(min)}$ = 2 mA
$$R_D = \frac{12\,V}{2\,mA} = 6\,k\Omega$$
For $I_{DSS(max)}$ = 6 mA
$$R_D = \frac{12\,V}{6\,mA} = 2\,k\Omega$$
To maintain A_v = 9 for the range of $g_m(y_{fs})$ values:
For $g_{m(min)}$ = 1500 μS

$$R_D = \frac{9}{1500\ \mu S} = 6\ k\Omega$$

For $g_{m(max)} = 3000\ \mu S$

$$R_D = \frac{9}{3000\ \mu S} = 3\ k\Omega$$

A drain resistance consisting of a 2.2 kΩ fixed resistor in series with a 5 kΩ variable resistor will provide more than sufficient range to maintain a gain of 9 over the specified range of g_m values. The dc voltage at the drain will vary with adjustment and depends on I_{DSS}.
The circuit cannot be modified to maintain both $V_{DS} = 12$ V and $A_v = 9$ over the full range of transistor parameter values.

EWB/Multisim Troubleshooting Problems

The solutions showing instrument connections for Problems 46 through 54 are available in the Solutions folder for Chapter 8 on the CD-ROM provided with the textbook. The solutions may be accessed using the password *ED5FLOYD*. The faults in the circuit files may be accessed using the password *book* (all lowercase).

46. Drain-source shorted

47. C_2 open

48. C_1 open

49. R_S shorted

50. Drain-source open

51. R_1 open

52. R_D open

53. R_2 open

54. C_2 open

Chapter 9
Power Amplifiers

Section 9-1 Class A Power Amplifiers

1. (a) $V_B = \left(\dfrac{R_2}{R_1 + R_2}\right)V_{CC} = \left(\dfrac{330\,\Omega}{1.0\,k\Omega + 330\,k\Omega}\right)15\,V = 3.72\,V$

$V_E = V_B - V_{BE} = 3.72 - 0.7\,V = 3.02\,V$

$I_{CQ} \cong I_E = \dfrac{V_E}{R_{E1} + R_{E2}} = \dfrac{3.02\,V}{8.2\,\Omega + 36\,\Omega} = \mathbf{68.4\,mA}$

$V_{CEQ} = V_{CC} - (I_C)(R_{E1} + R_{E2} + R_L)$

$\qquad = 15\,V - (68.4\,mA)(8.2\,\Omega + 35\,\Omega + 100\,\Omega) = \mathbf{5.14\,V}$

(b) $A_v = \dfrac{R_L}{R_{E1} + r'_e} = \dfrac{100\,\Omega}{8.2\,\Omega + 0.37\,\Omega} = \mathbf{11.7}$

$R_{in} = \beta_{ac}(R_{E1} + r'_e) \parallel R_1 \parallel R_2$

$\qquad = 100\,(8.2\,\Omega + 0.37\,\Omega) \parallel 330\,\Omega \parallel 1.0\,k\Omega = 192\,\Omega$

$A_p = A_v^2 \left(\dfrac{R_{in}}{R_L}\right) = 11.7^2 \left(\dfrac{192\,\Omega}{100\,\Omega}\right) = \mathbf{263}$

The computed voltage and power gains are slightly higher if r'_e is ignored.

2. (a) If R_L is removed, there is no collector current; hence, the power dissipated in the transistor is **zero**.

(b) Power is dissipated only in the bias resistors plus a small amount in R_{E1} and R_{E2}. Since the load resistor has been removed, the base voltage is altered. The base voltage can be found from the Thevenin equivalent drawn for the bias circuit in Figure 9-1.

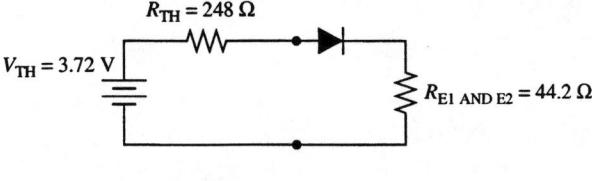

Figure 9-1

Applying the voltage-divider rule and including the base-emitter diode drop of 0.7 V result in a base voltage of 1.2 V. The power supply current is then computed as

$I_{CC} = \dfrac{V_{CC} - 1.2\,V}{R_1} = \dfrac{15\,V - 1.2\,V}{1.0\,k\Omega} = 13.8\,mA$

Chapter 9

Power from the supply is then computed as

$$P_T = I_{CC}V_{CC} = (13.8 \text{ mA})(15 \text{ V}) = \textbf{207 mW}$$

(c) $A_v = 11.7$ (see problem 1(b)). $V_{in} = 500 \text{ mV}_{pp} = 177 \text{ mV}_{rms}$.

$V_{out} = A_vV_{in} = (11.7)(177 \text{ mV}) = 2.07 \text{ V}$

$$P_{out} = \frac{V_{out}^2}{R_L} = \frac{2.07 \text{ V}^2}{100 \text{ }\Omega} = \textbf{42.8 mW}$$

3. The changes are shown in Figure 9-2. The advantage of this arrangement is that the load resistor is referenced to ground.

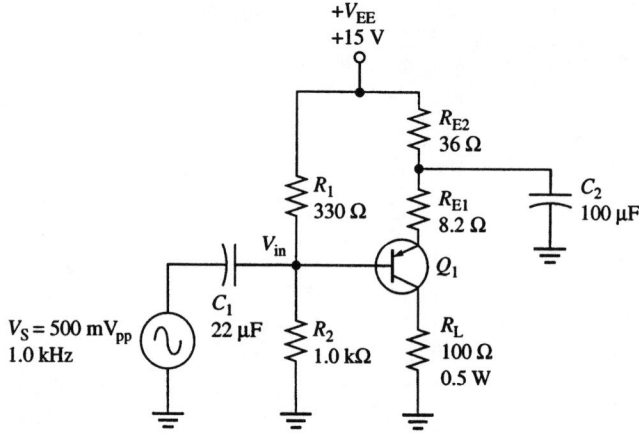

Figure 9-2

4. A CC amplifier has a voltage gain of approximately 1. Therefore,

$$A_p = \frac{R_{in}}{R_{out}} = \frac{2.2 \text{ k}\Omega}{50 \text{ }\Omega} = \textbf{44}$$

5. (a) $R_{IN(base)} = \beta_{DC}(R_{E1} + R_{E2}) = (125)(79.7) = 9.96 \text{ k}\Omega$

Since $R_{IN(base)} > 10R_2$, it can be neglected.

$$V_B = \left[\frac{R_2}{R_1 + R_2}\right]V_{CC} = \left(\frac{510 \text{ }\Omega}{680 \text{ }\Omega + 510 \text{ }\Omega}\right)12 \text{ V} = \left(\frac{510 \text{ }\Omega}{1190 \text{ }\Omega}\right)12 \text{ V} = 5.14 \text{ V}$$

$V_E = V_B - 0.7 \text{ V} = 5.14 \text{ V} - 0.7 \text{ V} = 4.44 \text{ V}$

$$I_{CQ} \cong I_E = \frac{V_E}{R_E} = \frac{4.44 \text{ V}}{79.7 \text{ }\Omega} = 55.7 \text{ mA}$$

$V_{CQ} = V_{CC} - I_{CQ}R_C = 12 \text{ V} - (55.7 \text{ mA})(100 \text{ }\Omega) = 6.43 \text{ V}$

$V_{CEQ} = V_C - V_E = 6.43 \text{ V} - 4.44 \text{ V} = 1.99 \text{ V}$

$R_c = R_C \| R_L = 100 \text{ }\Omega \| 100 \text{ }\Omega = 50 \text{ }\Omega$

$V_{ce(cutoff)} = V_{CEQ} + I_{CQ}R_c = 1.99 \text{ V} + 55.7 \text{ mA}(50 \text{ }\Omega) = 4.78 \text{ V}$

Since V_{CEQ} is closer to saturation, I_c is limited to

$$I_{c(p)} = \frac{V_{CEQ}}{R_c} = \frac{1.99 \text{ V}}{50 \text{ }\Omega} = \textbf{39.8 mA}$$

V_{out} is limited to

$V_{out(p)} = V_{CEQ} = \textbf{1.99 V}$

(b) $R_{\text{IN(base)}} = \beta_{\text{DC}}(R_{E1} + R_{E2}) = (120)(142\ \Omega) = 17\ \text{k}\Omega$

Since $R_{\text{IN(base)}} < 10R_2$, it is taken into account.

$$V_B = \left[\frac{R_2 \,\|\, R_{\text{IN(base)}}}{R_1 + R_2 \,\|\, R_{\text{IN(base)}}} \right] V_{\text{CC}} = \left(\frac{4.7\ \text{k}\Omega \,\|\, 17\ \text{k}\Omega}{12\ \text{k}\Omega + 4.7\ \text{k}\Omega \,\|\, 17\ \text{k}\Omega} \right) 12\ \text{V} = \left(\frac{3.68\ \text{k}\Omega}{15.68\ \text{k}\Omega} \right) 12\ \text{V} = 2.82\ \text{V}$$

$V_E = V_B - 0.7\ \text{V} = 2.82\ \text{V} - 0.7\ \text{V} = 2.12\ \text{V}$

$I_{\text{CQ}} \cong I_E = V_E/R_E = 2.12\ \text{V}/142\ \Omega = 14.9\ \text{mA}$

$V_{\text{CQ}} = V_{\text{CC}} - I_{\text{CQ}}R_C = 12\ \text{V} - (14.9\ \text{mA})(470\ \Omega) = 5.0\ \text{V}$

$V_{\text{CEQ}} = V_{\text{CQ}} - V_E = 5.0\ \text{V} - 2.12\ \text{V} = 2.88\ \text{V}$

$R_c = R_C \,\|\, R_L = 470\ \Omega \,\|\, 470\ \Omega = 235\ \Omega$

$V_{ce(cutoff)} = V_{\text{CEQ}} + I_{\text{CQ}}R_c = 2.88\ \text{V} + 14.9\ \text{mA}(235\ \Omega) = 6.38\ \text{V}$

Since V_{CEQ} is closer to saturation, I_c is limited to

$$I_{c(p)} = \frac{V_{\text{CEQ}}}{R_c} = \frac{2.88\ \text{V}}{235\ \Omega} = \textbf{12.3 mA}$$

V_{out} is limited to $V_{out(p)} = V_{\text{CEQ}} = \textbf{2.88 V}$

6.　　(a) $A_p = A_v^2 \left(\dfrac{R_{in}}{R_L} \right)$

$$A_v \cong \frac{R_c}{R_{E1}} = \frac{R_C \,\|\, R_L}{R_{E1}} = \frac{100\ \Omega \,\|\, 100\ \Omega}{4.7\ \Omega} = \frac{50\ \Omega}{4.7\ \Omega} = \textbf{10.6}$$

$R_{in} = R_1 \,\|\, R_2 \,\|\, R_{in(base)} = R_1 \,\|\, R_2 \,\|\, \beta_{ac}R_{E1}$

$R_{in} = 680\ \Omega \,\|\, 510\ \Omega \,\|\, (125)(4.7\ \Omega) = 680\ \Omega \,\|\, 510\ \Omega \,\|\, 588\ \Omega = 195\ \Omega$

$$A_p = (10.6)^2 \left(\frac{195\ \Omega}{100\ \Omega} \right) = \textbf{219}$$

(b)　$A_v \cong \dfrac{R_c}{R_{E1}} = \dfrac{R_C \,\|\, R_L}{R_{E1}} = \dfrac{470\ \Omega \,\|\, 470\ \Omega}{22\ \Omega} = \dfrac{235\ \Omega}{22\ \Omega} = \textbf{10.7}$

$R_{in} = 12\ \text{k}\Omega \,\|\, 4.7\ \text{k}\Omega \,\|\, (120)(22\ \Omega) = 12\ \text{k}\Omega \,\|\, 4.7\ \text{k}\Omega \,\|\, 2.64\ \text{k}\Omega = 1.48\ \text{k}\Omega$

$$A_p = (10.7)^2 \left(\frac{1.48\ \text{k}\Omega}{470\ \Omega} \right) = \textbf{361}$$

7. $R_{\text{IN(base)}} = \beta_{\text{DC}} R_E = 90(130\ \Omega) = 11.7\ \text{k}\Omega$

$R_2 \parallel R_{\text{IN(base)}} = 1.0\ \text{k}\Omega \parallel 11.7\ \text{k}\Omega = 921\ \Omega$

$$V_B = \left(\frac{R_2 \parallel R_{\text{IN(base)}}}{R_1 + R_2 \parallel R_{\text{in(base)}}} \right) V_{CC} = \left(\frac{921\ \Omega}{5.62\ \text{k}\Omega} \right) 24\ \text{V} = 3.93\ \text{V}$$

$V_E = V_B - 0.7\ \text{V} = 3.93\ \text{V} - 0.7\ \text{V} = 3.23\ \text{V}$

$$I_{CQ} \cong I_E = \frac{V_E}{R_E} = \frac{3.23\text{V}}{130\ \Omega} = 24.8\ \text{mA}$$

$V_C = V_{CC} - I_{CQ} R_C = 24\ \text{V} - (24.8\ \text{mA})(560\ \Omega) = 13.9\ \text{V}$

$V_{CEQ} = V_C - V_E = 13.9\ \text{V} - 3.23\ \text{V} = 10.7\ \text{V}$

$P_{\text{D(min)}} = P_{DQ} = I_{CQ} V_{CEQ} = (24.8\ \text{mA})(10.7\ \text{V}) = \textbf{265 mW}$

8. From Problem 7: $I_{CQ} = 24.8\ \text{mA}$ and $V_{CEQ} = 10.7\ \text{V}$

$V_{ce(cutoff)} = V_{CEQ} + I_{CQ} R_c = 10.7\ \text{V} + (24.8\ \text{mA})264\ \Omega = 17.2\ \text{V}$

The Q-point is closer to cutoff than to saturation.

$P_{out} = 0.5 I_{CQ}^2 R_c = 0.5(24.8\ \text{mA})^2 264\ \Omega = \textbf{81.2 mW}$

$$eff = \frac{P_{out}}{P_{DC}} = \frac{P_{out}}{V_{CC} I_{CC}} = \frac{P_{out}}{V_{CC} I_{CQ}} = \frac{81.2\,\text{mW}}{(24\,\text{V})(24.8\,\text{mA})} = 0.136$$

Section 9-2 Class B and Class AB Push-Pull Amplifiers

9. (a) $V_{B(Q1)} = 0\ \text{V} + 0.7\ \text{V} = \textbf{0.7 V}$

$\qquad V_{B(Q2)} = 0\ \text{V} - 0.7\ \text{V} = \textbf{-0.7 V}$

$\qquad V_E = \textbf{0 V}$

$$I_{CQ} = \frac{V_{CC} - (-V_{CC}) - 1.4\ \text{V}}{R_1 + R_2} = \frac{9\ \text{V} - (-9\ \text{V}) - 1.4\ \text{V}}{1.0\ \text{k}\Omega + 1.0\ \text{k}\Omega} = \textbf{8.3 mA}$$

$\qquad V_{CEQ(Q1)} = \textbf{9 V}$

$\qquad V_{CEQ(Q2)} = \textbf{-9 V}$

(b) $V_{out} = V_{in} = 5.0\ \text{V rms}$

$$P_{out} = \frac{(V_{out})^2}{R_L} = \frac{5.0\ \text{V}^2}{50\ \Omega} = \textbf{0.5 W}$$

10. $I_{c(sat)} = \dfrac{V_{CC}}{R_L} = \dfrac{9.0\ \text{V}}{50\ \Omega} = 180\ \text{mA}$

$V_{ce(cutoff)} = 9\ \text{V}$

These points define the ac load line as shown in Figure 9-3. The Q-point is at a collector current of 8.3 mA (see problem 9) and the dc load line rises vertically through this point.

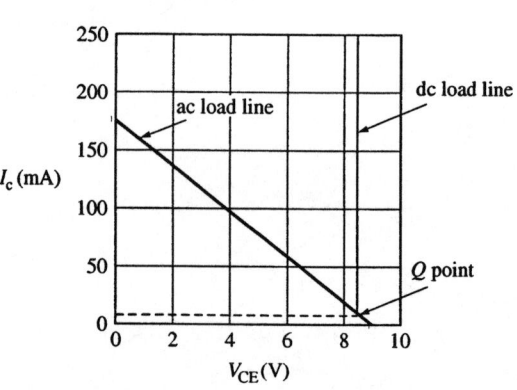

Figure 9-3

11. (a) $V_{B(Q1)} = 7.5\ \text{V} + 0.7\ \text{V} = \textbf{8.2 V}$

$V_{B(Q2)} = 7.5\ \text{V} - 0.7\ \text{V} = \textbf{6.8 V}$

$$V_E = \frac{15\ \text{V}}{2} = \textbf{7.5 V}$$

$$I_{CQ} = \frac{V_{CC} - 1.4\ \text{V}}{R_1 + R_2} = \frac{15\ \text{V} - 1.4\ \text{V}}{1.0\ \text{k}\Omega + 1.0\ \text{k}\Omega} = \textbf{6.8 mA}$$

$V_{CEQ(Q1)} = 15\ \text{V} - 7.5\ \text{V} = \textbf{7.5 V}$

$V_{CEQ(Q2)} = 0\ \text{V} - 7.5\ \text{V} = \textbf{-7.5 V}$

(b) $V_{in} = V_{out} = 10\ \text{V}_{pp} = 3.54\ \text{V rms}$

$$P_L = \frac{(V_L)^2}{R_L} = \frac{(3.54\ \text{V})^2}{75\ \Omega} = \textbf{167 mW}$$

12. (a) Maximum peak voltage = $7.5\ \text{V}_p$. $7.5\ \text{V}_p = 5.30\ \text{V rms}$

$$P_{L(max)} = \frac{(V_L)^2}{R_L} = \frac{(5.30\ \text{V})^2}{75\ \Omega} = \textbf{375 mW}$$

(b) Maximum peak voltage = $12\ \text{V}_p$. $12\ \text{V}_p = 8.48\ \text{V rms}$

$$P_{L(max)} = \frac{(V_L)^2}{R_L} = \frac{(8.48\ \text{V})^2}{75\ \Omega} = \textbf{960 mW}$$

13. (a) C_2 open or Q_2 open
(b) power supply off, open R_1, Q_1 base shorted to ground
(c) Q_1 has collector-to-emitter short
(d) one or both diodes shorted

14. (a) $I_{R1} \cong \dfrac{V_{DD} - (-V_{DD})}{R_1 + R_2 + R_3} = \dfrac{48\ \text{V}}{105.6\ \text{k}\Omega} = 455\ \mu\text{A}$

$V_B = V_{DD} - I_{R1}(R_1 + R_2) = 24\ \text{V} - 455\ \mu\text{A}(5.6\ \text{k}\Omega) = 21.5\ \text{V}$

$V_E = V_B + 0.7\ \text{V} = 21.5\ \text{V} + 0.7\ \text{V} = 22.2\ \text{V}$

$I_E = \dfrac{V_{DD} - V_E}{R_4 + R_5} = \dfrac{24\ \text{V} - 22.2\ \text{V}}{1.1\ \text{k}\Omega} = 1.64\ \text{mA}$

$V_{R6} = V_{TH(Q1)} - V_{TH(Q2)} = 2.75\ \text{V} - (-2.75\ \text{V}) = 5.5\ \text{V}$

$R_6 = \dfrac{V_{R6}}{I_{R6}} \cong \dfrac{V_{R6}}{I_E} = \dfrac{5.5\ \text{V}}{1.64\ \text{mA}} = \textbf{3.35 k}\boldsymbol{\Omega}$

(b) $r'_e \cong \dfrac{25\ \text{mV}}{I_E} = \dfrac{25\ \text{mV}}{1.64\ \text{mA}} = 15.2\ \Omega$

$A_v = \dfrac{R_7}{R_5 + r'_e} = \dfrac{15\ \text{k}\Omega}{115.2\ \Omega} = 130$

$V_{out} = A_v V_{in} = 130(50\ \text{mV}) = \textbf{6.5 V}$

(c) $P_L = \dfrac{V_{out}^2}{R_L} = \dfrac{(6.5\ \text{V})^2}{33\ \Omega} = \textbf{1.28 W}$

Chapter 9

Section 9-3 Class C Amplifiers

15. $P_{D(avg)} = \left(\dfrac{t_{on}}{T}\right)V_{CE(sat)}I_{C(sat)} = (0.1)(0.18 \text{ V})(25 \text{ mA}) = \textbf{450 } \boldsymbol{\mu}\textbf{W}$

16. $f_r = \dfrac{1}{2\pi\sqrt{LC}} = \dfrac{1}{2\pi\sqrt{(10 \text{ mH})(0.001 \,\mu\text{F})}} = \textbf{50.3 kHz}$

17. $V_{out(pp)} = 2V_{CC} = 2(12 \text{ V}) = \textbf{24 V}$

18. $P_{out} = \dfrac{0.5V_{CC}^2}{R_c} = \dfrac{0.5(15 \text{ V})^2}{50 \ \Omega} = 2.25 \text{ W}$

$P_{D(avg)} = \left(\dfrac{t_{on}}{T}\right)V_{CE(sat)}I_{C(sat)} = (0.1)(0.18 \text{ V})(25 \text{ mA}) = 0.45 \text{ mW}$

$\eta = \dfrac{P_{out}}{P_{out} + P_{D(avg)}} = \dfrac{2.25 \text{ W}}{2.25 \text{ W} + 0.45 \text{ mW}} = \textbf{0.9998}$

Section 9-4 Troubleshooting

19. With C_1 open, only the negative half of the input signal appears across R_L.

20. One of the transistors is open between the collector and emitter or a coupling capacitor is open.

21. (a) No dc supply voltage
 (b) Diode D_1 or D_2 open
 (c) Circuit is OK
 (d) Q_1 shorted from collector to emitter

System Application Problems

22. For the block diagram of textbook Figure 9-34 with no signal from the power amplifier or preamplifier, but with the microphone working, the problem is in the power amplifier or preamplifier. Check for an output from the preamp. If one is present, the preamp is not at fault.

23. For the circuit of Figure 9-35 with the base-emitter junction of the 2N6043 open, the dc output will be approximately 6 V with a signal output having the positive alternations of the input signal.

24. For the circuit of Figure 9-35 with the base-emitter junction of the 2N6040 open, the dc output will be 0 V with no signal output.

25. On the circuit board of Figure 9-49, the input coupling capacitor C_1 has been installed backwards. The positive lead should connect into the circuit.

Data Sheet Problems

26. From the 2N6040 data sheet of textbook Figure 9-36:
(a) $\beta_{DC(min)} = \mathbf{100}$ @ $I_C = 8.0$ A, $V_{CE} = 4$ V
$\beta_{DC(min)} = \mathbf{1000}$ @ $I_C = 4.0$ A, $V_{CE} = 4$ V
(b) For a 2N6041, $V_{CE(max)} = \mathbf{80\ V}$
(c) $P_{D(max)} = \mathbf{75\ W}$ @ $T_C = 25°C$
(d) $I_{C(max)} = 8.0$ A continuous or 16.0 A peak

27. $P_D = 75$ W $- (65°C - 25°C)(0.6$ W/°C$) = 75$ W $- 24$ W $= \mathbf{51\ W}$

28. $P_D = 2.2$ W $- (80°C - 25°C)(0.0175$ W/°C$) = 2.2$ W $- 963$ mW $= \mathbf{1.24\ W}$

29. As the frequency increases, the small-signal current gain **decreases**.

30. $h_{fe} \cong \mathbf{2800}$ @ $f = 2$ kHz
$h_{fe} \cong \mathbf{700}$ @ $f = 100$ kHz

Advanced Problems

31. T_C is much closer to the actual junction temperature than T_A. In a given operating environment, T_A is always less than T_C.

32. $I_{C(sat)} = \dfrac{24\ V}{330\ \Omega + 100\ \Omega} = \dfrac{24\ V}{430\ \Omega} = \mathbf{55.8\ mA}$

$V_{CE(cutoff)} = \mathbf{24\ V}$

$V_{BQ} = \left(\dfrac{1.0\ k\Omega}{1.0\ k\Omega + 4.7\ k\Omega}\right) 24\ V = 4.21\ V$

$V_{EQ} = 4.21\ V - 0.7\ V = 3.51\ V$

$I_{EQ} \cong I_{CQ} = \dfrac{3.51\ V}{100\ \Omega} = 35.1\ mA$

$R_c = 330\ \Omega \parallel 330\ \Omega = 165\ \Omega$

$V_{CQ} = 24\ V - (35.1\ mA)(165\ \Omega) = 12.4\ V$

$V_{CEQ} = 12.4\ V - 3.51\ V = 8.90\ V$

$I_{c(sat)} = 35.1\ mA + \dfrac{8.90\ V}{165\ \Omega} = \mathbf{89.1\ mA}$

$V_{ce(cutoff)} = 8.90\ V - (35.1\ mA)(165\ \Omega) = \mathbf{14.7\ V}$
See Figure 9-4.

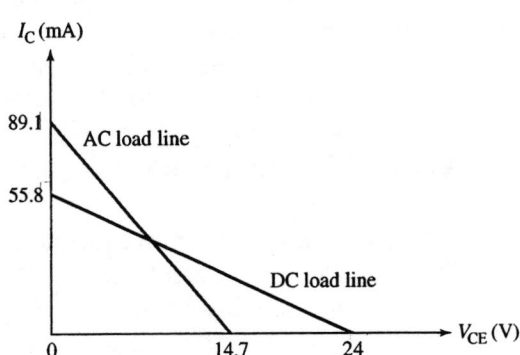

Figure 9-4

Chapter 9

33. See Figure 9-5.

$$I_{R1} \cong I_{R2} = \frac{15 \text{ V}}{86 \, \Omega} = 174 \text{ mA}$$

$$V_B \cong \left(\frac{18 \, \Omega}{86 \, \Omega} \right) 15 \text{ V} = 3.14 \text{ V}$$

$$V_E = 3.14 \text{ V} - 0.7 \text{ V} = 2.44 \text{ V}$$

$$I_E \cong I_C = \frac{2.44 \text{ V}}{4.85 \, \Omega} = 503 \text{ mA}$$

$$V_C = 15 \text{ V} - (10 \, \Omega)(503 \text{ mA}) = 9.97 \text{ V}$$

$$V_{CE} = 7.53 \text{ V}$$

$$r'_e = \frac{25 \text{ mV}}{503 \text{ mA}} = 0.05 \, \Omega$$

The ac resistance affecting the load line is

$$R_c + R_e + r'_e = 10 \, \Omega$$

$$\beta_{ac} = \beta_{DC} \geq 100$$

$$I_{c(sat)} = 503 \text{ mA} + \frac{7.53 \text{ V}}{10.2 \, \Omega} = 1.24 \text{ A}$$

$$V_{ce(cutoff)} = 7.53 \text{ V} + (503 \text{ mA})(10.2 \, \Omega) = 12.7 \text{ V}$$

The Q-point is closer to cutoff so
$P_{out} = (0.5)(503 \text{ mA})^2(10.2 \, \Omega) = 1.29 \text{ W}$
As loading occurs, the Q-point will still be closer
to cutoff. The circuit will have
$P_{out} \geq 1$ W for $R_L \geq 37.7 \, \Omega$. (39 Ω standard)

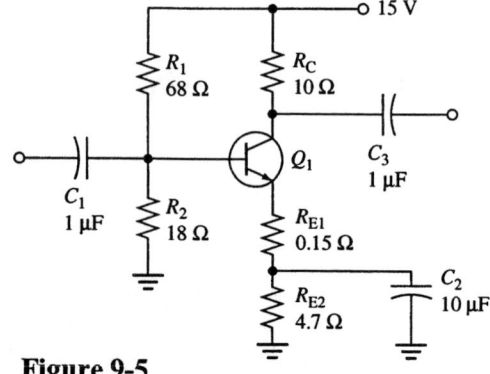

Figure 9-5

34. To modify the circuit of textbook Figure 9-39, to operate on dc power for 8 hours continuously, remove the rectifier connections (with a switch possibly) and connect the power terminals of the preamp and amplifier boards to a 12 V battery (possibly with the same switch as that which disconnects the power supply). Because the preamp operates on 9 V, a zener or other regulator must be used to set the proper voltage on this board.

EWB/Multisim Troubleshooting Problems

The solutions showing instrument connections for Problems 35 through 39 are available in the Solutions folder for Chapter 9 on the CD-ROM provided with the textbook. The solutions may be accessed using the password *ED5FLOYD*. The faults in the circuit files may be accessed using the password *book* (all lowercase).

35. C_{in} open

36. R_{E2} open

37. Q_1 collector-emitter open

38. D_2 shorted

39. Q_2 drain-source open

Chapter 10
Amplifier Frequency Response

Section 10-1 Basic Concepts

1. If $C_1 = C_2$, the critical frequencies are equal, and they will both cause the gain to decrease at 40 dB/decade below f_c.

2. At sufficiently high frequencies, the reactances of the coupling capacitors become very small and the capacitors appear effectively as shorts; thus, negligible signal voltage is dropped across them.

3. BJT: C_{be}, C_{bc}, and C_{ce}
    FET: C_{gs}, C_{gd}, and C_{ds}

4. Low-frequency response: C_1, C_2, and C_3
    High-frequency response: C_{bc}, C_{be}, and C_{ce}

5. $$V_E \cong \left(\frac{R_2}{R_1 + R_2}\right)V_{CC} - 0.7\,\text{V} = \left(\frac{4.7\,\text{k}\Omega}{37.7\,\text{k}\Omega}\right)20\,\text{V} - 0.7\,\text{V} = 1.79\,\text{V}$$

    $$I_E = \frac{V_E}{R_E} = \frac{1.79\,\text{V}}{560\,\Omega} = 3.2\,\text{mA}$$

    $$r_e' = \frac{25\,\text{mV}}{3.2\,\text{mA}} = 7.8\,\Omega$$

    $$A_v = \frac{R_c}{r_e'} = \frac{2.2\,\text{k}\Omega \,\|\, 5.6\,\text{k}\Omega}{7.8\,\Omega} = 202$$

    $$C_{in(miller)} = C_{bc}(A_v + 1) = 4\,\text{pF}(202 + 1) = \mathbf{812\ pF}$$

6. $$C_{out(miller)} = C_{bc}\left(\frac{A_v + 1}{A_v}\right) = 4\,\text{pF}\left(\frac{203}{202}\right) = \mathbf{4\ pF}$$

7. $I_D = 3.36\,\text{mA}$ using Eq. 8–5 and a programmable calculator.
    $$V_{GS} = -(3.36\,\text{mA})(1.0\,\text{k}\Omega) = -3.36\,\text{V}$$

    $$g_{m0} = \frac{2(10\,\text{mA})}{8\,\text{V}} = 2.5\,\text{mS}$$

    $$g_m = (2.5\,\text{mS})\left(1 - \frac{3.36\,\text{V}}{8\,\text{V}}\right) = 1.45\,\text{mS}$$

    $$A_v = g_m R_d = (1.45\,\text{mS})(1.0\,\text{k}\Omega \,\|\, 10\,\text{k}\Omega) = 1.32$$
    $$C_{gd} = C_{rss} = 3\,\text{pF}$$
    $$C_{in(miller)} = C_{gd}(A_v + 1) = 3\,\text{pF}(2.32) = \mathbf{6.95\ pF}$$

    $$C_{out(miller)} = C_{gd}\left(\frac{A_v + 1}{A_v}\right) = 3\,\text{pF}\left(\frac{2.32}{1.32}\right) = \mathbf{5.28\ pF}$$

Chapter 10

Section 10-2 The Decibel

8. $A_p = \dfrac{P_{out}}{P_{in}} = \dfrac{5\,\text{W}}{0.5\,\text{W}} = 10$

   $A_p(\text{dB}) = 10\log\left(\dfrac{P_{out}}{P_{in}}\right) = 10\log 10 = \textbf{10 dB}$

9. $V_{in} = \dfrac{V_{out}}{A_v} = \dfrac{1.2\,\text{V}}{50} = \textbf{24 mV rms}$

   $A_v(\text{dB}) = 20\log(A_v) = 20\log 50 = \textbf{34.0 dB}$

10.   The gain reduction is $20\log\left(\dfrac{25}{65}\right) = \textbf{--8.3 dB}$

11.   (a) $10\log\left(\dfrac{2\,\text{mW}}{1\,\text{mW}}\right) = \textbf{3.01 dBm}$

   (b) $10\log\left(\dfrac{1\,\text{mW}}{1\,\text{mW}}\right) = \textbf{0 dBm}$

   (c) $10\log\left(\dfrac{4\,\text{mW}}{1\,\text{mW}}\right) = \textbf{6.02 dBm}$

   (d) $10\log\left(\dfrac{0.25\,\text{mW}}{1\,\text{mW}}\right) = \textbf{--6.02 dBm}$

12. $V_B = \left(\dfrac{4.7\,\text{k}\Omega}{37.7\,\text{k}\Omega}\right)20\,\text{V} = 1.79\,\text{V}$

   $I_E = \dfrac{1.79\,\text{V}}{560\,\Omega} = 3.20\,\text{mA}$

   $r'_e = \dfrac{25\,\text{mV}}{3.2\,\text{mA}} = 7.81\,\Omega$

   $A_v = \dfrac{5.6\,\text{k}\Omega \parallel 2.2\,\text{k}\Omega}{7.81\,\Omega} = 202$

   $A_{v(dB)} = 20\log(202) = \textbf{46.1 dB}$
   At the critical frequencies,
   $A_{v(dB)} = 46.1\,\text{dB} - 3\,\text{dB} = \textbf{43.1 dB}$

Section 10-3 Low-Frequency Amplifier Response

13.   (a) $f_c = \dfrac{1}{2\pi RC} = \dfrac{1}{2\pi(100\,\Omega)(5\,\mu\text{F})} = \textbf{318 Hz}$

   (b) $f_c = \dfrac{1}{2\pi RC} = \dfrac{1}{2\pi(1.0\,\text{k}\Omega)(0.1\,\mu\text{F})} = \textbf{1.59 kHz}$

14. $R_{\text{IN(base)}} = \beta_{\text{DC}} R_{\text{E}} = 12.5 \text{ k}\Omega$

$$V_{\text{E}} = \left(\frac{R_2 \parallel R_{\text{IN(base)}}}{R_1 + R_2 \parallel R_{\text{IN(base)}}} \right) 9 \text{ V} - 0.7 \text{ V} = \left(\frac{4.7 \text{ k}\Omega \parallel 12.5 \text{ k}\Omega}{12 \text{ k}\Omega + 4.7 \text{ k}\Omega \parallel 12.5 \text{ k}\Omega} \right) 9 \text{ V} - 0.7 \text{ V} = 1.3 \text{ V}$$

$$I_{\text{E}} = \frac{V_{\text{E}}}{R_{\text{E}}} = \frac{1.3 \text{ V}}{100 \, \Omega} = 13 \text{ mA}$$

$$r_e' = \frac{25 \text{ mV}}{13 \text{ mA}} = 1.92 \, \Omega$$

$$R_{in(base)} = \beta_{ac} r_e' = (125)(1.92 \, \Omega) = 240 \, \Omega$$

$$R_{in} = 50 \, \Omega + R_{in(base)} \parallel R_1 \parallel R_2 = 50 \, \Omega + 240 \, \Omega \parallel 12 \text{ k}\Omega \parallel 4.7 \text{ k}\Omega = 274 \, \Omega$$

For the input network:

$$f_c = \frac{1}{2\pi R_{in} C_1} = \frac{1}{2\pi (274 \, \Omega)(1 \, \mu\text{F})} = \textbf{578 Hz}$$

For the output network:

$$f_c = \frac{1}{2\pi (R_{\text{C}} + R_L) C_3} = \frac{1}{2\pi (900 \, \Omega)(1 \, \mu\text{F})} = \textbf{177 Hz}$$

For the bypass network:

$$R_{\text{TH}} = R_1 \parallel R_2 \parallel R_s = 12 \text{ k}\Omega \parallel 4.7 \text{ k}\Omega \parallel 50 \, \Omega \cong 49.3 \, \Omega$$

$$f_c = \frac{1}{2\pi \left(r_e' + R_{\text{TH}} / \beta_{\text{DC}} \parallel R_{\text{E}} \right) C_2} = \frac{1}{2\pi (2.31 \, \Omega)(10 \, \mu\text{F})} = \textbf{6.89 kHz}$$

$$A_v = \frac{R_{\text{C}} \parallel R_L}{r_e'} = \frac{220 \, \Omega \parallel 680 \, \Omega}{1.92 \, \Omega} = 86.6$$

$A_v(\text{dB}) = 20 \log(86.6) = 38.8 \text{ dB}$

The **bypass network** produces the dominant low critical frequency. See Figure 10-1.

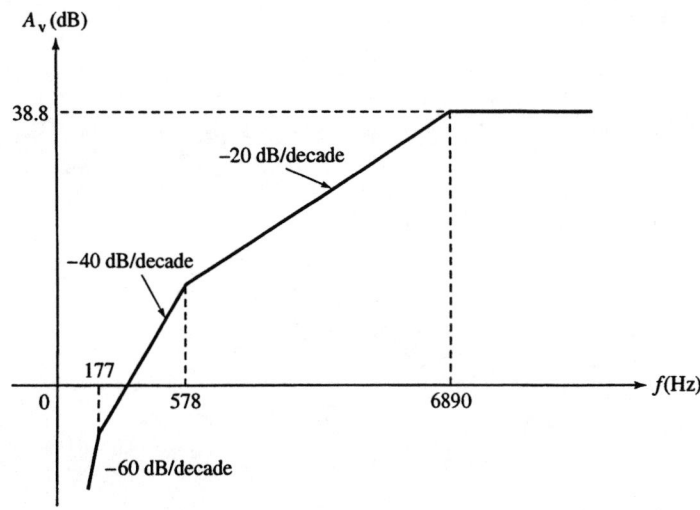

Figure 10-1

Chapter 10

15. From Problem 14:

$A_{v(mid)} = 86.6$

$A_{v(mid)}$ (dB) = 38.7 dB

For the input RC network: $f_c = 578$ Hz

For the output RC network: $f_c = 177$ Hz

For the bypass RC network: $f_c = 6.89$ kHz

The f_c of the bypass network is the dominant low critical frequency.

At $f = f_c = 6.89$ kHz:

$A_v = A_{v(mid)} - 3$ dB = 38.7 dB $-$ 3 dB = **35.7 dB**

At $f = 0.1f_c$:

$A_v = 38.75$ dB $-$ 20 dB = **18.7 dB**

At $10f_c$ (neglecting any high frequency effects):

$A_v = A_{v(mid)} =$ **38.7 dB**

16. At $f = f_c = X_C = R$

$$\theta = \tan^{-1}\left(\frac{X_C}{R}\right) = \tan^{-1}(1) = \mathbf{45°}$$

At $f = 0.1f_c$, $X_C = 10R$.

$\theta = \tan^{-1}(10) = \mathbf{84.3°}$

At $f = 10f_c$, $X_C = 0.1R$.

$\theta = \tan^{-1}(0.1) = \mathbf{5.7°}$

17. $R_{in(gate)} = \left|\dfrac{V_{GS}}{I_{GSS}}\right| = \left|\dfrac{-10\,\text{V}}{50\,\text{nA}}\right| = 200\,\text{M}\Omega$

$R_{in} = R_G \parallel R_{in(gate)} = 10\,\text{M}\Omega \parallel 200\,\text{M}\Omega = 9.52\,\text{M}\Omega$

For the input network:

$$f_c = \frac{1}{2\pi R_{in}C_1} = \frac{1}{2\pi(9.52\,\text{M}\Omega)(0.005\,\mu\text{F})} = \mathbf{3.34\ kHz}$$

For the output network:

$$f_c = \frac{1}{2\pi(R_D + R_L)C_2} = \frac{1}{2\pi(560\,\Omega + 10\,\text{k}\Omega)(0.005\,\mu\text{F})} = \mathbf{3.01\ kHz}$$

The **output network is dominant.** See Figure 10-2.

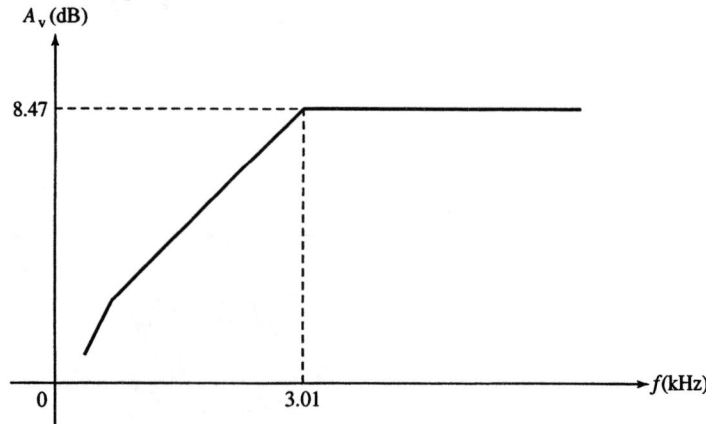

Figure 10-2

18. (a) $g_m = g_{m0} = \dfrac{2(15\text{ mA})}{6\text{ V}} = 5\text{ mS}$

$A_{v(mid)} = g_m(R_D \parallel R_L) = 5\text{ mS}(560\,\Omega \parallel 10\text{ k}\Omega) = 2.65$

$A_{v(mid)}(\text{dB}) = 8.47\text{ dB}$

At f_c:

$A_v = 8.47\text{ dB} - 3\text{ dB} = \mathbf{5.47\ dB}$

At $0.1f_c$:

$A_v = 8.47\text{ dB} - 20\text{ dB} = \mathbf{-11.5\ dB}$

At $10f_c$:

$A_v = A_{v(mid)} = \mathbf{8.47\ dB}$ (if $10f_c$ is still in midrange)

Section 10-4 High-Frequency Amplifier Response

19. From Problems 14 and 15:

$r_e' = 1.92\ \Omega$ and $A_{v(mid)} = 86.6$

Input network:

$C_{in(miller)} = C_{bc}(A_v + 1) = 10\text{ pF}(86.6) = 876\text{ pF}$

$C_T = C_{be} \parallel C_{in(miller)} = 25\text{ pF} + 876\text{ pF} = 901\text{ pF}$

$f_c = \dfrac{1}{2\pi(R_s \parallel R_1 \parallel R_2 \parallel \beta_{ac}r_e')C_T} = \dfrac{1}{2\pi(50\,\Omega \parallel 12\text{ k}\Omega \parallel 4.7\text{ k}\Omega \parallel 240\,\Omega)901\text{ pF}} = \mathbf{4.32\ MHz}$

Output network:

$C_{out(miller)} = C_{bc}\left(\dfrac{A_v + 1}{A_v}\right) = 10\text{ pF}\left(\dfrac{87.6}{86.6}\right) = 10.1\text{ pF}$

$f_c = \dfrac{1}{2\pi R_c C_{out(miller)}} = \dfrac{1}{2\pi(166\,\Omega)(10.1\text{ pF})} = \mathbf{94.9\ MHz}$

Therefore, the dominant high critical frequency is determined by the input network: $f_c = 4.32$ MHz. See Figure 10-3.

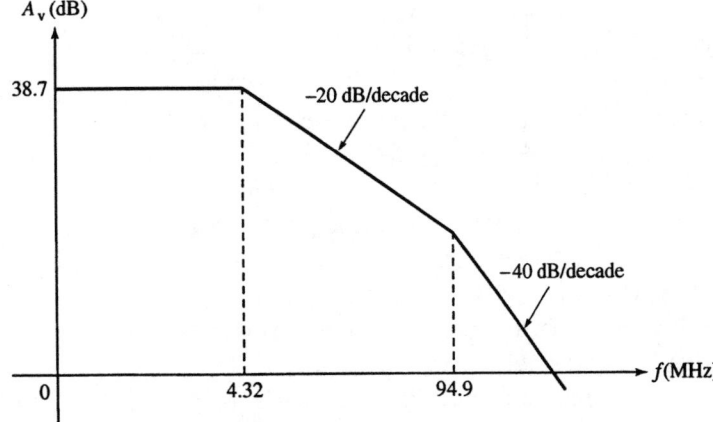

Figure 10-3

Chapter 10

20.   At $f = 0.1f_c = 458$ kHz:
$A_v = A_{v(mid)} = \textbf{38.7 dB}$
At $f = f_c = 4.58$ MHz:
$A_v = A_{v(mid)} - 3$ dB $= 38.7$ dB $- 3$ dB $= \textbf{35.7 dB}$
At $f = 10f_c = 45.8$ MHz:
$A_v = A_{v(mid)} - 20$ dB $= 38.7$ dB $- 20$ dB $= \textbf{18.7 dB}$
At $f = 100f_c = 458$ MHz:
The rolloff rate changes to -40 dB/decade at $f = 94.6$ MHz. So, for frequencies from
45.8 MHz to 94.6 MHz, the rolloff rate is -20 dB/decade and above 94.6 MHz it is
-40 dB/decade.
The change in frequency from 45.8 MHz to 94.63 MHz represents
$$\frac{94.6\,\text{MHz} - 45.8\,\text{MHz}}{458\,\text{MHz} - 45.8\text{MHz}} \times 100\% = 11.8\%$$
So, for 11.8% of the decade from 45.8 MHz to 458 MHz, the rolloff rate is -20 dB/decade
and for the remaining 88.2% of the decade, the rolloff rate is -40 dB/ decade.
$A_v = 18.7$ dB $- (0.118)(20$ dB$) - (0.882)(40$ dB$) = 18.7$ dB $- 2.36$ dB $- 35.3$ dB $= \textbf{--19 dB}$

21. $C_{gd} = C_{rss} = 4$ pF
$C_{gs} = C_{iss} - C_{rss} = 10$ pF $- 4$ pF $= 6$ pF
Input network:
$C_{in(miller)} = C_{gd}(A_v + 1) = 4$ pF$(2.65 + 1) = 14.6$ pF
$C_T = C_{gs} \parallel C_{in(miller)} = 6$ pF $+ 14.6$ pF $= 20.6$ pF
$$f_c = \frac{1}{2\pi R_s C_T} = \frac{1}{2\pi(600\,\Omega)(20.6\,\text{pF})} = \textbf{12.9 MHz}$$
Output network:
$$C_{out(miller)} = C_{gd}\left(\frac{A_v + 1}{A_v}\right) = 4\,\text{pF}\left(\frac{2.65 + 1}{2.65}\right) = 5.51\ \text{pF}$$
$$f_c = \frac{1}{2\pi R_d C_{out(miller)}} = \frac{1}{2\pi(530\,\Omega)(5.51\,\text{pF})} = \textbf{54.5 MHz}$$
The input network is dominant.

22.   From Problem 21: For the input network, $f_c = 12.9$ MHz and
for the output network, $f_c = 54.5$ MHz.
The dominant critical frequency is 12.9 MHz.
At $f = 0.1f_c = 1.29$ MHz: $A_v = A_{v(mid)} = \textbf{8.47 dB}$, $\theta = \textbf{0°}$
At $f = f_c = 12.9$ MHz: $A_v = A_{v(mid)} - 3$ dB $= 8.47$ dB $- 3$ dB $= \textbf{5.47 dB}$, $\theta = \tan^{-1}(1) = \textbf{45°}$
At $f = 10f_c = 129$ MHz:
From 12.9 MHz to 54.5 MHz the rolloff is -20 dB/decade. From 54.5 MHz to 129 MHz the
rolloff is -40 dB/decade.
The change in frequency from 12.9 MHz to 54.5 MHz represents
$$\frac{54.5\,\text{MHz} - 12.9\,\text{MHz}}{129\,\text{MHz} - 12.9\,\text{MHz}} \times 100\% = 35.8\%$$
So, for 35.8% of the decade, the rolloff rate is -20 dB/decade and for 64.2% of the decade,
the rate is -40 dB/decade.
$A_v = 5.47$ dB $- (0.358)(20$ dB$) - (0.642)(40$ dB$) = \textbf{--13.1 dB}$
At $f = 100f_c = 1290$ MHz: $A_v = -13.1$ dB $- 40$ dB $= \textbf{--53.1 dB}$

Section 10-5 Total Amplifier Frequency Response

23. f_{cl} = **136 Hz**
        f_{cu} = **8 kHz**

24.   From Problems 14 and 19:
        f_{cu} = 4.32 MHz and f_{cl} = 6.89 kHz
        $BW = f_{cu} - f_{cl}$ = 4.32 MHz – 6.89 kHz = **4.313 MHz**

25. $f_T = (BW)A_{v(mid)}$

$$BW = \frac{f_T}{A_{v(mid)}} = \frac{200 \text{ MHz}}{38} = 5.26 \text{ MHz}$$

Therefore, $f_{cu} \cong BW$ = **5.26 MHz**

26.   6 dB/octave rolloff:
        At $2f_{cu}$: A_v = 50 dB – 6 dB = **44 dB**
        At $4f_{cu}$: A_v = 50 dB – 12 dB = **38 dB**
        20 dB/decade rolloff:
        At $10f_{cu}$: A_v = 50 dB – 20 dB = **30 dB**

Section 10-6 Frequency Response of Multistage Amplifiers

27.   Dominant f'_{cl} = **230 Hz**
        Dominant f'_{cu} = **1.2 MHz**

28. BW = 1.2 MHz – 230 Hz $\cong$ **1.2 MHz**

29. $f'_{cl} = \dfrac{400 \text{ Hz}}{\sqrt{2^{1/2} - 1}} = \dfrac{400 \text{ Hz}}{0.643} = 622 \text{ Hz}$

$f'_{cu} = (800 \text{ kHz})\sqrt{2^{1/2} - 1} = 0.643(800 \text{ kHz}) = 515 \text{ kHz}$
BW = 515 kHz – 622 Hz $\cong$ **514 kHz**

30. $f'_{cl} = \dfrac{50 \text{ Hz}}{\sqrt{2^{1/3} - 1}} = \dfrac{50 \text{ Hz}}{0.510} = $ **98.1 Hz**

31. $f'_{cl} = \dfrac{125 \text{ Hz}}{\sqrt{2^{1/2} - 1}} = \dfrac{125 \text{ Hz}}{0.643} = 194 \text{ Hz}$

f'_{cu} 2.5 MHz
BW = 2.5 MHz – 194 Hz $\cong$ **2.5 MHz**

Chapter 10

Section 10-7 Frequency Response Measurement

32. $f_{cl} = \dfrac{0.35}{t_f} = \dfrac{0.35}{1\,\text{ms}} = \textbf{350 Hz}$

$f_{cu} = \dfrac{0.35}{t_r} = \dfrac{0.35}{20\,\text{ns}} = \textbf{17.5 MHz}$

33. Increase the frequency until the output voltage drops to 3.54 V (3 dB below the midrange output voltage). This is the upper critical frequency.

34. $t_r \cong 3\,\text{div} \times 5\,\mu\text{s/div} = 15\,\mu\text{s}$
$t_f \cong 6\,\text{div} \times 0.1\,\text{ms/div} = 600\,\mu\text{s}$

$f_{cl} = \dfrac{0.35}{t_f} = \dfrac{0.35}{600\,\mu\text{s}} = 583\,\text{Hz}$

$f_{cu} = \dfrac{0.35}{t_r} = \dfrac{0.35}{15\,\mu\text{s}} = 23.3\,\text{kHz}$

$BW = 23.3\,\text{kHz} - 583\,\text{Hz} = \textbf{22.7 kHz}$

System Application Problems

35. $V_{\text{B}} = \left(\dfrac{13\,\text{k}\Omega}{113\,\text{k}\Omega}\right)12\,\text{V} = 1.38\,\text{V}, \; V_{\text{E}} = 0.68\,\text{V}$

$I_{\text{E}} = 2.13\,\text{mA}, \; r'_e = 11.7\,\Omega$

$R_{in} = 22\,\text{k}\Omega \,\|\, 100\,\text{k}\Omega \,\|\, (112\,\Omega)(100) = 6.9\,\text{k}\Omega$ (*both stages*)

First stage:

$f_{cl(in)} = \dfrac{1}{2\pi(6.9\,\text{k}\Omega)(1\,\mu\text{F})} = \textbf{23.1 Hz}$

$R_{out} = 4.7\,\text{k}\Omega + 6.9\,\text{k}\Omega = 11.6\,\text{k}\Omega$

$f_{cl(out)} = \dfrac{1}{2\pi(11.6\,\text{k}\Omega)(1\,\mu\text{F})} = \textbf{13.7 Hz}$

$R_{bypass} = 220\,\Omega \,\|\, (112\,\Omega + 22\,\text{k}\Omega \,\|\, 100\,\text{k}\Omega/100) = 125\,\Omega$

$f_{cl(bypass)} = \dfrac{1}{2\pi(125\,\Omega)(100\,\mu\text{F})} = \textbf{12.7 Hz}$

Second stage:

$f_{cl(in)} = \textbf{13.7 Hz}$ (same as $f_{cl(out)}$ of first stage)

$R_{out} = 4.7\,\text{k}\Omega + 10\,\text{k}\Omega = 14.7\,\text{k}\Omega$

$f_{cl(out)} = \dfrac{1}{2\pi(14.7\,\text{k}\Omega)(1\,\mu\text{F})} = \textbf{10.8 Hz}$

$R_{bypass} = 220\,\Omega \,\|\, (112\,\Omega + 22\,\text{k}\Omega \,\|\, 100\,\text{k}\Omega \,\|\, 4.7\,\text{k}\Omega/100) = 88.8\,\Omega$

$f_{cl(bypass)} = \dfrac{1}{2\pi(88.8\,\Omega)(100\,\mu\text{F})} = \textbf{17.9 Hz}$

$f_{cl(in)}$ **of first stage is the dominant lower critical frequency.**

36. Changing to 1 μF coupling capacitors does not significantly affect the overall bandwidth because the upper critical frequency is much greater than the dominant lower critical frequency.

37. Increasing the load resistance on the output of the second stage has no effect on the dominant lower critical frequency because the critical frequency of the output circuit will decrease and the critical frequency of the first stage input circuit will remain dominant.

38. $V_B = \left(\dfrac{13\,\text{k}\Omega}{113\,\text{k}\Omega}\right)12\,\text{V} = 1.38\,\text{V},\ V_E = 0.68\,\text{V}$

$I_E = 2.13\,\text{mA},\ r_e' = 11.7\,\Omega$

$R_{in} = 22\,\text{k}\Omega \,\|\, 100\,\text{k}\Omega \,\|\, (112\,\Omega)(100) = 6.9\,\text{k}\Omega\ (\textit{both stages})$

First stage:

$f_{cl(in)} = \dfrac{1}{2\pi(6.9\,\text{k}\Omega)(10\,\mu\text{F})} = \mathbf{2.31\ Hz}$

$R_{out} = 4.7\,\text{k}\Omega + 6.9\,\text{k}\Omega = 11.6\,\text{k}\Omega$

$f_{cl(out)} = \dfrac{1}{2\pi(11.6\,\text{k}\Omega)(10\,\mu\text{F})} = \mathbf{1.37\ Hz}$

$R_{bypass} = 220\,\Omega \,\|\, (112\,\Omega + 22\,\text{k}\Omega \,\|\, 100\,\text{k}\Omega / 100) = 125\,\Omega$

$f_{cl(bypass)} = \dfrac{1}{2\pi(125\,\Omega)(100\,\mu\text{F})} = \mathbf{12.7\ Hz}$

Second stage:
$f_{cl(in)} = \mathbf{1.37\ Hz}$ (same as $f_{cl(out)}$ of first stage)
$R_{out} = 4.7\,\text{k}\Omega + 10\,\text{k}\Omega = 14.7\,\text{k}\Omega$

$f_{cl(out)} = \dfrac{1}{2\pi(14.7\,\text{k}\Omega)(10\,\mu\text{F})} = \mathbf{1.08\ Hz}$

$R_{bypass} = 220\,\Omega \,\|\, (112\,\Omega + 22\,\text{k}\Omega \,\|\, 100\,\text{k}\Omega \,\|\, 4.7\,\text{k}\Omega / 100) = 88.8\,\Omega$

$f_{cl(bypass)} = \dfrac{1}{2\pi(88.8\,\Omega)(100\,\mu\text{F})} = \mathbf{17.9\ Hz}$

First stage:
$R_c = 4.7\,\text{k}\Omega \,\|\, 100\,\text{k}\Omega \,\|\, 22\,\text{k}\Omega \,\|\, (100)(100\,\Omega + 11.7\,\Omega) = 2.8\,\text{k}\Omega$

$A_{v1} = \dfrac{2.8\,\text{k}\Omega}{112\,\Omega} = 25$

$C_{in(Miller)} = (25 + 1)4\,\text{pF} = 112\,\text{pF}$
$C_{in(Tot)} = 112\,\text{pF} + 8\,\text{pF} = 120\,\text{pF}$

$C_{out(Miller)} = \left(\dfrac{25+1}{25}\right)4\,\text{pF} = 4.16\,\text{pF}$

$f_{cu(in)} = \dfrac{1}{2\pi(6.9\,\text{k}\Omega)(120\,\text{pF})} = \mathbf{192\ kHz}$

$f_{cu(out)} = \dfrac{1}{2\pi(2.8\,\text{k}\Omega)(4.16\,\mu\text{F})} = \mathbf{13.7\ MHz}$

Chapter 10

Second stage:

$R_c = 4.7\,\text{k}\Omega \parallel 10\,\text{k}\Omega = 3.2\,\text{k}\Omega$

$A_{v1} = \dfrac{3.2\,\text{k}\Omega}{112\,\Omega} = 28.6$

$C_{in(Miller)} = (28.6 + 1)4\,\text{pF} = 119\,\text{pF}$
$C_{in(tot)} = 119\,\text{pF} + 8\,\text{pF} = 127\,\text{pF}$

$C_{out(Miller)} = \left(\dfrac{28.6 + 1}{28.6}\right)4\,\text{pF} = 4.14\,\text{pF}$

$f_{cu(in)} = \dfrac{1}{2\pi(2.8\,\text{k}\Omega)(127\,\text{pF})} = \textbf{448 kHz}$

$f_{cu(out)} = \dfrac{1}{2\pi(3.2\,\text{k}\Omega)(4.14\,\text{pF})} = \textbf{12.0 MHz}$

$t_f = \dfrac{0.35}{17.9\,\text{Hz}} = \textbf{19.5 ms}$

$t_f = \dfrac{0.35}{192\,\text{kHz}} = \textbf{1.82 }\boldsymbol{\mu}\textbf{s}$

Data Sheet Problems

39. $C_{in(tot)} = (25 + 1)4\,\text{pF} + 8\,\text{pF} = \textbf{112 pF}$

40. $BW_{min} = \dfrac{f_T}{A_{v(mid)}} = \dfrac{300\,\text{MHz}}{50} = \textbf{6 MHz}$

41. $C_{gd} = C_{rss} = \textbf{1.3 pF}$
$C_{gs} = C_{iss} - C_{rss} = 5\,\text{pF} - 1.3\,\text{pF} = \textbf{3.7 pF}$
$C_{ds} = C_d - C_{rss} = 5\,\text{pF} - 1.3\,\text{pF} = \textbf{3.7 pF}$

Advanced Problems

42.   From Problem 12: $r_e' = 7.81\,\Omega$ and $I_E = 3.2\,\text{mA}$
$V_C \cong 20\,\text{V} - (3.2\,\text{mA})(2.2\,\text{k}\Omega) = 13\,\text{V dc}$
The maximum peak output signal can be approximately 6 V.
The maximum allowable gain for the two stages is

$A_{v(max)} = \dfrac{6\,\text{V}}{1.414(10\,\text{mV})} = 424$

For stage 1:

$R_c = 2.2\,\text{k}\Omega \parallel 33\,\text{k}\Omega \parallel 4.7\,\text{k}\Omega \parallel (150)(7.81\,\Omega) = 645\,\Omega$

$A_{v1} = \dfrac{645\,\Omega}{7.81\,\Omega} = 82.6$

For stage 2:

$R_c = 2.2\,\text{k}\Omega \,\|\, 5.6\,\text{k}\Omega = 1.58\,\text{k}\Omega$

$A_{v1} = \dfrac{1.58\,\text{k}\Omega}{7.81\,\Omega} = 202$

$A_{v(tot)} = (82.6)(202) = 16{,}685$

The amplifier will **not operate linearly** with a 10 mV rms input signal.
The gains of both stages can be reduced or the gain of the second stage only can be reduced.
One approach is leave the gain of the first stage as is and bypass a portion of the emitter resistance in the second stage to achieve a gain of 424/82.6 = 5.13.

$A_v = \dfrac{R_c}{R_e + r_e'} = 5.13$

$R_e = \dfrac{R_c - 5.13 r_e'}{5.13} = \dfrac{1.58\,\text{k}\Omega - 40.1\,\Omega}{5.13} = 300\,\Omega$

Modification: Replace the 560 Ω emitter resistor in the second stage with an unbypassed 300 Ω resistor and a bypassed 260 Ω resistor (closest standard value is 270 Ω).

43. From Problems 17, 18, and 21:

$C_T = C_{gs} \,\|\, C_{in(miller)} = 20.6\,\text{pF}$

$C_{out(miller)} = 4\,\text{pF}\left(\dfrac{2.65 + 1}{2.65}\right) = 5.51\,\text{pF}$

Stage 1:

$f_{cl(in)} = \dfrac{1}{2\pi R_{in} C_1} = \dfrac{1}{2\pi (9.52\,\text{M}\Omega)(0.005\,\mu\text{F})} = 3.34\,\text{Hz}$

$f_{cl(out)} = \dfrac{1}{2\pi (9.52\,\text{M}\Omega)(0.005\,\mu\text{F})} = 3.34\,\text{Hz since } R_{in(2)} \gg 560\,\Omega$

$f_{cu(in)} = \dfrac{1}{2\pi (600\,\Omega)(20.6\,\text{pF})} = 12.9\,\text{MHz}$

$f_{cu(out)} = \dfrac{1}{2\pi (560\,\Omega)(20.6\,\text{pF} + 5.51\,\text{pF})} = 10.5\,\text{MHz}$

Stage 2:

$f_{cl(in)} = \dfrac{1}{2\pi R_{in} C_1} = \dfrac{1}{2\pi (9.52\,\text{M}\Omega)(0.005\,\mu\text{F})} = 3.34\,\text{Hz}$

$f_{cl(out)} = \dfrac{1}{2\pi (10.6\,\text{k}\Omega)(0.005\,\mu\text{F})} = 3.01\,\text{kHz}$

$f_{cu(in)} = \dfrac{1}{2\pi (560\,\Omega)(20.6\,\text{pF} + 5.51\,\text{pF})} = 10.5\,\text{MHz}$

$f_{cu(out)} = \dfrac{1}{2\pi (560\,\Omega \,\|\, 10\,\text{k}\Omega)(5.51\,\text{pF})} = 54.5\,\text{MHz}$

Overall:

$f_{cl(out)} = 3.01\,\text{kHz and } f_{cu(in)} = 10.5\,\text{MHz}$

$BW \cong \textbf{10.5 MHz}$

Chapter 10

44. $R_{in(1)} = 22\,\text{k}\Omega \parallel (100)(320\,\Omega) = 13\,\text{k}\Omega$

$V_{B(1)} = \left(\dfrac{13\,\text{k}\Omega}{113\,\text{k}\Omega}\right)12\,\text{V} = 1.38,\ V_{E(1)} = 0.684\,\text{V}$

$I_{E(1)} = \dfrac{0.684\,\text{V}}{320\,\Omega} = 2.14\,\text{mA},\ r'_e = 11.7\,\Omega$

$R_{c(1)} = 4.7\,\text{k}\Omega \parallel 33\,\text{k}\Omega \parallel 22\,\text{k}\Omega \parallel (100)(100\,\Omega) = 2.57\,\text{k}\Omega$

$A_{v(1)} = \dfrac{2.57\,\text{k}\Omega}{112\,\Omega} = 23$

$R_{in(2)} = 22\,\text{k}\Omega \parallel (100)(1010\,\Omega) = 18\,\text{k}\Omega$

$V_{B(2)} = \left(\dfrac{18\,\text{k}\Omega}{51\,\text{k}\Omega}\right)12\,\text{V} = 4.42,\ V_{E(1)} = 3.54\,\text{V}$

$I_{E(2)} = \dfrac{3.54\,\text{V}}{1.01\,\text{k}\Omega} = 3.51\,\text{mA},\ r'_e = 7.13\,\Omega$

$R_{c(2)} = 3\,\text{k}\Omega \parallel 10\,\text{k}\Omega = 2.31\,\text{k}\Omega$

$A_{v(2)} = \dfrac{2.31\,\text{k}\Omega}{107.13\,\Omega} = 24 \text{ maximum}$

$A_{v(2)} = \dfrac{2.31\,\text{k}\Omega}{101\,\text{k}\Omega + 7.13\,\Omega} = 2.27 \text{ minimum}$

$A_{v(tot)} = (23)(24) = 554 \text{ maximum}$
$A_{v(tot)} = (23)(2.27) = 52.3 \text{ minimum}$
This is a bit high, so adjust $R_{c(1)}$ to 3 kΩ, then

$A_{v(1)} = \dfrac{3\,\text{k}\Omega \parallel 22\,\text{k}\Omega \parallel 33\,\text{k}\Omega \parallel 101\,\text{k}\Omega}{112\,\Omega} = 21.4$

Now,
$A_{v(tot)} = (21.3)(24) = \textbf{513} \text{ maximum}$
$A_{v(tot)} = (21.3)(2.27) = \textbf{48.5} \text{ minimum}$
Thus, A_v is within 3% of the desired specifications.

Frequency response for stage 1:
$R_{in} = 22\,\text{k}\Omega \parallel 100\,\text{k}\Omega \parallel 32\,\text{k}\Omega = 11.5\,\text{k}\Omega$

$f_{cl(in)} = \dfrac{1}{2\pi(11.5\,\text{k}\Omega)(10\,\mu\text{F})} = 1.38\,\text{Hz}$

$R_{emitter} = 220\,\Omega \parallel (100\,\Omega + 11.7\,\Omega + (22\,\text{k}\Omega \parallel 100\,\text{k}\Omega)100) = 125\,\Omega$

$f_{cl(bypass)} = \dfrac{1}{2\pi(125\,\Omega)(100\,\mu\text{F})} = 12.7\,\text{Hz}$

$R_{out} = 3\,\text{k}\Omega + (33\,\text{k}\Omega \parallel 22\,\text{k}\Omega \parallel (100)(107\,\Omega)) = 8.91\,\text{k}\Omega$

$f_{cl(out)} = \dfrac{1}{2\pi(8.91\,\text{k}\Omega)(10\,\mu\text{F})} = 1.79\,\text{Hz}$

Frequency response for stage 2:

$f_{cl(in)} = 1.79$ Hz (same as $f_{cl(out)}$ for stage 1)

$R_{out} = 3$ kΩ + 10 kΩ = 13 kΩ

$$f_{cl(out)} = \frac{1}{2\pi(13\,\text{k}\Omega)(10\,\mu\text{F})} = 1.22 \text{ Hz}$$

This means that $C_{E(2)}$ is the frequency limiting capacitance.

$R_{emitter}$ 910 $\Omega\|$ (100 Ω + 7 Ω + (22 k$\Omega\|$ 33 k$\Omega\|$ 3 kΩ)/100) = 115 Ω

For $f_{cl}' = 1$ kHz:

$$C_{E(2)} = \frac{1}{2\pi(115\,\Omega)(1\,\text{kHz})} = 1.38\ \mu\text{F}$$

1.5 μF is the closest standard value and gives

$$f_{cl(bypass)} = \frac{1}{2\pi(115\,\Omega)(1.5\,\mu\text{F})} = \textbf{922 Hz}$$

This value can be moved closer to 1 kHz by using additional parallel bypass capacitors in stage 2 to fine-tune the response.

EWB/Multisim Troubleshooting Problems

The solutions showing instrument connections for Problems 45 through 48 are available in the Solutions folder for Chapter 10 on the CD-ROM provided with the textbook. The solutions may be accessed using the password *ED5FLOYD*. The faults in the circuit files may be accessed using the password *book* (all lowercase).

45. R_C open

46. Output capacitor open

47. R_2 open

48. Drain-source shorted

Chapter 11
Thyristors and Other Devices

Section 11-1 The Basic 4-Layer Device

1. $V_A = V_{BE} - V_{CE(sat)} = 0.7\,V + 0.2\,V = 0.9\,V$

   $V_{R_S} = V_{BIAS} - V_A = 25\,V - 0.9\,V = 24.1\,V$

   $$I_A = \frac{V_{R_S}}{R_S} = \frac{24.1\,V}{1.0\,k\Omega} = \mathbf{24.1\ mA}$$

2.   (a) $R_{AK} = \dfrac{V_{AK}}{I_A} = \dfrac{15\,V}{1\,\mu A} = \mathbf{15\ M\Omega}$

   (b) From 15 V to 50 V for an increase of 35 V.

Section 11-2 The Silicon-Controlled Rectifier (SCR)

3.   See Section 11-2 in the textbook.

4.   Neglecting the SCR voltage drop,

   $$R_{max} = \frac{30\,V}{10\,mA} = \mathbf{3\ k\Omega}$$

Section 11-3 SCR Applications

5.   Add a transistor to provide inversion of the negative half-cycle in order to obtain a positive gate trigger.

6. D_1 and D_2 are full-wave rectifier diodes.

7.   See Figure 11-1.

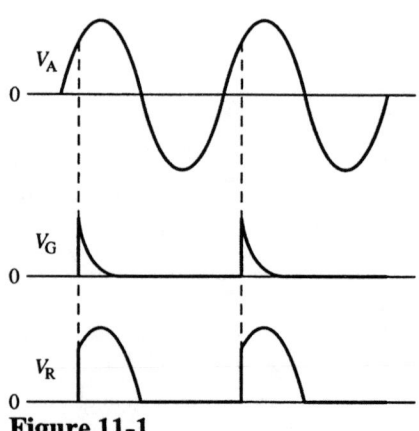

Figure 11-1

Section 11-4 The Diac and Triac

8. $V_{in(p)} = 1.414V_{in(rms)} = 1.414(25 \text{ V}) = 35.4 \text{ V}$

$I_p = V_{in(p)} = \dfrac{35.35 \text{ V}}{1.0 \text{ k}\Omega} = 35.4 \text{ mA}$

Current at breakover $= \dfrac{20 \text{ V}}{1.0 \text{ k}\Omega} = 20 \text{ mA}$

See Figure 11-2.

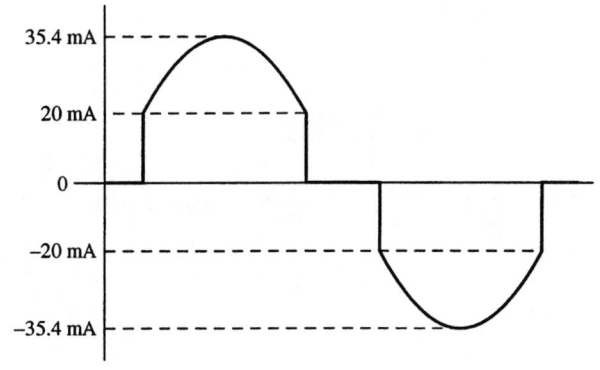

Figure 11-2

9. $I_p = \dfrac{15 \text{ V}}{4.7 \text{ k}\Omega} = 3.19 \text{ mA}$
See Figure 11-3.

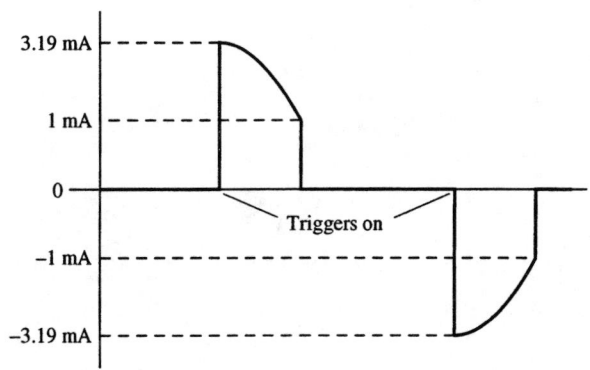

Figure 11-3

Section 11-5 The Silicon-Controlled Switch (SCS)

10.   See Section 11-5 in the text.

11.   Anode, cathode, anode gate, and cathode gate

Chapter 11

Section 11-6 The Unijunction Transistor (UJT)

12. $\eta = \dfrac{r'_{B1}}{r'_{B1} + r'_{B2}} = \dfrac{2.5\,k\Omega}{2.5\,k\Omega + 4\,k\Omega} = \mathbf{0.385}$

13. $V_p = \eta V_{BB} + V_{pn} = 0.385(15\ \text{V}) + 0.7\ \text{V} = \mathbf{6.48\ V}$

14. $\dfrac{V_{BB} - V_v}{I_v} < R_1 < \dfrac{V_{BB} - V_P}{I_p}$

$\dfrac{12\ \text{V} - 0.8\ \text{V}}{15\ \text{mA}} < R_1 < \dfrac{12\ \text{V} - 10\ \text{V}}{10\ \mu\text{A}}$

$\mathbf{747\ \Omega < R_1 < 200\ k\Omega}$

Section 11-7 The Programmable UJT (PUT)

15.   (a) $V_A = \left(\dfrac{R_3}{R_2 + R_3}\right) V_B + 0.7\ \text{V} = \left(\dfrac{10\,k\Omega}{22\,k\Omega}\right) 20\ \text{V} + 0.7\ \text{V} = \mathbf{9.79\ V}$

(b) $V_A = \left(\dfrac{R_3}{R_2 + R_3}\right) V_B + 0.7\ \text{V} = \left(\dfrac{47\,k\Omega}{94\,k\Omega}\right) 9\ \text{V} + 0.7\ \text{V} = \mathbf{5.2\ V}$

16.   (a) From Problem 15(a), $V_A = 9.79$ V at turn on.

$I = \dfrac{9.79\ \text{V}}{470\ \Omega} = 20.8$ mA at turn on

$I_p = \dfrac{10\ \text{V}}{470\ \Omega} = 21.3$ mA

See Figure 11-4.

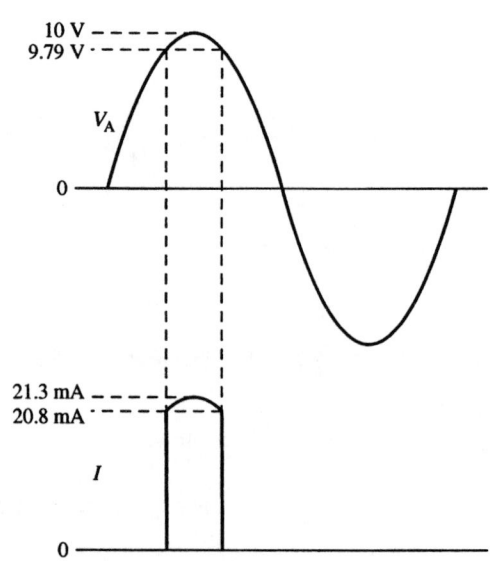

Figure 11-4

(b) From Problem 15(b), $V_A = 5.2$ V at turn on.

$$I = \frac{5.2\ \text{V}}{330\ \Omega} = 15.8\ \text{mA at turn on}$$

$$I_p = \frac{10\ \text{V}}{330\ \Omega} = 30.3\ \text{mA}$$

See Figure 11-5.

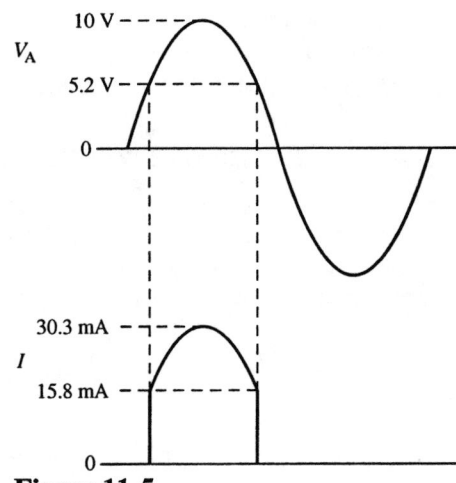

Figure 11-5

17. $$V_A = \left(\frac{R_3}{R_2 + R_3}\right) 6\ \text{V} + 0.7\ \text{V} = \left(\frac{10\ \text{k}\Omega}{20\ \text{k}\Omega}\right) 6\ \text{V} + 0.7\ \text{V} = 3.7\ \text{V at turn on}$$

$V_{R1} \cong V_A = 3.7$ V at turn on.
See Figure 11-6.

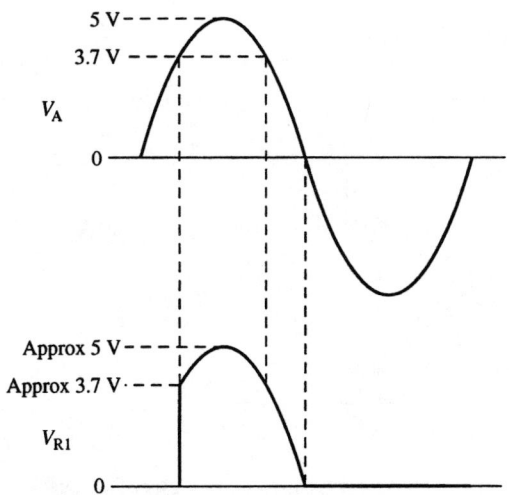

Figure 11-6

Chapter 11

Section 11-8 The Phototransistor

18. $I_C = \beta_{DC}I_\lambda = (200)(100\ \mu A) = \textbf{20 mA}$

19. (a) $V_{OUT} = \textbf{12 V}$
     (b) $V_{OUT} = \textbf{0 V}$

20. $I_{\lambda 1} = (50\ \text{lm/m}^2)(1\ \mu A/\text{lm/m}^2) = 50\ \mu A$
     $I_E = \beta_{DC1}\beta_{DC2}I_{\lambda 1} = (100)(150)(50\ \mu A) = \textbf{750 mA}$

Section 11-9 The Light-Activated SCR (LASCR)

21. When the switch is closed, the battery V_2 causes illumination of the lamp. The light energy causes the LASCR to conduct and thus energize the relay. When the relay is energized, the contacts close and 115 V ac are applied to the motor.

22. See Figure 11-7.

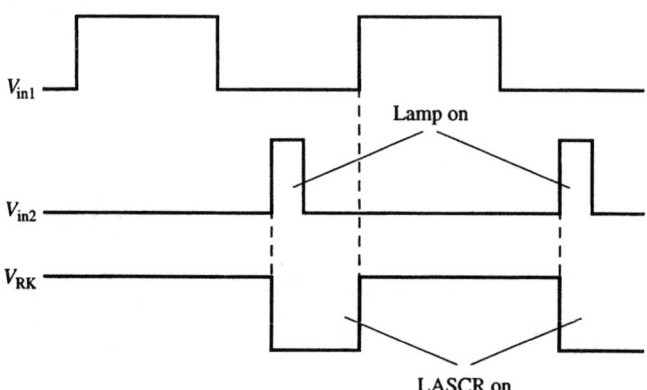

Figure 11-7

Section 11-10 Optical Couplers

23. $I_{out} = (0.30)(100\ \text{mA}) = \textbf{30 mA}$

24. $\dfrac{I_{OUT}}{I_{IN}} = 0.6$

     $I_{IN} = \dfrac{I_{OUT}}{0.6} = \dfrac{10\ \text{mA}}{0.6} = \textbf{16.7 mA}$

System Application Problems

25. The motor runs fastest at **0 V** for the motor speed control circuit.

26. If the rheostat resistance decreases, the SCR turns on **earlier** in the ac cycle.

27. As the PUT gate voltage increases in the circuit, the PUT triggers on later in the ac cycle causing the SCR to fire later in the cycle, conduct for a shorter time, and decrease the power to the motor.

Advanced Problems

28. D_1: 15 V zener (1N4744)
R_1: 100 Ω, 1 W
R_2: 100 Ω, 1 W
Q_1: Any SCR with a 1 A minimum rating (1.5 A would be better)
R_3: 150 Ω, 1 W

29.   See Figure 11-8.

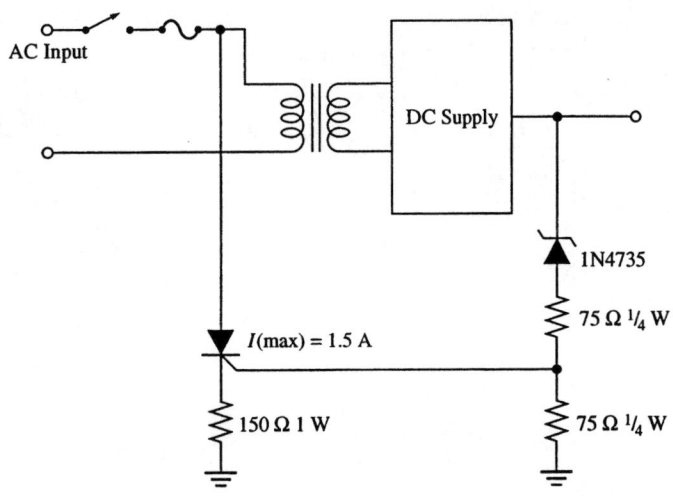

Figure 11-8

30. $V_p = \eta V_{BB} + V_{pn} = (0.75)(12\,\text{V}) + 0.7\,\text{V} = 9.7\,\text{V}$
$I_v = 10$ mA and $I_p = 20\ \mu\text{A}$

$$R_1 < \frac{12\,\text{V} - 9.7\,\text{V}}{20\,\mu\text{A}} = 115\,\text{k}\Omega$$

$$R_1 > \frac{12\,\text{V} - 1\,\text{V}}{10\,\text{mA}} = 1.1\,\text{k}\Omega$$

Select $R_1 = 51$ kΩ as an intermediate value.
During the charging cycle:

$$V(t) = V_F - (V_F - V_0)e^{-t_1/R_1C}$$

$$9.7\,\text{V} = 12\,\text{V} - (12\,\text{V} - 1\,\text{V})e^{-t_1/R_1C}$$

$$-\frac{t_1}{R_1C} = \ln\left(\frac{2.3\,\text{V}}{11\,\text{V}}\right)$$

$$t_1 = -R_1C\ln\left(\frac{2.3\,\text{V}}{11\,\text{V}}\right) = 1.56R_1C = 79.8 \times 10^3 C$$

During the discharging cycle (assuming $R_2 \gg R_{B1}$):

$$V(t) = V_F - (V_F - V_0)e^{-t_2/R_2C}$$

$$1\text{ V} = 0\text{ V} - (0\text{ V} - 9.3\text{ V})e^{-t_2/R_2C}$$

$$-\frac{t_2}{R_2C} = \ln\left(\frac{1\text{ V}}{9.3\text{ V}}\right)$$

$$t_2 = -R_2C\ln\left(\frac{1\text{ V}}{9.3\text{ V}}\right) = 2.23R_2C$$

Let $R_2 = 100$ kΩ, so $t_2 = 223 \times 10^3 C$.

Since $f = 2.5$ kHz, $T = 400$ μs

$$T = t_1 + t_2 = 79.8 \times 10^3 C + 223 \times 10^3 C = 303 \times 10^3 C = 400\text{ }\mu\text{s}$$

$$C = \frac{400\text{ }\mu\text{s}}{303 \times 10^3} = 0.0013\text{ }\mu\text{F}$$

See Figure 11-9.

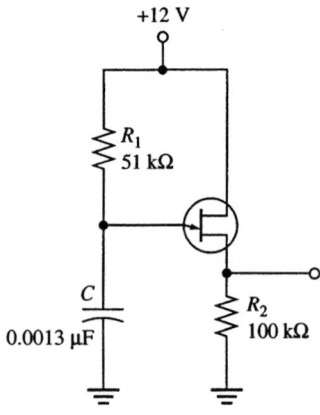

Figure 11-9

EWB/Multisim Troubleshooting Problems

The solutions showing instrument connections for Problems 31 through 33 are available in the Solutions folder for Chapter 11 on the CD-ROM provided with the textbook. The solutions may be accessed using the password *ED5FLOYD*. The faults in the circuit files may be accessed using the password *book* (all lowercase).

31.   Shockley diode shorted (EWB only)

32.   Gate-cathode open

33. R_1 shorted

Chapter 12
Operational Amplifiers

Section 12-1 Introduction to Operational Amplifiers

1.   *Practical op-amp*: High open-loop gain, high input impedance. low output impedance, and high CMRR.
     Ideal op-amp: Infinite open-loop gain, infinite input impedance, zero output impedance, and infinite CMRR.

2.   Op amp 2 is more desirable because it has a higher input impedance, a lower output impedance, and a higher open-loop gain.

Section 12-2 Op-Amp Input Modes and Parameters

3.   (a) Single-ended input
     (b) Differential input
     (c) Common-mode

4.   CMRR(dB) = 20 log(250,000) = **108 dB**

5. $\text{CMRR(dB)} = 20\ \log\left(\dfrac{A_{ol}}{A_{cm}}\right) = 20\log\left(\dfrac{175,000}{0.18}\right) =$ **120 dB**

6. $\text{CMRR} = \dfrac{A_{ol}}{A_{cm}}$

     $A_{cm} = \dfrac{A_{ol}}{\text{CMRR}} = \dfrac{90,000}{300,000} =$ **0.3**

7. $I_{\text{BIAS}} = \dfrac{8.3\ \mu A - 7.9\ \mu A}{2} =$ **8.1 μA**

8.   Input bias current is the average of the two input currents. Input offset current is the difference between the two input currents.

     $I_{\text{OS}} = \left|8.3\ \mu A - 7.9\ \mu A\right| =$ **400 nA**

9.   Slew rate $= \dfrac{24\ \text{V}}{15\ \mu s} =$ **1.6 V/μs**

10. $\Delta t = \dfrac{\Delta V_{out}}{\text{slew rate}} = \dfrac{20\ \text{V}}{0.5\ \text{V/}\mu s} =$ **40 μs**

Chapter 12

Section 12-4 Op-Amps with Negative Feedback

11. (a) Voltage-follower
     (b) Noninverting
     (c) Inverting

12. $B = \dfrac{R_i}{R_i + R_f} = \dfrac{1.0\,k\Omega}{101\,k\Omega} = \mathbf{9.90 \times 10^{-3}}$

     $V_f = BV_{out} = (9.90 \times 10^{-3})5\,V = 0.0495\,V = \mathbf{49.5\,mV}$

13. (a) $A_{cl(NI)} = \dfrac{1}{B} = \dfrac{1}{1.5\,k\Omega\,/\,561.5\,k\Omega} = \mathbf{374}$

     (b) $V_{out} = A_{cl(NI)}V_{in} = (374)(10\,mV) = \mathbf{3.74\,V\ rms}$

     (c) $V_f = \left(\dfrac{1.5\,k\Omega}{561.5\,k\Omega}\right)3.74\,V = \mathbf{9.99\,mV\ rms}$

14. (a) $A_{cl(NI)} = \dfrac{1}{B} = \dfrac{1}{4.7\,k\Omega\,/\,51.7\,k\Omega} = \mathbf{11}$

     (b) $A_{cl(NI)} = \dfrac{1}{B} = \dfrac{1}{10\,k\Omega\,/\,1.01\,M\Omega} = \mathbf{101}$

     (c) $A_{cl(NI)} = \dfrac{1}{B} = \dfrac{1}{4.7\,k\Omega\,/\,224.7\,k\Omega} = \mathbf{47.8}$

     (d) $A_{cl(NI)} = \dfrac{1}{B} = \dfrac{1}{1.0\,k\Omega\,/\,23\,k\Omega} = \mathbf{23}$

15. (a) $1 + \dfrac{R_f}{R_i} = A_{cl(NI)}$

     $R_f = R_i(A_{cl(NI)} - 1) = 1.0\,k\Omega(50 - 1) = \mathbf{49\,k\Omega}$

     (b) $\dfrac{R_f}{R_i} = A_{cl(I)}$

     $R_f = -R_i(A_{cl(I)}) = -10\,k\Omega(-300) = \mathbf{3\,M\Omega}$

     (c) $R_f = R_i(A_{cl(NI)} - 1) = 12\,k\Omega(7) = \mathbf{84\,k\Omega}$

     (d) $R_f = -R_i(A_{cl(I)}) = -2.2\,k\Omega(-75) = \mathbf{165\,k\Omega}$

16. (a) $A_{cl(VF)} = \mathbf{1}$

     (b) $A_{cl(I)} = -\left(\dfrac{R_f}{R_i}\right) = -\left(\dfrac{100\,k\Omega}{100\,k\Omega}\right) = \mathbf{-1}$

     (c) $A_{cl(NI)} = \dfrac{1}{\left(\dfrac{R_i}{R_i + R_f}\right)} = \dfrac{1}{\left(\dfrac{47\,k\Omega}{47\,k\Omega + 1.0\,M\Omega}\right)} = \mathbf{22}$

     (d) $A_{cl(I)} = -\left(\dfrac{R_f}{R_i}\right) = -\left(\dfrac{330\,k\Omega}{33\,k\Omega}\right) = \mathbf{-10}$

17.   (a) $V_{out} \cong V_{in} =$ **10 mV, in phase**

      (b) $V_{out} = A_{cl}V_{in} = -\left(\dfrac{R_f}{R_i}\right)V_{in} = -(1)(10 \text{ mV}) =$ **−10 mV, 180° out of phase**

      (c) $V_{out} = \left(\dfrac{1}{\left(\dfrac{R_i}{R_i + R_f}\right)}\right)V_{in} = \left(\dfrac{1}{\left(\dfrac{47 \text{ k}\Omega}{1047 \text{ k}\Omega}\right)}\right)10 \text{ mV} =$ **223 mV, in phase**

      (d) $V_{out} = -\left(\dfrac{R_f}{R_i}\right)V_{in} = -\left(\dfrac{330 \text{ k}\Omega}{33 \text{ k}\Omega}\right)10 \text{ mV} =$ **−100 mV, 180° out of phase**

18.   (a) $I_{in} = \dfrac{V_{in}}{R_{in}} = \dfrac{1 \text{ V}}{2.2 \text{ k}\Omega} =$ **455 μA**

      (b) $I_f \cong I_{in} =$ **455 μA**

      (c) $V_{out} = -I_f R_f = -(455 \text{ }\mu\text{A})(22 \text{ k}\Omega) =$ **−10 V**

      (d) $A_{cl(I)} = -\left(\dfrac{R_f}{R_i}\right) = -\left(\dfrac{22 \text{ k}\Omega}{2.2 \text{ k}\Omega}\right) =$ **−10**

Section 12-5 Effects of Negative Feedback on Op-Amp Impedances

19.   (a) $B = \dfrac{2.7 \text{ k}\Omega}{562.5 \text{ k}\Omega} = 0.0048$

         $Z_{in(NI)} = (1 + A_{ol})Z_{in} = [1 + (175{,}000)(0.0048)]10 \text{ M}\Omega =$ **8.41 GΩ**

         $Z_{out(NI)} = \dfrac{Z_{out}}{1 + A_{ol}B} = \dfrac{75 \text{ }\Omega}{1 + (175{,}000)(0.0048)} =$ **89.2 mΩ**

      (b) $B = \dfrac{1.5 \text{ k}\Omega}{48.5 \text{ k}\Omega} = 0.031$

         $Z_{in(NI)} = (1 + A_{ol})Z_{in} = [1 + (200{,}000)(0.031)]1 \text{ M}\Omega =$ **6.20 GΩ**

         $Z_{out(NI)} = \dfrac{Z_{out}}{1 + A_{ol}B} = \dfrac{25 \text{ }\Omega}{1 + (200{,}000)(0.031)} =$ **4.04 mΩ**

      (c) $B = \dfrac{56 \text{ k}\Omega}{1.056 \text{ M}\Omega} = 0.053$

         $Z_{in(NI)} = (1 + A_{ol})Z_{in} = [1 + (50{,}000)(0.053)]2 \text{ M}\Omega =$ **5.30 GΩ**

         $Z_{out(NI)} = \dfrac{Z_{out}}{1 + A_{ol}B} = \dfrac{50 \text{ }\Omega}{1 + (50{,}000)(0.053)} =$ **19.0 mΩ**

Chapter 12

20. (a) $Z_{in(VF)} = (1 + A_{ol})Z_{in} = (1 + 220,000)6 \text{ M}\Omega = 1.32 \times 10^{12} \, \Omega = \mathbf{1.32 \ T\Omega}$

$$Z_{out(VF)} = \frac{Z_{out}}{1 + A_{ol}} = \frac{100 \, \Omega}{1 + 220,000} = \mathbf{455 \ \mu\Omega}$$

(b) $Z_{in(VF)} = (1 + A_{ol})Z_{in} = (1 + 100,000)5 \text{ M}\Omega = 5 \times 10^{11} \, \Omega = \mathbf{500 \ G\Omega}$

$$Z_{out(VF)} = \frac{Z_{out}}{1 + A_{ol}} = \frac{60 \, \Omega}{1 + 100,000} = \mathbf{600 \ \mu\Omega}$$

(c) $Z_{in(VF)} = (1 + A_{ol})Z_{in} = (1 + 50,000)800 \text{ k}\Omega = \mathbf{40 \ G\Omega}$

$$Z_{out(VF)} = \frac{Z_{out}}{1 + A_{ol}} = \frac{75 \, \Omega}{1 + 500,000} = \mathbf{1.5 \ m\Omega}$$

21. (a) $Z_{in(I)} \cong R_i = \mathbf{10 \ k\Omega}$

$$B = \frac{R_i}{R_i + R_f} = \frac{10 \text{ k}\Omega}{160 \text{ k}\Omega} = 0.0625$$

$$Z_{out(I)} = \frac{Z_{out}}{1 + A_{ol}B} = \frac{40 \, \Omega}{1 + (125,000)(0.0625)} = \mathbf{5.12 \ m\Omega}$$

(b) $Z_{in(I)} \cong R_i = \mathbf{100 \ k\Omega}$

$$B = \frac{100 \text{ k}\Omega}{1.1 \text{ M}\Omega} = 0.090$$

$$Z_{out(I)} = \frac{Z_{out}}{1 + A_{ol}B} = \frac{50 \, \Omega}{1 + (75,000)(0.90)} = \mathbf{7.41 \ m\Omega}$$

(c) $Z_{in(I)} \cong R_i = \mathbf{470 \ \Omega}$

$$B = \frac{470 \, \Omega}{10,470 \, \Omega} = 0.045$$

$$Z_{out(I)} = \frac{Z_{out}}{1 + A_{ol}B} = \frac{70 \, \Omega}{1 + (250,000)(0.045)} = \mathbf{6.22 \ m\Omega}$$

Section 12-6 Bias Current and Offset Voltage Compensation

22. (a) $R_{comp} = R_{in} = \mathbf{75 \ \Omega}$ placed in the feedback path.

$I_{OS} = |42 \ \mu\text{A} - 40 \ \mu\text{A}| = 2\mu\text{A}$

(b) $V_{OUT(error)} = A_v I_{OS} R_{in} = (1)(2 \ \mu\text{A})(75 \ \Omega) = \mathbf{150 \ \mu V}$

23. (a) $R_c = R_i \parallel R_f = 2.7 \text{ k}\Omega \parallel 560 \text{ k}\Omega = \mathbf{2.69 \ k\Omega}$

(b) $R_c = R_i \parallel R_f = 1.5 \text{ k}\Omega \parallel 47 \text{ k}\Omega = \mathbf{1.45 \ k\Omega}$

(c) $R_c = R_i \parallel R_f = 56 \text{ k}\Omega \parallel 1.0 \text{ M}\Omega = \mathbf{53 \ k\Omega}$

See Figure 12-1.

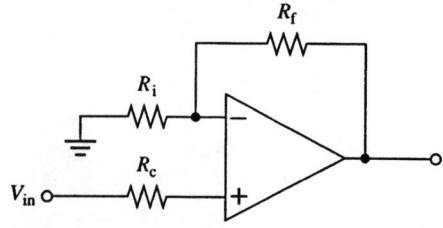

Figure 12-1

24. $V_{\text{OUT(error)}} = A_v V_{\text{IO}} = (1)(2 \text{ nV}) = \mathbf{2 \text{ nV}}$

25. $V_{\text{OUT(error)}} = (1 + A_{ol})V_{\text{IO}}$

$$V_{\text{IO}} = \frac{V_{\text{OUT(error)}}}{A_{ol}} = \frac{35 \text{ mV}}{200{,}000} = \mathbf{175 \text{ nV}}$$

Section 12-7 Open-Loop Response

26. $A_{cl} = 120 \text{ dB} - 50 \text{ dB} = \mathbf{70 \text{ dB}}$

27. The gain is ideally **175,000** at 200 Hz. The midrange dB gain is
$20 \log(175{,}000) = 105 \text{ dB}$
The actual gain at 200 Hz is
$A_v(\text{dB}) = 105 \text{ dB} - 3 \text{ dB} = 102 \text{ dB}$

$$A_v = \log^{-1}\left(\frac{102}{20}\right) = \mathbf{125{,}892}$$

$BW_{ol} = \mathbf{200 \text{ Hz}}$

28. $\dfrac{f_c}{f} = \dfrac{X_C}{R}$

$$X_C = \frac{R f_c}{f} = \frac{(1.0 \text{ k}\Omega)(5 \text{ kHz})}{3 \text{ kHz}} = \mathbf{1.67 \text{ k}\Omega}$$

29. (a) $\dfrac{V_{out}}{V_{in}} = \dfrac{1}{\sqrt{1 + \left(\dfrac{f}{f_c}\right)^2}} = \dfrac{1}{\sqrt{1 + \left(\dfrac{1 \text{ kHz}}{12 \text{ kHz}}\right)^2}} = \mathbf{0.997}$

(b) $\dfrac{V_{out}}{V_{in}} = \dfrac{1}{\sqrt{1 + \left(\dfrac{f}{f_c}\right)^2}} = \dfrac{1}{\sqrt{1 + \left(\dfrac{5 \text{ kHz}}{12 \text{ kHz}}\right)^2}} = \mathbf{0.923}$

(c) $\dfrac{V_{out}}{V_{in}} = \dfrac{1}{\sqrt{1 + \left(\dfrac{f}{f_c}\right)^2}} = \dfrac{1}{\sqrt{1 + \left(\dfrac{12 \text{ kHz}}{12 \text{ kHz}}\right)^2}} = \mathbf{0.707}$

(d) $\dfrac{V_{out}}{V_{in}} = \dfrac{1}{\sqrt{1 + \left(\dfrac{f}{f_c}\right)^2}} = \dfrac{1}{\sqrt{1 + \left(\dfrac{20 \text{ kHz}}{12 \text{ kHz}}\right)^2}} = \mathbf{0.515}$

(e) $\dfrac{V_{out}}{V_{in}} = \dfrac{1}{\sqrt{1 + \left(\dfrac{f}{f_c}\right)^2}} = \dfrac{1}{\sqrt{1 + \left(\dfrac{100 \text{ kHz}}{12 \text{ kHz}}\right)^2}} = \mathbf{0.119}$

Chapter 12

30. (a) $A_{ol} = \dfrac{A_{ol(mid)}}{\sqrt{1+\left(\dfrac{f}{f_{c(ol)}}\right)^2}} = \dfrac{80{,}000}{\sqrt{1+\left(\dfrac{100\,\text{Hz}}{1\,\text{kHz}}\right)^2}} = \textbf{79,603}$

(b) $A_{ol} = \dfrac{A_{ol(mid)}}{\sqrt{1+\left(\dfrac{f}{f_{c(ol)}}\right)^2}} = \dfrac{80{,}000}{\sqrt{1+\left(\dfrac{1\,\text{kHz}}{1\,\text{kHz}}\right)^2}} = \textbf{56,569}$

(c) $A_{ol} = \dfrac{A_{ol(mid)}}{\sqrt{1+\left(\dfrac{f}{f_{c(ol)}}\right)^2}} = \dfrac{80{,}000}{\sqrt{1+\left(\dfrac{10\,\text{kHz}}{1\,\text{kHz}}\right)^2}} = \textbf{7960}$

(d) $A_{ol} = \dfrac{A_{ol(mid)}}{\sqrt{1+\left(\dfrac{f}{f_{c(ol)}}\right)^2}} = \dfrac{80{,}000}{\sqrt{1+\left(\dfrac{1\,\text{MHz}}{1\,\text{kHz}}\right)^2}} = \textbf{80}$

31. (a) $f_c = \dfrac{1}{2\pi RC} = \dfrac{1}{2\pi(10\,\text{k}\Omega)(0.01\,\mu\text{F})} = 1.59\,\text{kHz};\quad \theta = \tan^{-1}\left(\dfrac{f}{f_c}\right) = \tan^{-1}\left(\dfrac{2\,\text{kHz}}{1.59\,\text{kHz}}\right) = \textbf{--51.5°}$

(b) $f_c = \dfrac{1}{2\pi RC} = \dfrac{1}{2\pi(1.0\,\text{k}\Omega)(0.01\,\mu\text{F})} = 15.9\,\text{kHz};\quad \theta = \tan^{-1}\left(\dfrac{f}{f_c}\right) = \tan^{-1}\left(\dfrac{2\,\text{kHz}}{15.9\,\text{kHz}}\right) = \textbf{--7.17°}$

(c) $f_c = \dfrac{1}{2\pi RC} = \dfrac{1}{2\pi(100\,\text{k}\Omega)(0.01\,\mu\text{F})} = 159\,\text{Hz};\quad \theta = \tan^{-1}\left(\dfrac{f}{f_c}\right) = \tan^{-1}\left(\dfrac{2\,\text{kHz}}{159\,\text{Hz}}\right) = \textbf{--85.5°}$

32. (a) $\theta = \tan^{-1}\left(\dfrac{f}{f_c}\right) = \tan^{-1}\left(\dfrac{100\,\text{Hz}}{8.5\,\text{kHz}}\right) = \textbf{--0.674°}$

(b) $\theta = \tan^{-1}\left(\dfrac{f}{f_c}\right) = \tan^{-1}\left(\dfrac{400\,\text{Hz}}{8.5\,\text{kHz}}\right) = \textbf{--2.69°}$

(c) $\theta = \tan^{-1}\left(\dfrac{f}{f_c}\right) = \tan^{-1}\left(\dfrac{850\,\text{Hz}}{8.5\,\text{kHz}}\right) = \textbf{--5.71°}$

(d) $\theta = \tan^{-1}\left(\dfrac{f}{f_c}\right) = \tan^{-1}\left(\dfrac{8.5\,\text{kHz}}{8.5\,\text{kHz}}\right) = \textbf{--45.0°}$

(e) $\theta = \tan^{-1}\left(\dfrac{f}{f_c}\right) = \tan^{-1}\left(\dfrac{25\,\text{kHz}}{8.5\,\text{kHz}}\right) = \textbf{--71.2°}$

(f) $\theta = \tan^{-1}\left(\dfrac{f}{f_c}\right) = \tan^{-1}\left(\dfrac{85\,\text{kHz}}{8.5\,\text{kHz}}\right) = \textbf{--84.3°}$

See Figure 12-2.

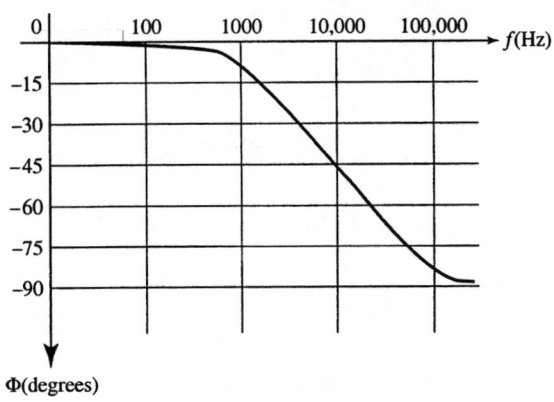

Figure 12-2

33. (a) $A_{ol(mid)} = 30 \text{ dB} + 40 \text{ dB} + 20 \text{ dB} = \textbf{90 dB}$

(b) $\theta_1 = -\tan^{-1}\left(\dfrac{f}{f_c}\right) = -\tan^{-1}\left(\dfrac{10 \text{ kHz}}{600 \text{ Hz}}\right) = -86.6°$

$\theta_2 = -\tan^{-1}\left(\dfrac{f}{f_c}\right) = -\tan^{-1}\left(\dfrac{10 \text{ kHz}}{50 \text{ kHz}}\right) = -11.3°$

$\theta_3 = -\tan^{-1}\left(\dfrac{f}{f_c}\right) = -\tan^{-1}\left(\dfrac{10 \text{ kHz}}{200 \text{ kHz}}\right) = -2.86°$

$\theta_{tot} = -86.6° - 11.3° - 2.86° - 180° = \textbf{-281°}$

34. (a) 0 dB/decade
(b) −20 dB/decade
(c) −40 dB/decade
(d) −60 dB/decade

Section 12-8 Closed-Loop Response

35. (a) $A_{cl(I)} = -\left(\dfrac{R_f}{R_i}\right) = -\left(\dfrac{68 \text{ k}\Omega}{2.2 \text{ k}\Omega}\right) = -30.9;$ $A_{cl(I)}(\text{dB}) = 20 \log(30.9) = \textbf{29.8 dB}$

(b) $A_{cl(NI)} = \dfrac{1}{B} = \dfrac{1}{15 \text{ k}\Omega / 235 \text{ k}\Omega} = 15.7;$ $A_{cl(NI)}(\text{dB}) = 20 \log(15.7) = \textbf{23.9 dB}$

(c) $A_{cl(VF)} = 1;$ $A_{cl(VF)}(\text{dB}) = 20 \log(1) = \textbf{0 dB}$
These are all closed-loop gains.

36. $BW_{cl} = BW_{ol}(1 + BA_{ol(mid)}) = 1500 \text{ Hz}[1 + (0.015)(180,000)] = \textbf{4.05 MHz}$

Chapter 12

37. $A_{ol}(\text{dB}) = 89 \text{ dB}$

$A_{ol} = 28{,}184$

$A_{cl}f_{c(cl)} = A_{ol}f_{c(ol)}$

$A_{cl} = \dfrac{A_{ol}f_{c(ol)}}{f_{c(cl)}} = \dfrac{(28{,}184)(750 \text{ Hz})}{5.5 \text{ kHz}} = 3843$

$A_{cl}(\text{dB}) = 20 \log(3843) = \textbf{71.7 dB}$

38. $A_{cl} = \dfrac{A_{ol}f_{c(ol)}}{f_{c(cl)}} = \dfrac{(28{,}184)(750 \text{ Hz})}{5.5 \text{ kHz}} = 3843$

Unity-gain bandwidth $= A_{cl}f_{c(cl)} = (3843)(5.5 \text{ kHz}) = \textbf{21.1 MHz}$

39. (a) $A_{cl(VF)} = \textbf{1}$

$BW = f_{c(cl)} = \dfrac{\text{Unity - gain } BW}{A_{cl}} = \dfrac{28 \text{ MHz}}{1} = \textbf{2.8 MHz}$

(b) $A_{cl(I)} = -\dfrac{100 \text{ k}\Omega}{2.2 \text{ k}\Omega} = \textbf{-45.5}$

$BW = \dfrac{2.8 \text{ MHz}}{45.5} = \textbf{61.6 kHz}$

(c) $A_{cl(NI)} = 1 + \dfrac{12 \text{ k}\Omega}{1.0 \text{ k}\Omega} = \textbf{13}$

$BW = \dfrac{2.8 \text{ MHz}}{13} = \textbf{215 kHz}$

(d) $A_{cl(I)} = -\dfrac{1 \text{ M}\Omega}{5.6 \text{ k}\Omega} = \textbf{-179}$

$BW = \dfrac{2.8 \text{ MHz}}{179} = \textbf{15.7 kHz}$

40. (a) $A_{cl} = \dfrac{150 \text{ k}\Omega}{22 \text{ k}\Omega} = 6.8$

$f_{c(cl)} = \dfrac{A_{ol}f_{c(ol)}}{A_{cl}} = \dfrac{(120{,}000)(150 \text{ Hz})}{6.8} = 2.65 \text{ MHz}$

$BW = f_{c(cl)} = \textbf{2.65 MHz}$

(b) $A_{cl} = \dfrac{1.0 \text{ M}\Omega}{10 \text{ k}\Omega} = 100$

$f_{c(cl)} = \dfrac{A_{ol}f_{c(ol)}}{A_{cl}} = \dfrac{(195{,}000)(50 \text{ Hz})}{100} = 97.5 \text{ kHz}$

$BW = f_{c(cl)} = \textbf{97.5 kHz}$

Section 12-9 Troubleshooting

41.   (a) Faulty op-amp or open R_1
            (b) R_2 open, forcing open-loop operation

42.   (a) Circuit becomes a voltage-follower and the output replicates the input.
            (b) Output will saturate.
            (c) No effect on the ac; may add or subtract a small dc voltage to the output.
            (d) The voltage gain will change from 10 to 0.1.

43.   The gain becomes a fixed -100 with no effect as the potentiometer is adjusted.

System Application Problems

44.   The push-pull stage will operate nonlinearly if D_1 or D_2 is shorted, Q_1 or Q_2 is faulty, the op-amp stage has excessive gain, or if R_6 is open or shorted.

45.   If a 2.2 MΩ resistor is used for R_3, the gain of the op amp will be ten times too high, probably causing a clipped output waveform.

46.   If D_1 opens, the emitter current of Q_1 is diverted to the base of Q_2 producing saturation. Q_3 will also saturate. The result is a signal voltage of **0 V** on the output.

Data Sheet Problems

47.   From the data sheet of textbook Figure 12-67:

$$B = \frac{470\,\Omega}{47\,k\Omega + 470\,\Omega} = 0.0099$$

$A_{ol} = 200{,}000$ (typical)
$Z_{in} = 2.0\ M\Omega$ (typical)
$Z_{out} = 25\ \Omega$ (typical)
$Z_{in(NI)} = (1 + 0.0099)(200{,}000)(2\ M\Omega) = (1 + 1980)2\ M\Omega = \mathbf{3.96\ G\Omega}$

48.   From the data sheet in Figure 12-67:

$$Z_{in(I)} = R_i = \frac{R_f}{A_{cl}} = \frac{100\,k\Omega}{100} = \mathbf{1\ k\Omega}$$

49. $A_{ol} = 50\ V/mV = \dfrac{50\ V}{1\ mV} = \dfrac{50{,}000\ V}{1\ V} = \mathbf{50{,}000}$

50.   Slew rate $= 0.5\ V/\mu s$
            $\Delta V = 8\ V - (-8\ V) = 16\ V$

$$\Delta t = \frac{16\ V}{0.5\ V/\mu s} = \mathbf{32\ \mu s}$$

Chapter 12

Advanced Problems

51. Using available standard values of $R_f = 150\ \text{k}\Omega$ and $R_i = 1.0\ \text{k}\Omega$,

$$A_v = 1 + \frac{150\ \text{k}\Omega}{1.0\ \text{k}\Omega} = 151$$

$$B = \frac{1.0\ \text{k}\Omega}{151\ \text{k}\Omega} = 6.62 \times 10^{-3}$$

$Z_{in(\text{NI})} = (1 + (6.62 \times 10^{-3})(50{,}000))300\ \text{k}\Omega = 99.6\ \text{M}\Omega$

The compensating resistor is

$$R_c = R_i \,\|\, R_f = 150\ \text{k}\Omega \,\|\, 1.0\ \text{k}\Omega = 993\ \Omega$$

See Figure 12-3.

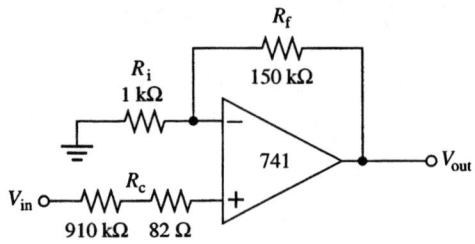

Figure 12-3

52. See Figure 12-4. 2% tolerance resistors are used to achieve a 5% gain tolerance.

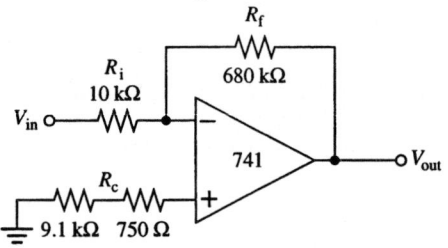

Figure 12-4

53. From textbook Figure 12-68:
$f_c = 10\ \text{kHz}$ at $A_v = 40\ \text{dB} = 100$
In this circuit

$$A_v = 1 + \frac{33\ \text{k}\Omega}{333\ \Omega} = 100.1 \cong 100$$

The compensating resistor is
$$R_c = 33\ \text{k}\Omega \,\|\, 333\ \Omega = 330\ \Omega$$
See Figure 12-5.

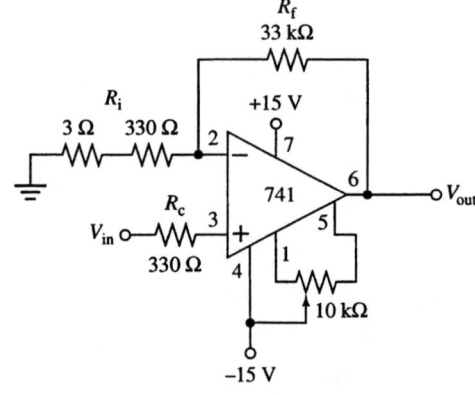

Figure 12-5

54. From textbook Figure 12-69:
For a ±10 V output swing minimum, the load must be 600 Ω for a ±10 V and ≈ 620 Ω for −10 V. So, the minimum load is **620 Ω**.

55. For the amplifier,
$$A_v = -\frac{100\,k\Omega}{2\,k\Omega} = -50$$
The compensating resistor is
$$R_c = 100\,k\Omega \parallel 2\,k\Omega = 1.96\,k\Omega \cong 2\,k\Omega$$
See Figure 12-6.

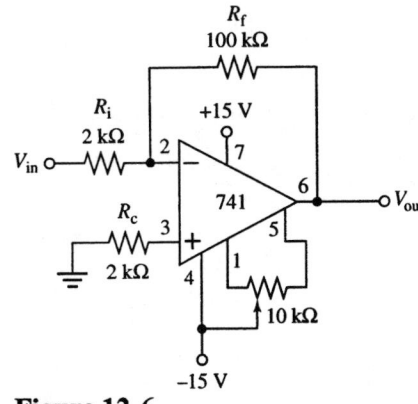

Figure 12-6

56. From textbook Figure 12-68 the maximum 741 closed loop gain with $BW = 5$ kHz is approximately 60 dB − (20 dB)log(5 kHz)/1 kHz = 60 dB − (20 dB)(0.7) = **46 dB**
$$A_{v(dB)} = 20 \log A_v$$
$$A_v = \log^{-1}\left(\frac{A_{v(dB)}}{20}\right) = \log^{-1}\left(\frac{46}{20}\right) = \mathbf{200}$$

EWB/Multisim Troubleshooting Problems

The solutions showing instrument connections for Problems 57 through 72 are available in the Solutions folder for Chapter 12 on the CD-ROM provided with the textbook. The solutions may be accessed using the password *ED5FLOYD*. The faults in the circuit files may be accessed using the password *book* (all lowercase).

57. R_f open

58. R_i open

59. R_f leaky

60. R_i shorted

61. R_f shorted

62. Op-amp input to output open

63. R_f leaky

64. R_i leaky

65. R_i shorted

66. R_i open

67. R_f open

68. R_f leaky

69. R_f open

70. R_f shorted

71. R_i open

72. R_i leaky

Chapter 13
Basic Op-Amp Applications

Section 13-1 Comparators

1. $V_{out(p)} = A_{ol}V_{in} = (80,000)(0.15\ mV)(1.414) = 16.9\ V$
      Since 12 V is the peak limit, the op-amp saturates.
      $V_{out(pp)} = $ **24 V with distortion due to clipping.**

2.   (a) Maximum negative
      (b) Maximum positive
      (c) Maximum negative

3. $V_{UTP} = \left(\dfrac{R_2}{R_1 + R_2}\right)(+10\ V) = \left(\dfrac{18\ k\Omega}{65\ k\Omega}\right)10\ V = $ **2.77 V**

      $V_{LTP} = \left(\dfrac{R_2}{R_1 + R_2}\right)(-10\ V) = \left(\dfrac{18\ k\Omega}{65\ k\Omega}\right)(-10\ V) = $ **−2.77 V**

4. $V_{HYS} = V_{UTP} - V_{LTP} = 2.77\ V - (-2.77\ V) = $ **5.54 V**

5.   See Figure 13-1.

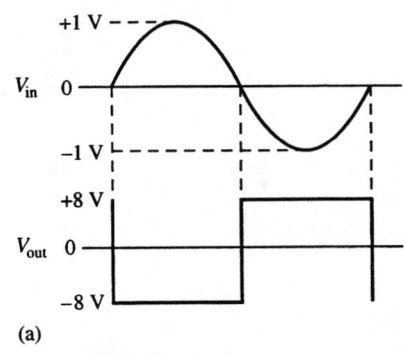
(a)

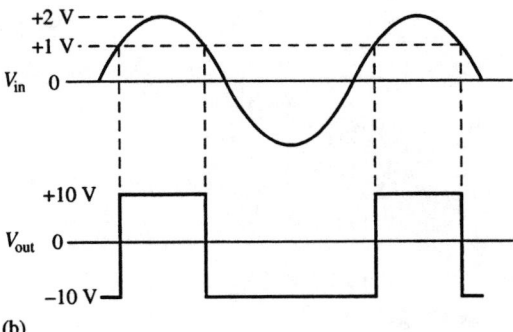
(b)

Figure 13-1

119

Chapter 13

6. $V_{UTP} = \left(\dfrac{R_2}{R_1 + R_2}\right)\left(+V_{out(max)}\right) = \left(\dfrac{18\,k\Omega}{51\,k\Omega}\right)11\,V = 3.88\,V$

$V_{LTP} = -3.88\,V$

$V_{HYS} = V_{UTP} - V_{LTP} = 3.88\,V - (-3.88\,V) = \mathbf{7.76\,V}$

$V_{UTP} = \left(\dfrac{R_2}{R_1 + R_2}\right)\left(+V_{out(max)}\right) = \left(\dfrac{68\,k\Omega}{218\,k\Omega}\right)11\,V = 3.43\,V$

$V_{LTP} = -3.43\,V$

$V_{HYS} = V_{UTP} - V_{LTP} = 3.43\,V - (-3.43\,V) = \mathbf{6.86\,V}$

7. When the zener is forward-biased:

$V_{out} = \left(\dfrac{18\,k\Omega}{18\,k\Omega + 47\,k\Omega}\right)V_{out} - 0.7\,V$

$V_{out} = (0.277)V_{out} - 0.7\,V$

$V_{out}(1 - 0.277) = -0.7\,V$

$V_{out} = \dfrac{-0.7\,V}{1 - 0.277} = \mathbf{-0.968\,V}$

When the zener is reverse-biased:

$V_{out} = \left(\dfrac{18\,k\Omega}{18\,k\Omega + 47\,k\Omega}\right)V_{out} + 6.2\,V$

$V_{out} = (0.277)V_{out} + 6.2\,V$

$V_{out}(1 - 0.277) = +6.2\,V$

$V_{out} = \dfrac{+6.2\,V}{1 - 0.277} = \mathbf{+8.57\,V}$

8. $V_{out} = \left(\dfrac{10\,k\Omega}{10\,k\Omega + 47\,k\Omega}\right)V_{out} \pm (4.7\,V + 0.7\,V)$

$V_{out} = (0.175)V_{out} \pm 5.4\,V$

$V_{out} = \dfrac{\pm 5.4\,V}{1 - 0.175} = \pm 6.55\,V$

$V_{UTP} = (0.175)(+6.55\,V) = +1.15\,V$

$V_{LTP} = (0.175)(-6.55\,V) = -1.15\,V$

See Figure 13-2.

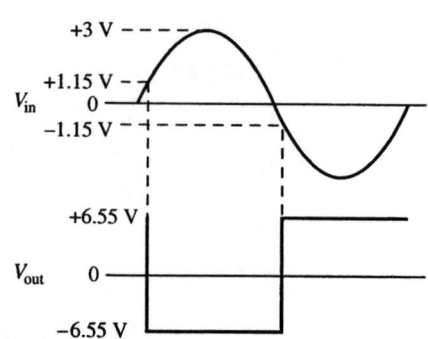

Figure 13-2

Section 13-2 Summing Amplifiers

9. (a) $V_{OUT} = -\dfrac{R_f}{R_i}(+1\,V + 1.5\,V) = -1(1\,V + 1.5\,V) = \mathbf{-2.5\,V}$

  (b) $V_{OUT} = -\dfrac{R_f}{R_i}(0.1\,V + 1\,V + 0.5\,V) = -\dfrac{22\,k\Omega}{10\,k\Omega}(1.6\,V) = \mathbf{-3.52\,V}$

10. (a) $V_{R1} = \mathbf{1\,V}$
$V_{R2} = \mathbf{1.8\,V}$

  (b) $I_{R1} = \dfrac{1\,V}{22\,k\Omega} = 45.5\,\mu A$

  $I_{R2} = \dfrac{1.8\,V}{22\,k\Omega} = 81.8\,\mu A$

  $I_f = I_{R1} + I_{R2} = 45.5\,\mu A + 81.8\,\mu A = \mathbf{127\,\mu A}$

  (c) $V_{OUT} = -I_f R_f = -(127.27\,\mu A)(22\,k\Omega) = \mathbf{-2.8\,V}$

11. $5V_{in} = \left(\dfrac{R_f}{R}\right)V_{in}$

  $\dfrac{R_f}{R} = 5$

  $R_f = 5R = 5(22\,k\Omega) = \mathbf{110\,k\Omega}$

12. See Figure 13-3.

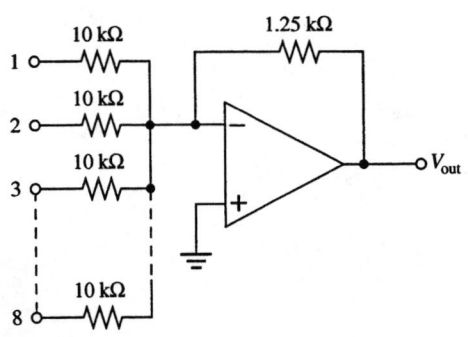

Figure 13-3

13. $V_{OUT} = -\left[\left(\dfrac{R_f}{R_1}\right)V_1 + \left(\dfrac{R_f}{R_2}\right)V_2 + \left(\dfrac{R_f}{R_3}\right)V_3 + \left(\dfrac{R_f}{R_4}\right)V_4\right]$

  $= -\left[\left(\dfrac{10\,k\Omega}{10\,k\Omega}\right)2\,V + \left(\dfrac{10\,k\Omega}{33\,k\Omega}\right)3\,V + \left(\dfrac{10\,k\Omega}{91\,k\Omega}\right)3\,V + \left(\dfrac{10\,k\Omega}{180\,k\Omega}\right)6\,V\right]$

  $= -(2\,V + 0.91\,V + 0.33\,V + 0.33\,V) = \mathbf{-3.57\,V}$

  $I_f = \dfrac{V_{OUT}}{R_f} = \dfrac{3.57\,V}{10\,k\Omega} = \mathbf{357\,\mu A}$

Chapter 13

14. $R_f = 100\ \text{k}\Omega$

Input resistors: $R_1 = 100\ \text{k}\Omega$, $R_2 = 50\ \text{k}\Omega$, $R_3 = 25\ \text{k}\Omega$, $R_4 = 12.5\ \text{k}\Omega$,
$R_5 = 6.25\ \text{k}\Omega$, $R_6 = 3.125\ \text{k}\Omega$

Section 13-3 Integrators and Differentiators

15. $\dfrac{dV_{out}}{dt} = -\dfrac{V_{\text{IN}}}{RC} = -\dfrac{5\ \text{V}}{(56\ \text{k}\Omega)(0.02\ \mu\text{F})} = -4.46\ \text{mV}/\mu\text{s}$

16. See Figure 13-4.

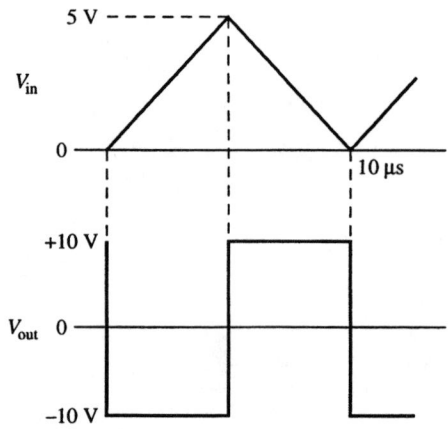

Figure 13-4

17. $I = \dfrac{CV_{pp}}{T/2} = \dfrac{(0.001\ \mu\text{F})(5\ \text{V})}{10\ \mu\text{s}/2} = 1\ \text{mA}$

18. $V_{out} = \pm RC\left(\dfrac{V_{pp}}{T/2}\right) = \pm(15\ \text{k}\Omega)(0.05\ \mu\text{F})\left(\dfrac{2\ \text{V}}{0.5\ \text{ms}}\right) = \pm 3\ \text{V}$

See Figure 13-5.

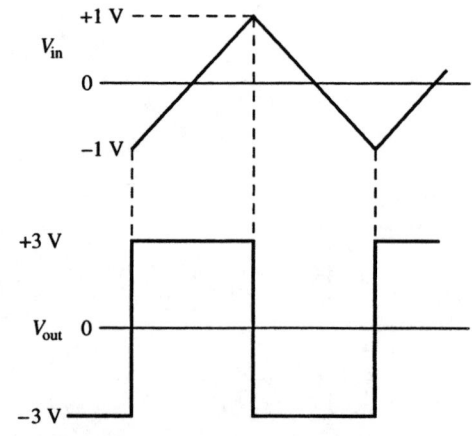

Figure 13-5

19. For the 10 ms interval when the switch is in position 2:

$$\frac{\Delta V_{out}}{\Delta t} = -\frac{V_{IN}}{RC} = -\frac{5\,\text{V}}{(10\,\text{k}\Omega)(10\,\mu\text{F})} = -\frac{5\,\text{V}}{0.1\,\text{s}} = -50\,\text{V/s} = -50\,\text{mV/ms}$$

$\Delta V_{out} = (-50\,\text{mV/ms})(10\,\text{ms}) = -500\,\text{mV} = -0.5\,\text{V}$

For the 10 ms interval when the switch is in position 1:

$$\frac{\Delta V_{out}}{\Delta t} = -\frac{V_{IN}}{RC} = -\frac{-5\,\text{V}}{(10\,\text{k}\Omega)(10\,\mu\text{F})} = -\frac{-5\,\text{V}}{0.1\,\text{s}} = +50\,\text{V/s} = +50\,\text{mV/ms}$$

$\Delta V_{out} = (+50\,\text{mV/ms})(10\,\text{ms}) = +500\,\text{mV} = +0.5\,\text{V}$

See Figure 13-6.

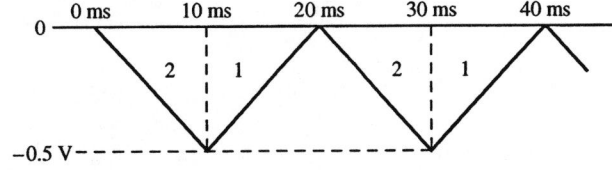

Figure 13-6

Section 13-4 Troubleshooting

20.
$$V_B = \left(\frac{R_2}{R_1 + R_2}\right)V_{out} \pm (V_Z + 0.7\,\text{V})$$

$$V_B = \frac{\pm (V_Z + 0.7\,\text{V})}{1 - \left(\dfrac{R_2}{R_1 + R_2}\right)}$$

Normally, V_B should be

$$V_B = \frac{\pm (4.3\,\text{V} + 0.7\,\text{V})}{1 - 0.5} = \pm 10\,\text{V}$$

Since the negative portion of V_B is only -1.4 V, zener D_2 **must be shorted**:

$$V_B = \frac{-(0\,\text{V} + 0.7\,\text{V})}{1 - 0.5} = 1.4\,\text{V}$$

21. The output should be as shown in Figure 13-7. V_2 has no effect on the output. This indicates that R_2 **is open**.

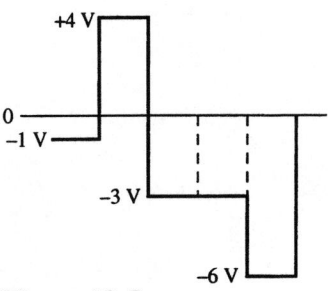

Figure 13-7

22. $A_v = \dfrac{2.5\,\text{k}\Omega}{10\,\text{k}\Omega} = 0.25$

The output should be as shown in Figure 13-8. An **open R_2** (V_2 is missing) will produce the observed output, which is incorrect.

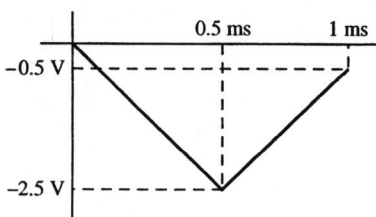

Figure 13-8

23. The D_2 input is missing (acts as a constant 0). This indicates an **open 50 kΩ resistor**.

System Application Problems

24. The first thing that you should always do is visually inspect the circuit for bad contacts or loose connections, shorts from solder splashes or wire clippings, incorrect components, and incorrectly installed components. In this case, after careful inspection, you will find that the **middle op-amp IC is installed incorrectly** (notice where pin 1 is as indicated by the dot).

25. An open integrator capacitor will cause the output of IC2 to saturate positively.

26. If a 1.0 kΩ resistor is used for R_1, the output of IC2 will be ten times larger for the sample-and-hold operation most likely causing the integrator to ramp into saturation.

Advanced Problems

27. For a 741S op amp with a 12 V/μs slew rate and 500 kHz sample pulse rate, the ramp up and ramp down must take

$\tau = \dfrac{1}{500\,\text{kHz}} = 2\,\mu s$

With a fixed interval of 1 μs for ramp up, this leaves a 1 μs ramp down interval.
If $-V_{\text{REF}} = -8$ V as in the system application, with a -8 V/μs ramp down rate, the ramp down can accommodate an 8 V ramp-up peak corresponding to +8 V input. However, if full slew rate is utilized as a -12 V reference voltage is used, a +12 V input can be accommodated.

28. A maximum of +0.5 can be used.

29. $100\,\text{mV}/\mu s = 5\,\text{V}/R_iC$

$R_iC = \dfrac{5\,\text{V}}{100\,\text{mV}/\mu s} = 50\,\mu s$

For $C = 3300$ pF:

$R_i = \dfrac{50\,\mu s}{3300\,\text{pF}} = 15.15\,\text{k}\Omega = 15\,\text{k}\Omega + 150\,\Omega$

For a 5 V peak-peak triangle waveform:

$$t_{ramp\ up} = t_{ramp\ down} = \frac{5\ \text{V}}{100\ \text{mV}/\mu s} = 50\ \mu s$$

$\tau = 2(50\ \mu s) = 100\ \mu s$

$f_{in} = 1/100\ \mu s = \textbf{100 kHz}$

See Figure 13-9.

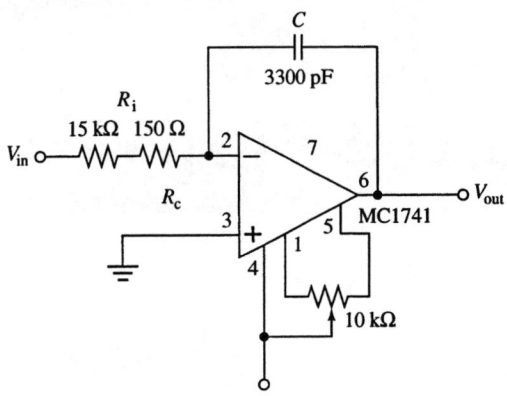

Figure 13-9

EWB/Multisim Troubleshooting Problems

The solutions showing instrument connections for Problems 30 through 39 are available in the Solutions folder for Chapter 13 on the CD-ROM provided with the textbook. The solutions may be accessed using the password *ED5FLOYD*. The faults in the circuit files may be accessed using the password *book* (all lowercase).

30. R_1 open

31. Op-amp inputs shorted together

32. Op-amp + input to output shorted

33. D_1 shorted

34. Top 10 kΩ resistor open

35. Middle 10 kΩ resistor shorted

36. R_f leaky

37. R_f open

38. C leaky

39. C open

Chapter 14
Special-Purpose Op-Amp Circuits

Section 14-1 Instrumentation Amplifiers

1. $A_{v(1)} = 1 + \dfrac{R_1}{R_G} = 1 + \dfrac{100\,k\Omega}{1.0\,k\Omega} = \mathbf{101}$

   $A_{v(2)} = 1 + \dfrac{R_2}{R_G} = 1 + \dfrac{100\,k\Omega}{1.0\,k\Omega} = \mathbf{101}$

2. $A_{cl} = 1 + \dfrac{2R}{R_G} = 1 + \dfrac{200\,k\Omega}{1.0\,k\Omega} = \mathbf{201}$

3. $V_{out} = A_{cl}(V_{in(2)} - V_{in(1)}) = 202(10\,mV - 5\,mV) = \mathbf{1.005\ V}$

4. $A_v = 1 + \dfrac{2R}{R_G}$

   $\dfrac{2R}{R_G} = A_v - 1$

   $R_G = \dfrac{2R}{A_v - 1} = \dfrac{2(100\,k\Omega)}{1000 - 1} = \dfrac{200\,k\Omega}{999} = 200.2\,\Omega \cong \mathbf{200\ \Omega}$

5. $R_G = \dfrac{50.5\,k\Omega}{A_v - 1}$

   $A_v = \dfrac{50.5\,k\Omega}{1.0\,k\Omega} + 1 = \mathbf{51.5}$

6.   Using the graph in textbook Figure 14-6,
   $BW \cong \mathbf{300\ kHz}$

7.   Change R_G to
   $R_G = \dfrac{50.5\,k\Omega}{A_v - 1} = \dfrac{50.5\,k\Omega}{24 - 1} \cong \mathbf{2.2\ k\Omega}$

8. $R_G = \dfrac{50.5\,k\Omega}{A_v - 1} = \dfrac{50.5\,k\Omega}{20 - 1} \cong \mathbf{2.7\ k\Omega}$

Section 14-2 Isolation Amplifiers

9. $A_{v(total)} = (30)(10) = \textbf{300}$

10. (a) $A_{v1} = \dfrac{R_{f1}}{R_{i1}} + 1 = \dfrac{18\,\text{k}\Omega}{8.2\,\text{k}\Omega} + 1 = 3.2$

    $A_{v2} = \dfrac{R_{f1}}{R_{i1}} + 1 = \dfrac{150\,\text{k}\Omega}{15\,\text{k}\Omega} + 1 = 11$

    $A_{v(tot)} = A_{v1}A_{v2} = (3.2)(11) = \textbf{35.2}$

    (b) $A_{v1} = \dfrac{R_{f1}}{R_{i1}} + 1 = \dfrac{330\,\text{k}\Omega}{1.0\,\text{k}\Omega} + 1 = 331$

    $A_{v2} = \dfrac{R_{f1}}{R_{i1}} + 1 = \dfrac{47\,\text{k}\Omega}{15\,\text{k}\Omega} + 1 = 4.13$

    $A_{v(tot)} = A_{v1}A_{v2} = (331)(4.13) = \textbf{1,367}$

11. $A_{v2} = 4.13$ (from Problem 10)
    $A_{v1}A_{v2} = 100$

    $\dfrac{R_{f1}}{R_{i1}} + 1 = A_{v1} = \dfrac{100}{4.13} = 24.2$

    Change R_f (18 kΩ) to 23.2 kΩ.
    Use **23.2 kΩ** ± 1% standard value resistor.

12. $A_{v1} = 331$ (from Problem 10)
    $A_{v1}A_{v2} = 440$

    $\dfrac{R_{f2}}{R_{i2}} + 1 = A_{v2} = \dfrac{440}{331} = 1.33$

    Change R_f (47 kΩ) to 3.3 kΩ.
    Change R_i (15 kΩ) to 10 kΩ.

13. Connect pin 6 to pin 10 and pin 14 to pin 15.

Section 14-3 Operational Transconductance Amplifiers (OTAs)

14. $g_m = \dfrac{I_{out}}{V_{in}} = \dfrac{10\,\mu\text{A}}{10\,\text{mV}} = \textbf{1 mS}$

15. $I_{out} = g_m V_{in} = (5000\,\mu\text{S})(100\,\text{mV}) = \textbf{500}\,\mu\textbf{A}$
    $V_{out} = I_{out}R_L = (500\,\mu\text{A})(10\,\text{k}\Omega) = \textbf{5 V}$

16. $g_m = \dfrac{I_{out}}{V_{in}}$

    $I_{out} = g_m V_{in} = (4000\,\mu\text{S})(100\,\text{mV}) = 400\,\mu\text{A}$

    $R_L = \dfrac{V_{out}}{I_{out}} = \dfrac{3.5\,\text{V}}{400\,\mu\text{A}} = \textbf{8.75 k}\Omega$

Chapter 14

17. $I_{BIAS} = \dfrac{+12\,V - (-12\,V) - 0.7\,V}{R_{BIAS}} = \dfrac{+12\,V - (-12\,V) - 0.7\,V}{220\,k\Omega} = \dfrac{23.3\,V}{220\,k\Omega} = 106\,\mu A$

From the graph in Figure 14-44:

$g_m = K I_{BIAS} \cong (16\,\mu S/\mu A)(106\,\mu A) = 1.70\,mS$

$A_v = \dfrac{V_{out}}{V_{in}} = \dfrac{I_{out} R_L}{V_{in}} = g_m R_L = (1.70\,mS)(6.8\,k\Omega) = \mathbf{11.6}$

18. The maximum voltage gain occurs when the 10 kΩ potentiometer is set to 0 Ω and was determined in Problem 17.

$A_{v(max)} = \mathbf{11.6}$

The minimum voltage gain occurs when the 10 kΩ potentiometer is set to 10 kΩ.

$I_{BIAS} = \dfrac{+12\,V - (-12\,V) - 0.7\,V}{220\,k\Omega + 10\,k\Omega} = \dfrac{23.3\,V}{230\,k\Omega} = 101\,\mu A$

$g_m \cong (16\,\mu S/\mu A)(101\,\mu A) = 1.62\,mS$

$A_{v(min)} = g_m R_L = (1.62\,mS)(6.8\,k\Omega) = \mathbf{11.0}$

19. The V_{MOD} waveform is applied to the bias input.

The gain and output voltage for each value of V_{MOD} is determined as follows using $K = 16\,\mu S/\mu A$. The output waveform is shown in Figure 14-1.

For $V_{MOD} = +8\,V$:

$I_{BIAS} = \dfrac{+8\,V - (-9\,V) - 0.7\,V}{39\,k\Omega} = \dfrac{16.3\,V}{39\,k\Omega} = 418\,\mu A$

$g_m = K I_{BIAS} \cong (16\,\mu S/\mu A)(418\,\mu A) = 6.69\,mS$

$A_v = \dfrac{V_{out}}{V_{in}} = \dfrac{I_{out} R_L}{V_{in}} = g_m R_L = (6.69\,mS)(10\,k\Omega) = 66.9$

$V_{out} = A_v V_{in} = (66.9)(100\,mV) = \mathbf{6.69\,V}$

For $V_{MOD} = +6\,V$:

$I_{BIAS} = \dfrac{+6\,V - (-9\,V) - 0.7\,V}{39\,k\Omega} = \dfrac{14.3\,V}{39\,k\Omega} = 367\,\mu A$

$g_m = K I_{BIAS} \cong (16\,\mu S/\mu A)(367\,\mu A) = 5.87\,mS$

$A_v = \dfrac{V_{out}}{V_{in}} = \dfrac{I_{out} R_L}{V_{in}} = g_m R_L = (5.87\,mS)(10\,k\Omega) = 58.7$

$V_{out} = A_v V_{in} = (58.7)(100\,mV) = \mathbf{5.87\,V}$

For $V_{MOD} = +4$ V:

$$I_{BIAS} = \frac{+4\,V - (-9\,V) - 0.7\,V}{39\,k\Omega} = \frac{12.3\,V}{39\,k\Omega} = 315\,\mu A$$

$$g_m = KI_{BIAS} \cong (16\,\mu S/\mu A)(315\,\mu A) = 5.04\,mS$$

$$A_v = \frac{V_{out}}{V_{in}} = \frac{I_{out}R_L}{V_{in}} = g_m R_L = (5.04\,mS)(10\,k\Omega) = 50.4$$

$$V_{out} = A_v V_{in} = (50.4)(100\,mV) = \mathbf{5.04\ V}$$

For $V_{MOD} = +2$ V:

$$I_{BIAS} = \frac{+2\,V - (-9\,V) - 0.7\,V}{39\,k\Omega} = \frac{10.3\,V}{39\,k\Omega} = 264\,\mu A$$

$$g_m = KI_{BIAS} \cong (16\,\mu S/\mu A)(264\,\mu A) = 4.22\,mS$$

$$A_v = \frac{V_{out}}{V_{in}} = \frac{I_{out}R_L}{V_{in}} = g_m R_L = (4.22\,mS)(10\,k\Omega) = 42.2$$

$$V_{out} = A_v V_{in} = (42.2)(100\,mV) = \mathbf{4.22\ V}$$

For $V_{MOD} = +1$ V:

$$I_{BIAS} = \frac{+1\,V - (-9\,V) - 0.7\,V}{39\,k\Omega} = \frac{9.3\,V}{39\,k\Omega} = 238\,\mu A$$

$$g_m = KI_{BIAS} \cong (16\,\mu S/\mu A)(238\,\mu A) = 3.81\,mS$$

$$A_v = \frac{V_{out}}{V_{in}} = \frac{I_{out}R_L}{V_{in}} = g_m R_L = (3.81\,mS)(10\,k\Omega) = 38.1$$

$$V_{out} = A_v V_{in} = (38.1)(100\,mV) = \mathbf{3.81\ V}$$

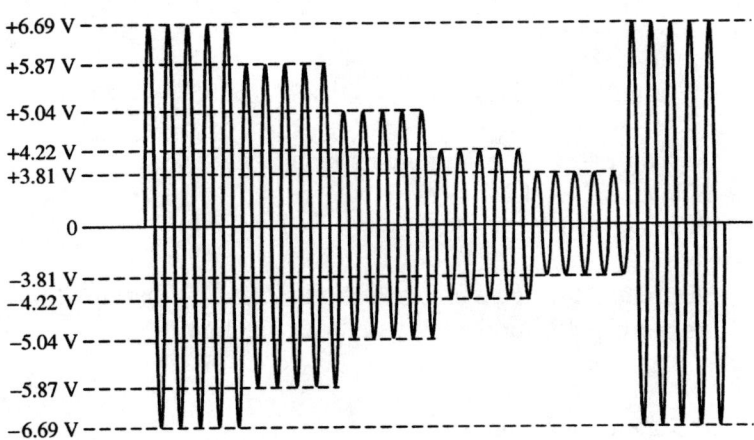

Figure 14-1

20. $$I_{BIAS} = \frac{+9V - (-9\,V) - 0.7\,V}{39\,k\Omega} = \frac{17.3\,V}{39\,k\Omega} = 444\,\mu A$$

$$V_{TRIG(+)} = I_{BIAS}R_1 = (444\,\mu A)(10\,k\Omega) = \mathbf{+4.44\ V}$$

$$V_{TRIG(-)} = -I_{BIAS}R_1 = (-444\,\mu A)(10\,k\Omega) = \mathbf{-4.44\ V}$$

Chapter 14

21. See Figure 14-2.

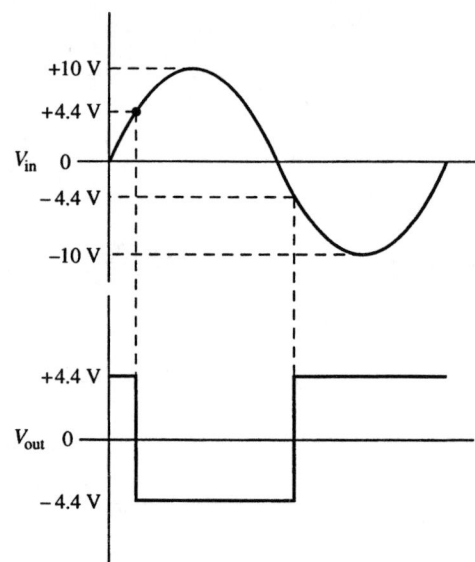

Figure 14-2

Section 14-4 Log and Antilog Amplifiers

22. (a) $\ln(0.5) = -0.693$
(b) $\ln(2) = 0.693$
(c) $\ln(50) = 3.91$
(d) $\ln(130) = 4.87$

23. (a) $\log_{10}(0.5) = -0.301$
(b) $\log_{10}(2) = 0.301$
(c) $\log_{10}(50) = 1.70$
(d) $\log_{10}(130) = 2.11$

24. Antilog $x = 10^x$ or e^x, depending on the base used.
INV ln $= e^{1.6} = 4.95$
INV log $= 10^{1.6} = 39.8$

25. The output of a log amplifier is limited to **0.7 V** because the output voltage is limited to the barrier potential of the transistor's *pn* junction.

26. $V_{out} \cong -(0.025 \text{ V})\ln\left(\dfrac{V_{in}}{I_s R_{in}}\right)$

$= -(0.025 \text{ V})\ln\left(\dfrac{3 \text{ V}}{(100 \text{ nA})(82 \text{ k}\Omega)}\right) = -(0.025 \text{ V})\ln(365.9) = \mathbf{-148\ mV}$

27. $V_{out} \cong -(0.025 \text{ V})\ln\left(\dfrac{V_{in}}{I_{EBO} R_{in}}\right)$

$= -(0.025 \text{ V})\ln\left(\dfrac{1.5 \text{ V}}{(60 \text{ nA})(47 \text{ k}\Omega)}\right) = -(0.025 \text{ V})\ln(531.9) = \mathbf{-157\ mV}$

28. $V_{out} = -R_f I_{EBO} \text{ antilog}\left(\dfrac{V_{in}}{25\,\text{mV}}\right) = -R_f I_{EBO} e^{\left(\frac{V_{in}}{25\,\text{mV}}\right)}$

$V_{out} = -(10\,\text{k}\Omega)(60\,\text{nA})\,e^{\left(\frac{0.225\,\text{V}}{25\,\text{mV}}\right)} = -(10\,\text{k}\Omega)(60\,\text{nA})e^9 = -(10\,\text{k}\Omega)(60\,\text{nA})(8103) = \textbf{-4.86 V}$

29. $V_{out(max)} \cong -(0.025\,\text{V})\ln\left(\dfrac{V_{in}}{I_{EBO}R_{in}}\right) = -(0.025\,\text{V})\ln\left(\dfrac{1\,\text{V}}{(60\,\text{nA})(47\,\text{k}\Omega)}\right)$

$= -(0.025\,\text{V})\ln(354.6) = \textbf{-147 mV}$

$V_{out(min)} \cong -(0.025\,\text{V})\ln\left(\dfrac{V_{in}}{I_{EBO}R_{in}}\right) = -(0.025\,\text{V})\ln\left(\dfrac{100\,\text{mV}}{(60\,\text{nA})(47\,\text{k}\Omega)}\right)$

$= -(0.025\,\text{V})\ln(35.5) = \textbf{-89.2 mV}$

The signal compression allows larger signals to be reduced without causing smaller amplitudes to be lost (in this case, the 1 V peak is reduced 85% but the 100 mV peak is reduced only 10%).

Section 14-5 Converters and Other Op-Amp Circuits

30. (a) $V_{IN} = V_Z = 4.7\,\text{V}$

$I_L = \dfrac{V_{IN}}{R_i} = \dfrac{4.7\,\text{V}}{1.0\,\text{k}\Omega} = \textbf{4.7 mA}$

(b) $V_{IN} = \left(\dfrac{10\,\text{k}\Omega}{20\,\text{k}\Omega}\right)12\,\text{V} = 6\,\text{V}$

$R_i = 10\,\text{k}\Omega \parallel 10\,\text{k}\Omega + 100\,\Omega = 5.1\,\text{k}\Omega$

$I_L = \dfrac{V_{IN}}{R_i} = \dfrac{6\,\text{V}}{5.1\,\text{k}\Omega} = \textbf{1.18 mA}$

31. See Figure 14-3.

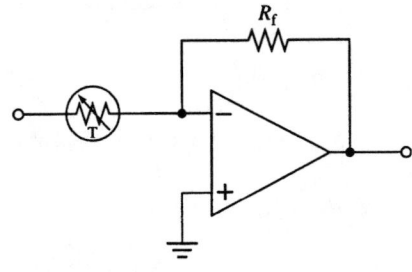

Figure 14-3

Chapter 14

Troubleshooting Problems

32. The circuit on this board is represented by the schematic in textbook Figure 14-38. For the isolation amplifier IC_1:

$$A_{v1} = \frac{R_3}{R_2} + 1 = \frac{330\,k\Omega}{86\,k\Omega} + 1 = 3.84 + 1 = 4.84$$

$$A_{v2} = \frac{R_5}{R_4} + 1 = \frac{120\,k\Omega}{100\,k\Omega} + 1 = 2.2$$

$$A_{v(total)} = A_{v1}A_{v2} = (4.84)(2.2) = 10.6$$

For the IC_2 filter:

$$A_{v(mid)} = \frac{R_8}{R_9} + 1 = \frac{3.3\,k\Omega}{5.6\,k\Omega} + 1 = 0.59 + 1 = 1.59$$

$$f_c = \frac{1}{2\pi RC} = \frac{1}{2\pi(100\,k\Omega)(0.015\,\mu F)} = 106\,Hz,\text{ so the 50 Hz input is in the midrange.}$$

For IC_3:

$$A_v = \frac{R_{15} + R_{16}}{R_{10}} = \frac{125\,k\Omega}{1.0\,k\Omega} = 125,\text{ assuming } R_{16}\text{ is set at 25 k}\Omega.$$

TP 1 is at the output of IC_2:
$V_{TP\,1} = (1.59)(10.6\,mV) = \textbf{16.9 mV @ 50 Hz}$
TP 2 is at pin 2 of IC_2:

$$V_{TP\,2} = \left(\frac{5.6\,k\Omega}{8.9\,k\Omega}\right)V_{TP\,1} = \textbf{10.6 mV @ 50 Hz}$$

TP 3 is at the output of IC_1:
$V_{TP\,3} = A_{v(tot)}V_{in} = (10.6)(1\,mV) = \textbf{10.6 mV @ 50 Hz}$
TP 4 is at the supply voltage of **+15 V DC.**
TP 5 is at the output of IC_3:
$V_{TP\,5} = A_v V_{TP\,1} = (125)(16.9\,mV) = \textbf{2.11 V @ 50 Hz}$

33. The IC_2 filter was found in Problem 32 to have a critical frequency of 106 Hz. Therefore, the 1 kHz input signal is outside of the bandwidth.
$V_{TP\,1} \cong \textbf{0 V}$
$V_{TP\,2} \cong \textbf{0 V}$
The voltage gain of IC_1 was found in Problem 32 to be 10.6.
$V_{TP\,3} = (10.6)(2\,mV) = \textbf{21.2 mV @ 1 kHz}$
$V_{TP\,4} = \textbf{+15 V DC}$
$V_{TP\,5} \cong \textbf{0 V}$

EWB/Multisim Troubleshooting Problems

The solutions showing instrument connections for Problems 34 through 38 are available in the Solutions folder for Chapter 14 on the CD-ROM provided with the textbook. The solutions may be accessed using the password *ED5FLOYD*. The faults in the circuit files may be accessed using the password *book* (all lowercase).

34. R_G leaky

35. R open

36. R_f open

37. Zener diode open

38. Lower 10 kΩ resistor open

Chapter 15
Active Filters

___

Section 15-1 Basic Filter Responses

1. (a) Band-pass
    (b) High-pass
    (c) Low-pass
    (d) Band-stop

2. $BW = f_c = $ **800 Hz**

3. $f_c = \dfrac{1}{2\pi RC} = \dfrac{1}{2\pi(2.2\text{ k}\Omega)(0.0015\ \mu\text{F})} = $ **48.2 Hz**

    No, the upper response roll-off due to internal device capacitances is unknown.

4. The roll-off is **20 dB/decade** because this is a single-pole filter.

5. $BW = f_{ch} - f_{cl} = 3.9\text{ kHz} - 3.2\text{ kHz} = 0.7\text{ kHz} = $ **700 Hz**

    $f_0 = \sqrt{f_{cl}f_{ch}} = \sqrt{(3.2\text{ kHz})(3.9\text{ kHz})} = 3.53\text{ kHz}$

    $Q = \dfrac{f_0}{BW} = \dfrac{3.53\text{ kHz}}{700\text{ Hz}} = $ **5.04**

6. $Q = \dfrac{f_0}{BW}$

    $f_0 = Q(BW) = 15(1\text{ kHz}) = $ **15 kHz**

Section 15-2 Filter Response Characteristics

7. (a) 2nd order, 1 stage

    $DF = 2 - \dfrac{R_3}{R_4} = 2 - \dfrac{1.2\text{ k}\Omega}{1.2\text{ k}\Omega} = 2 - 1 = 1$ **Not Butterworth**

    (b) 2nd order, 1 stage

    $DF = 2 - \dfrac{R_3}{R_4} = 2 - \dfrac{560\ \Omega}{1.0\text{ k}\Omega} = 2 - 0.56 = 1.44$ **Approximately Butterworth**

    (c) 3rd order, 2 stages, 1st stage (2 poles):

    $DF = 2 - \dfrac{R_3}{R_4} = 2 - \dfrac{330\ \Omega}{1.0\text{ k}\Omega} = $ **1.67**

    2nd stage (1 pole):

    $DF = 2 - \dfrac{R_6}{R_7} = $ **1.67**   **Not Butterworth**

8.   (a) From Table 15-1 in the textbook, the damping factor must be 1.414; therefore,

$$\frac{R_3}{R_4} = 0.586$$

$R_3 = 0.586R_4 = 0.586(1.2 \text{ k}\Omega) = \textbf{703 } \Omega$
Nearest standard value: **720 Ω**

   (b) $\dfrac{R_3}{R_4} = 0.56$

   This is an approximate Butterworth response
   (as close as you can get using standard 5% resistors).

   (c) From Table 15-1, the damping factor of both stages must be 1, therefore

$$\frac{R_3}{R_4} = 1$$

$R_3 = R_4 = R_6 = R_7 = \textbf{1 k}\Omega$ (for both stages)

9.   (a) Chebyshev
   (b) Butterworth
   (c) Bessel
   (d) Butterworth

Section 15-3 Active Low-Pass Filters

10.   **High Pass**
   1st stage:

$$DF = 2 - \frac{R_3}{R_4} = 2 - \frac{1.0 \text{ k}\Omega}{6.8 \text{ k}\Omega} = 1.85$$

   2nd stage:

$$DF = 2 - \frac{R_7}{R_8} = 2 - \frac{6.8 \text{ k}\Omega}{5.6 \text{ k}\Omega} = 0.786$$

   From Table 15-1 in the textbook:
   1st stage $DF = 1.848$ and 2nd stage $DF = 0.765$
   Therefore, this filter is **approximately Butterworth**.
   Roll-off rate = **80 dB/decade**

11. $f_c = \dfrac{1}{2\pi\sqrt{R_1 R_2 C_1 C_2}} = \dfrac{1}{2\pi\sqrt{R_5 R_6 C_3 C_4}} = \dfrac{1}{2\pi\sqrt{(4.7 \text{ k}\Omega)(6.8 \text{ k}\Omega)(0.22 \text{ }\mu\text{F})(0.1 \text{ }\mu\text{F})}} = \textbf{190 Hz}$

12. $R = R_1 = R_2 = R_5 = R_6$ and $C = C_1 = C_2 = C_3 = C_4$
   Let $C = \textbf{0.22 } \mu\text{F}$ (for both stages).

$$f_c = \frac{1}{2\pi\sqrt{R^2 C^2}} = \frac{1}{2\pi RC}$$

$$R = \frac{1}{2\pi f_c C} = \frac{1}{2\pi(190 \text{ Hz})(0.22 \text{ }\mu\text{F})} = 3.81 \text{ k}\Omega$$

   Choose $R = \textbf{3.9 k}\Omega$ (for both stages)

Chapter 15

13. See Figure 15-1.

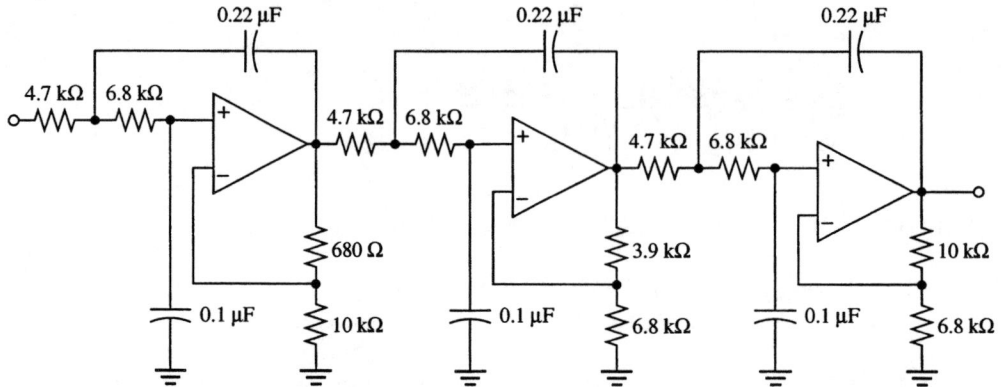

Figure 15-1

14. See Figure 15-2.

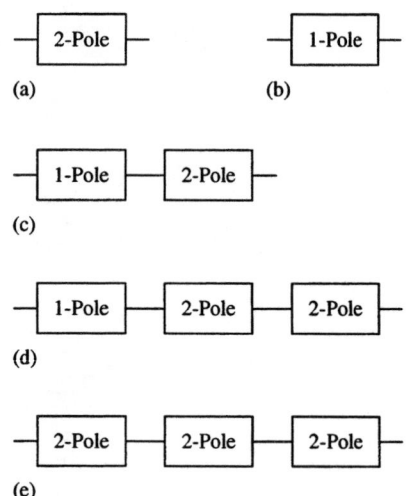

Figure 15-2

Section 15-4 Active High-Pass Filters

15. Exchange the positions of the resistors and the capacitors. See Figure 15-3.

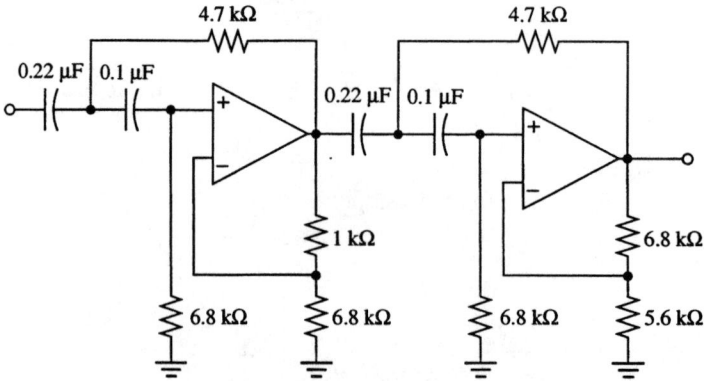

Figure 15-3

16. $f_c = \dfrac{1}{2\pi RC}$

$f_0 = \dfrac{190\,\text{Hz}}{2} = 95\,\text{Hz}$

$R = \dfrac{1}{2\pi f_c C} = \dfrac{1}{2\pi(95\,\text{Hz})(0.22\,\mu\text{F})} = 7615\,\Omega$

Let $R = 7.5\,\text{k}\Omega$. Change all resistors to **7.5 kΩ**.

17.   (a) Decrease R_1 and R_2 or C_1 and C_2.
(b) Increase R_3 or decrease R_4.

Section 15-5 Active Band-Pass Filters

18.   (a) Cascaded high-pass/low-pass filters
(b) Multiple feedback
(c) State variable

19.   (a) 1st stage:

$f_{c1} = \dfrac{1}{2\pi RC} = \dfrac{1}{2\pi(1.0\,\text{k}\Omega)(0.047\,\mu\text{F})} = 3.39\,\text{kHz}$

2nd stage:

$f_{c2} = \dfrac{1}{2\pi RC} = \dfrac{1}{2\pi(1.0\,\text{k}\Omega)(0.022\,\mu\text{F})} = 7.23\,\text{kHz}$

$f_0 = \sqrt{f_{c1}f_{c2}} = \sqrt{(3.39\,\text{kHz})(7.23\,\text{kHz})} = \textbf{4.95 kHz}$

$BW = 7.23\,\text{kHz} - 3.39\,\text{Hz} = \textbf{3.84 kHz}$

(b) $f_0 = \dfrac{1}{2\pi C}\sqrt{\dfrac{R_1 + R_2}{R_1 R_2 R_3}} = \dfrac{1}{2\pi(0.022\,\mu\text{F})}\sqrt{\dfrac{47\,\text{k}\Omega + 1.8\,\text{k}\Omega}{(47\,\text{k}\Omega)(1.8\,\text{k}\Omega)(150\,\text{k}\Omega)}} = \textbf{449 Hz}$

$Q = \pi f_0 C R_3 = \pi(449\,\text{Hz})(0.022\,\mu\text{F})(150\,\text{k}\Omega) = 4.66$

$BW = \dfrac{f_0}{Q} = \dfrac{449\,\text{Hz}}{4.66} = \textbf{96.4 Hz}$

(c) For each integrator:

$f_c = \dfrac{1}{2\pi RC} = \dfrac{1}{2\pi(10\,\text{k}\Omega)(0.001\,\mu\text{F})} = 1.59\,\text{kHz}$

$f_0 = f_c = \textbf{15.9 kHz}$

$Q = \dfrac{1}{3}\left(\dfrac{R_5}{R_6} + 1\right) = \dfrac{1}{3}\left(\dfrac{560\,\text{k}\Omega}{10\,\text{k}\Omega} + 1\right) = \dfrac{1}{3}(56 + 1) = 19$

$BW = \dfrac{f_0}{Q} = \dfrac{15.9\,\text{kHz}}{19} = \textbf{838 Hz}$

Chapter 15

20. $Q = \dfrac{1}{3}\left(\dfrac{R_5}{R_6} + 1\right)$

Select $R_6 = \textbf{10 k}\Omega$.

$Q = \dfrac{R_5}{3R_6} + \dfrac{1}{3} = \dfrac{R_5 + R_6}{3R_6}$

$3R_6Q = R_5 + R_6$

$R_5 = 3R_6Q - R_6 = 3(1.0\ \text{k}\Omega)(50) - 10\ \text{k}\Omega = 150\ \text{k}\Omega - 10\ \text{k}\Omega = \textbf{140 k}\Omega$

$f_0 = \dfrac{1}{2\pi(12\ \text{k}\Omega)(0.01\ \mu\text{F})} = 1.33\ \text{kHz}$

$BW = \dfrac{f_0}{Q} = \dfrac{1.33\ \text{kHz}}{50} = \textbf{26.6 Hz}$

Section 15-6 Active Band-Stop Filters

21. See Figure 15-4.

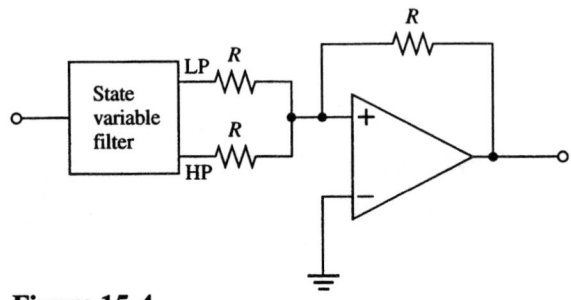

Figure 15-4

22. $f_0 = f_c = \dfrac{1}{2\pi RC}$

Let C remain $0.01\ \mu$F.

$R = \dfrac{1}{2\pi f_0 C} = \dfrac{1}{2\pi(120\ \text{Hz})(0.01\ \mu\text{F})} = \textbf{133 k}\Omega$

Change R in the integrators from 12 kΩ to 133 kΩ.

EWB/Multisim Troubleshooting Problems

The solutions showing instrument connections for Problems 23 through 31 are available in the Solutions folder for Chapter 15 on the CD-ROM provided with the textbook. The solutions may be accessed using the password *ED5FLOYD*. The faults in the circuit files may be accessed using the password *book* (all lowercase).

23. R_4 shorted

24. R_3 open

25. C_3 shorted

26. R_5 open

27. R_1 open

28. R_2 shorted

29. R_1 open

30. C_2 open

31. R_7 open

Chapter 16
Oscillators

Section 16-1 The Oscillator

1. An oscillator requires no input other than the dc supply voltage.

2. Amplifier and positive feedback circuit

Section 16-2 Feedback Oscillator Principles

3. Unity gain around the closed loop is required for sustained oscillation.
   $A_{cl} = A_v B = 1$

   $B = \dfrac{1}{A_v} = \dfrac{1}{75} = 0.0133$

4. To ensure startup:
   $A_{cl} > 1$
   since $A_v = 75$, B must be greater than 1/75 in order to produce the condition
   $A_v B > 1$.
   For example, if $B = 1/50$,

   $A_v B = 75\left(\dfrac{1}{50}\right) = 1.5$

Section 16-3 Oscillators with RC Feedback Circuits

5. $\dfrac{V_{out}}{V_{in}} = \dfrac{1}{3}$

   $V_{out} = \left(\dfrac{1}{3}\right)V_{in} = \dfrac{2.2\,\text{V}}{3} = 733\ \text{mV}$

6. $f_r = \dfrac{1}{2\pi RC} = \dfrac{1}{2\pi(6.2\ \text{k}\Omega)(0.02\ \mu\text{F})} = 1.28\ \text{kHz}$

7. $R_1 = 2R_2$
   $R_2 = \dfrac{R_1}{2} = \dfrac{100\ \text{k}\Omega}{2} = 50\ \text{k}\Omega$

8. When dc power is first applied, both zener diodes appear as opens because there is insufficient output voltage. This places R_3 in series with R_1, thus increasing the closed-loop gain to a value greater than unity to assure that oscillation will begin.

9. $R_f = (A_v - 1)(R_3 + r'_{ds}) = (3 - 1)(820\ \Omega + 350\ \Omega) = 2.34\ \text{k}\Omega$

10. $f_r = \dfrac{1}{2\pi(1.0\,\text{k}\Omega)(0.015\,\mu\text{F})} = \textbf{10.6 kHz}$

11. $B = \dfrac{1}{29}$

$A_{cl} = \dfrac{1}{B} = 29$

$A_{cl} = \dfrac{R_f}{R_i}$

$R_f = A_{cl}R_i = 29(4.7\,\text{k}\Omega) = \textbf{136 k}\boldsymbol{\Omega}$

$f_r = \dfrac{1}{2\pi\sqrt{6}\big((4.7\,\text{k}\Omega)(0.02\,\mu\text{F})\big)} = \textbf{691 Hz}$

Section 16-4 Oscillators with LC Feedback Circuits

12.   (a) *Colpitts*: C_1 and C_3 are the feedback capacitors.

$f_r = \dfrac{1}{2\pi\sqrt{L_1 C_T}}$

$C_T = \dfrac{C_1 C_3}{C_1 + C_3} = \dfrac{(100\,\mu\text{F})(1000\,\text{pF})}{1100\,\text{pF}} = 90.9\,\text{pF}$

$f_r = \dfrac{1}{2\pi\sqrt{(5\,\text{mH})(90.9\,\text{pF})}} = \textbf{236 kHz}$

(b) *Hartley*:

$f_r = \dfrac{1}{2\pi\sqrt{L_T C_2}}$

$L_T = L_1 + L_2 = 1.5\,\text{mH} + 10\,\text{mH} = 11.5\,\text{mH}$

$f_r = \dfrac{1}{2\pi\sqrt{(11.5\,\text{mH})(470\,\text{pF})}} = \textbf{68.5 kHz}$

13. $B = \dfrac{50\,\text{pF}}{470\,\text{pF}} = 0.106$

The condition for sustained oscillation is

$A_v = \dfrac{1}{B} = \dfrac{1}{0.106} = \textbf{9.4}$

Section 16-5 Relaxation Oscillators

14.   Triangular waveform.

$f = \dfrac{1}{4R_1 C}\left(\dfrac{R_2}{R_3}\right) = \dfrac{1}{4(22\,\text{k}\Omega)(0.022\,\mu\text{F})}\left(\dfrac{56\,\text{k}\Omega}{18\,\text{k}\Omega}\right) = \textbf{1.61 kHz}$

15. Change f to 10 kHz by changing R_1:

$$f = \frac{1}{4R_1C}\left(\frac{R_2}{R_3}\right)$$

$$R = \frac{1}{4fC}\left(\frac{R_2}{R_3}\right) = \frac{1}{4(10\text{ kHz})(0.022\ \mu F)}\left(\frac{56\text{ k}\Omega}{18\text{ k}\Omega}\right) = \textbf{3.54 k}\Omega$$

16. $$T = \frac{V_p - V_F}{\left(\dfrac{|V_{IN}|}{RC}\right)}$$

$$V_p = \left(\frac{R_5}{R_4 + R_5}\right)12\text{ V} = \left(\frac{47\text{ k}\Omega}{147\text{ k}\Omega}\right)12\text{ V} = 3.84\text{ V}$$

PUT triggers at about $+3.84$ V $+ 0.7$ V $= 4.54$ V
Amplitude $= +4.54$ V $- 1$ V $= \textbf{3.54 V}$

$$V_{IN} = \left(\frac{R_2}{R_1 + R_2}\right)(-12\text{ V}) = \left(\frac{22\text{ k}\Omega}{122\text{ k}\Omega}\right)(-12\text{ V}) = -2.16\text{ V}$$

$$T = \frac{4.54\text{ V} - 1\text{ V}}{\left(\dfrac{2.16\text{ V}}{(100\text{ k}\Omega)(0.002\ \mu F)}\right)} = 328\ \mu s$$

$$f = \frac{1}{T} = \frac{1}{328\ \mu s} = \textbf{3.05 kHz}$$

See Figure 16-1.

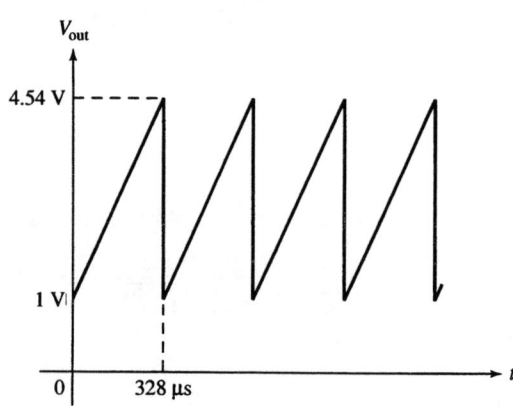

Figure 16-1

17. $V_G = 5$ V. Assume $V_{AK} = 1$ V.

$$V_G = \left(\frac{R_5}{R_4 + R_5}\right)12\text{ V}$$

Change R_4 to get $V_G = 5$ V.
5 V$(R_4 + 47$ k$\Omega) = (47$ k$\Omega)12$ V
$R_4(5$ V$) = (47$ k$\Omega)12$ V $- (47$ k$\Omega)5$ V

$$R_4 = \frac{(12\text{ V} - 5\text{ V})47\text{ k}\Omega}{5\text{ V}} = \textbf{65.8 k}\Omega$$

18. $\quad T = \dfrac{V_p - V_F}{\left(\dfrac{V_{IN}}{RC}\right)}$

$V_p = \left(\dfrac{V_{IN}}{RC}\right)T + V_F = \left(\dfrac{3\,V}{(4.7\,k\Omega)(0.001\,\mu F)}\right)10\,\mu s + 1\,V = 7.38\,V$

$V_{pp(out)} = V_p - V_F = 7.38\,V - 1\,V = \mathbf{6.38\,V}$

Section 16-6 The 555 Timer as an Oscillator

19. $\quad \dfrac{1}{3}V_{CC} = \dfrac{1}{3}(10\,V) = \mathbf{3.33\,V}$

$\dfrac{2}{3}V_{CC} = \dfrac{2}{3}(10\,V) = \mathbf{6.67\,V}$

20. $\quad f = \dfrac{1.44}{(R_1 + 2R_2)C_{ext}} = \dfrac{1.44}{(1.0\,k\Omega + 6.6\,k\Omega)(0.047\,\mu F)} = \mathbf{4.03\,kHz}$

21. $\quad f = \dfrac{1.44}{(R_1 + 2R_2)C_{ext}}$

$C_{ext} = \dfrac{1.44}{(R_1 + 2R_2)f} = \dfrac{1.44}{(1.0\,k\Omega + 6.6\,k\Omega)(25\,kHz)} = \mathbf{0.0076\,\mu F}$

22. $\quad$ Duty cycle (dc) $= \dfrac{R_1 + R_2}{R_1 + 2R_2} \times 100\%$

$dc(R_1 + 2R_2) = (R_1 + R_2)100$

$75(3.3\,k\Omega + 2R_2) = (3.3\,k\Omega + R_2)100$

$75(3.3\,k\Omega + 150R_2 = 100(3.3\,k\Omega) + 100R_2$

$150R_2 - 100R_2 = 100(3.3\,k\Omega) - 75(3.3\,k\Omega)$

$50R_2 = 25(3.3\,k\Omega)$

$R_2 = \dfrac{25(3.3\,k\Omega)}{50} = \mathbf{1.65\,k\Omega}$

EWB/Multisim Troubleshooting Problems

The solutions showing instrument connections for Problems 23 through 28 are available in the Solutions folder for Chapter 16 on the CD-ROM provided with the textbook. The solutions may be accessed using the password *ED5FLOYD*. The faults in the circuit files may be accessed using the password *book* (all lowercase).

23. $\quad$ Drain-to-source shorted

24. $\quad C_3$ open

25. $\quad$ Collector-to-emitter shorted

26. R_1 open

27. R_2 open

28. R_1 leaky

Chapter 17
Communications Circuits

Section 17-1 Basic Receivers

1. See Figure 17-1.

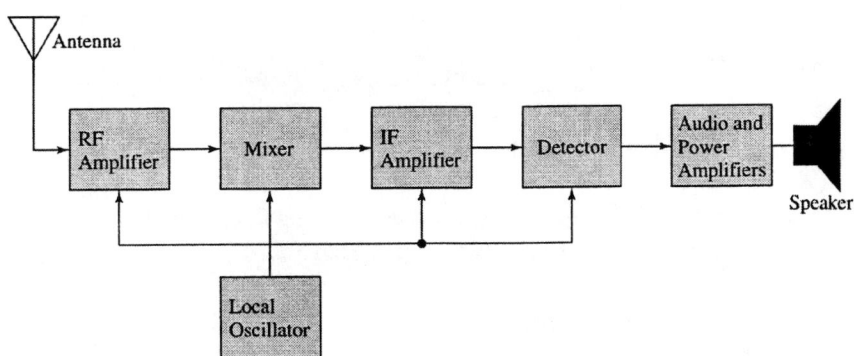

Figure 17-1

2. See Figure 17-2.

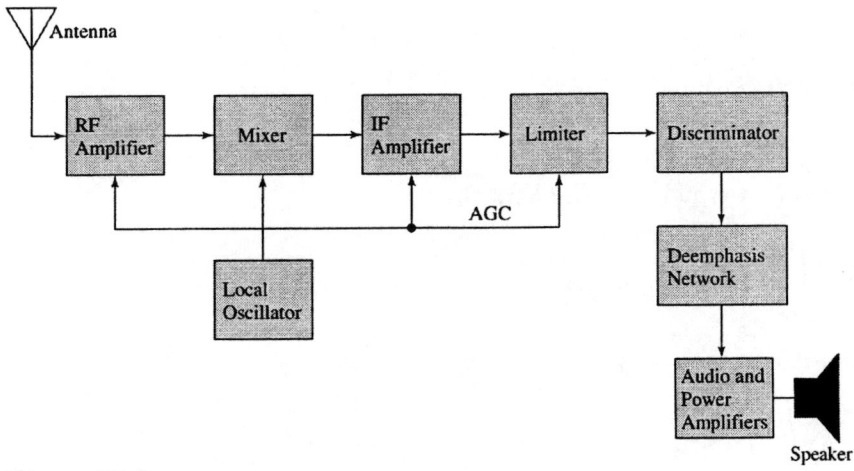

Figure 17-2

3. $f_{LO} = 680$ kHz + 455 kHz = **1135 kHz**

4. $f_{LO} = 97.2$ MHz + 10.7 MHz = **107.9 MHz**

5. $f_{RF} = 101.9$ MHz − 10.7 MHz = **91.2 MHz**
   $f_{IF} = $ **10.7 MHz** (always)

Chapter 17

Section 17-2 The Linear Multiplier

6. (a) $V_{out} \cong -2.5$ V
    (b) $V_{out} \cong -1.6$ V
    (c) $V_{out} \cong +1.0$ V
    (d) $V_{out} \cong +10$ V

7. $I_3 = \dfrac{\left|-12\text{ V}\right| - 0.7\text{ V}}{(12\text{ k}\Omega + 2.8\text{ k}\Omega) + 500\ \Omega} = \dfrac{11.3\text{ V}}{15.3\text{ k}\Omega} = \textbf{739 } \mu\textbf{A}$

8. Using I_3 from Problem 7: $K = \dfrac{2R_L}{R_X R_Y I_3} = \dfrac{2(6.8\text{ k}\Omega)}{(12\text{ k}\Omega)(12\text{ k}\Omega)(739\ \mu\text{A})} = \textbf{0.128}$

9. $V_{out} = KV_X V_Y = 0.8(+3.5\text{ V})(-2.9\text{ V}) = \textbf{--8.12 V}$

10. Connect pin 4 to pin 9 and pin 8 to pin 12. Apply the input between pins 9 and 12. For a "true" squaring circuit, the component values must produce a $K = 1$.

11. (a) $V_{out} = KV_1 V_2 = (0.1)(+2\text{ V})(+1.4\text{ V}) = \textbf{+0.28 V}$
    (b) $V_{out} = KV_1 V_2 = KV_1^2 (0.1)(-3.2\text{ V})^2 = \textbf{+1.024 V}$
    (c) $V_{out} = \dfrac{-V_1}{V_2} = \dfrac{-(6.2\text{ V})}{-3\text{ V}} = \textbf{+2.07 V}$
    (d) $V_{out} = \sqrt{V_1} = \sqrt{6.2\text{ V}} = \textbf{+2.49 V}$

Section 17-3 Amplitude Modulation

12. $f_{diff} = f_1 - f_2 = 100\text{ kHz} - 30\text{ kHz} = \textbf{70 kHz}$
    $f_{sum} = f_1 + f_2 = 100\text{ kHz} + 30\text{ kHz} = \textbf{130 kHz}$

13. $f_1 = \dfrac{9\text{ cycles}}{1\text{ ms}} = 9000\text{ cycles/s} = 9\text{ kHz}$

    $f_2 = \dfrac{1\text{ cycle}}{1\text{ ms}} = 1000\text{ cycles/s} = 1\text{ kHz}$

    $f_{diff} = f_1 - f_2 = 9\text{ kHz} - 1\text{ kHz} = \textbf{8 kHz}$
    $f_{sum} = f_1 + f_2 = 9\text{ kHz} + 1\text{ kHz} = \textbf{10 kHz}$

14. $f_c = 1000\text{ kHz}$
    $f_{diff} = 1000\text{ kHz} - 3\text{ kHz} = \textbf{997 kHz}$
    $f_{sum} = 1000\text{ kHz} + 3\text{ kHz} = \textbf{1003 kHz}$

15. $f_1 = \dfrac{18 \text{ cycles}}{10 \ \mu s} = 1.8 \text{ MHz}$

$f_2 = \dfrac{1 \text{ cycle}}{10 \ \mu s} = 100 \text{ kHz}$

$f_{diff} = f_1 - f_2 = 1.8 \text{ MHz} - 100 \text{ kHz} = \textbf{1.7 MHz}$
$f_{sum} = f_1 + f_2 = 1.8 \text{ MHz} + 100 \text{ kHz} = \textbf{1.9 MHz}$
$f_c = \textbf{1.8 MHz}$

16. $f_c = 1.2 \text{ MHz}$ by inspection
$f_m = f_c - f_{diff} = 1.2 \text{ MHz} - 1.1955 \text{ MHz} = \textbf{4.5 kHz}$

17. $f_c = \dfrac{f_{diff} + f_{sum}}{2} = \dfrac{847 kHz + 853 kHz}{2} = \textbf{850 kHz}$

$f_m = f_c - f_{diff} = 850 \text{ kHz} - 847 \text{ kHz} = \textbf{3 kHz}$

18. $f_{diff(min)} = 600 \text{ kHz} - 3 \text{ kHz} = \textbf{597 kHz}$
$f_{diff(max)} = 600 \text{ kHz} - 300 \text{ Hz} = \textbf{599.7 kHz}$
$f_{sum(min)} = 600 \text{ kHz} + 300 \text{ Hz} = \textbf{600.3 kHz}$
$f_{sum(max)} = 600 \text{ kHz} + 3 \text{ kHz} = \textbf{603 kHz}$
See Figure 17-3.

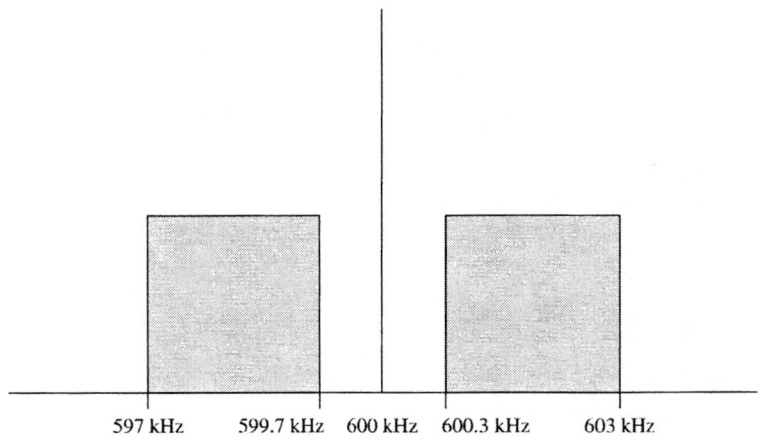

597 kHz   599.7 kHz   600 kHz   600.3 kHz   603 kHz

Figure 17-3

Section 17-4 The Mixer

19. $(\sin A)(\sin B) = \dfrac{1}{2}[\cos(A - B) - \cos(A + B)]$

$V_{in(1)} = 0.2 \text{ V} \sin [2\pi(2200 \text{ kHz})t]$
$V_{in(2)} = 0.15 \text{ V} \sin [2\pi(3300 \text{ kHz})t]$
$V_{in(1)}V_{in(2)} = (0.2 \text{ V})(0.15 \text{ V}) \sin [2\pi(2200 \text{ kHz})t] \sin [2\pi(3300 \text{ kHz})t]$

$V_{out} = \dfrac{(0.2 \text{ V})(0.15 \text{ V})}{2} [\cos 2\pi(3300 \text{ kHz} - 2200 \text{ kHz})t - \cos 2\pi(3300 \text{ kHz} + 2200 \text{ kHz})t]$

$V_{out} = 15 \text{ mV} \cos [2\pi(1100 \text{ kHz})t] - 15 \text{ mV} \cos [2\pi(5500 \text{ kHz})t]$

20. $f_{IF} = f_{LO} - f_c = 986.4 \text{ kHz} - 980 \text{ kHz} = \textbf{6.4 kHz}$

Chapter 17

Section 17-5 AM Demodulation

21. See Figure 17-4.

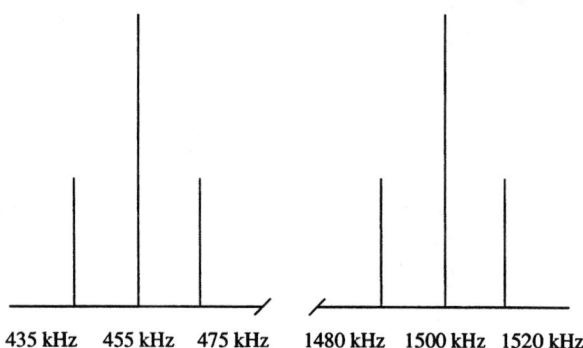

435 kHz   455 kHz   475 kHz   1480 kHz   1500 kHz   1520 kHz

Figure 17-4

22. See Figure 17-5.

23. See Figure 17-6.

435 kHz   455 kHz   475 kHz   20 kHz

Figure 17-5   **Figure 17-6**

Section 17-6 IF and Audio Amplifiers

24. $f_c - f_m = 1.2 \text{ MHz} - 8.5 \text{ kHz} = 1.1915 \text{ MHz}$
$f_c + f_m = 1.2 \text{ MHz} + 8.5 \text{ kHz} = 1.2085 \text{ MHz}$
$f_c = 1.2 \text{ MHz}$
$f_{LO} - f_m = 455 \text{ kHz} - 8.5 \text{ kHz} = 446.5 \text{ kHz}$
$f_{LO} + f_m = 455 \text{ kHz} + 8.5 \text{ kHz} = 463.5 \text{ kHz}$
$f_{LO} = 455 \text{ kHz}$

25. The **IF amplifier** has a 450 kHz to 460 kHz passband.
The **audio/power amplifiers** have a 10 Hz to 5 kHz bandpass.

26. C_4 between pins 1 and 8 makes the gain 200.
With R_1 set for minimum input, $V_{in} = 0$ V.
$V_{out(min)} = A_v V_{in(min)} = 200(0$ V$) = $ **0 V**
With R_1 set for maximum input, $V_{in} = 10$ mV rms.
$V_{out(max)} = A_v V_{in(max)} = 200(10$ mV$) = $ **2 V rms**

Section 17-7 Frequency Modulation

27. The modulating input signal is applied to the control voltage terminal of the VCO. As the input signal amplitude varies, the output frequency of the VCO varies proportionately.

28. An FM signal differs from an AM signal in that the information is contained in frequency variations of the carrier rather than amplitude variations.

29. Varactor

Section 17-8 The Phase-Locked Loop (PLL)

30. See Figure 17-7.

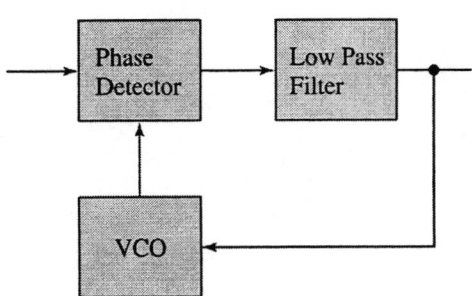

Figure 17-7

31. (a) The VCO signal is locked onto the incoming signal and therefore its frequency is equal to the incoming frequency of **10 MHz**.

(b) $V_c = \dfrac{V_i V_o}{2} \cos\theta_e \dfrac{(250\,\text{mV})(400\,\text{mV})}{2} \cos(30° - 15°) = (0.050)(0.966) = $ **48.3 mV**

32. $\Delta f_o = +3.6$ kHz, $\qquad \Delta V_c = +0.5$ V
$K = \dfrac{\Delta f_o}{\Delta V_c} = \dfrac{+3.6\,\text{kHz}}{+0.5\,\text{V}} = $ **7.2 kHz/V**

33. $K = 1.5$ kHz/V, $\qquad \Delta V_c = +0.67$ V
$K = \dfrac{\Delta f_o}{\Delta V_c}$
$\Delta f_o = K\Delta V_c = (1.5\,\text{kHz/V})(+0.67\,\text{V}) = $ **1005 Hz**

Chapter 17

34. For a PLL to acquire lock the following conditions are needed:
    (1) The difference frequency, $f_0 - f_i$ must fall within the filter's bandwidth.
    (2) The maximum frequency deviation of the VCO frequency, Δf_{max}, must be sufficient to permit f_0 to change to equal f_i.

35. The free-running frequency:

$$f_0 = \frac{1.2}{4R_1C_1} = \frac{1.2}{4(3.9\,\text{k}\Omega)(330\,\text{pF})} = \textbf{233 kHz}$$

The lock range:

$$f_{lock} = \pm\frac{8f_o}{V_{CC}} = \pm\frac{8(233\,\text{kHz})}{18\,\text{V}} = \pm\frac{1.864\,\text{MHz}}{18\,\text{V}} = \textbf{±104 kHz}$$

The capture range:

$$f_{cap} = \pm\frac{1}{2\pi}\sqrt{\left(\frac{2\pi f_{lock}}{3600 \times C_2}\right)}$$

$$= \pm\frac{1}{2\pi}\sqrt{\left(\frac{2\pi(103.6\,\text{kHz})}{3600 \times 0.22\,\mu\text{F}}\right)} = \pm\frac{1}{2\pi}\sqrt{\left(\frac{650.9\,\text{kHz}}{792\,\mu\text{F}}\right)} = \textbf{±4.56 kHz}$$

There are no *EWB*/Multisim Troubleshooting Problems in this chapter.

Chapter 18
Voltage Regulators

Section 18-1 Voltage Regulation

1. Percent line regulation $= \left(\dfrac{\Delta V_{OUT}}{\Delta V_{IN}} \right) 100\% = \left(\dfrac{2\,mV}{6\,V} \right) 100\% = \mathbf{0.0333\%}$

2. Percent line regulation $= \left(\dfrac{\Delta V_{OUT} / V_{OUT}}{\Delta V_{IN}} \right) 100\% = \left(\dfrac{2\,mV/8\,V}{6\,V} \right) 100\% = \mathbf{0.00417\%/V}$

3. Percent load regulation $= \left(\dfrac{V_{NL} / V_{FL}}{\Delta V_{FL}} \right) 100\% = \left(\dfrac{10\,V - 9.90\,V}{9.90\,V} \right) 100\% = \mathbf{1.01\%}$

4. From Problem 3, the percent load regulation is 1.01%. For a full load current of 250 mA, this can be expressed as

    $\dfrac{1.01\%}{250\,mA} = \mathbf{0.00404\%/mA}$

Section 18-2 Basic Series Regulators

5. See Figure 18-1.

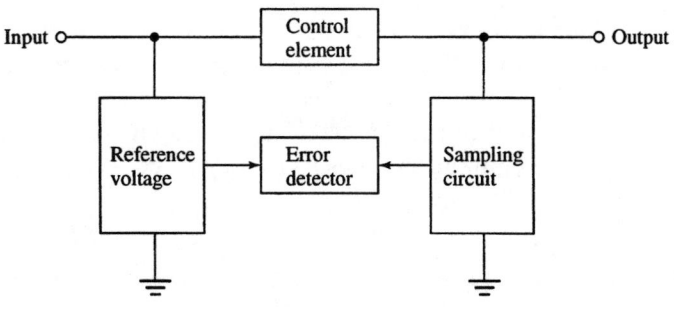

Figure 18-1

6. $V_{OUT} = \left(1 + \dfrac{R_2}{R_3} \right) V_{REF} = \left(1 + \dfrac{33\,k\Omega}{10\,k\Omega} \right) 2.4\,V = \mathbf{10.3\,V}$

7. $V_{OUT} = \left(1 + \dfrac{R_2}{R_3} \right) V_{REF} = \left(1 + \dfrac{5.6\,k\Omega}{2.2\,k\Omega} \right) 2.4\,V = \mathbf{8.51\,V}$

Chapter 18

8. For $R_3 = 2.2 \text{ k}\Omega$:

$$V_{OUT} = \left(1 + \frac{R_2}{R_3}\right)V_{REF} = \left(1 + \frac{5.6 \text{ k}\Omega}{2.2 \text{ k}\Omega}\right)2.4 \text{ V} = 8.5 \text{ V}$$

For $R_3 = 4.7 \text{ k}\Omega$:

$$V_{OUT} = \left(1 + \frac{R_2}{R_3}\right)V_{REF} = \left(1 + \frac{5.6 \text{ k}\Omega}{4.7 \text{ k}\Omega}\right)2.4 \text{ V} = 5.23 \text{ V}$$

The output voltage **decreases by 3.27 V** when R_3 is changed from 2.2 kΩ to 4.7 kΩ.

9. $\quad V_{OUT} = \left(1 + \frac{R_2}{R_3}\right)V_{REF} = \left(1 + \frac{5.6 \text{ k}\Omega}{2.2 \text{ k}\Omega}\right)2.7 \text{ V} = \textbf{9.57 V}$

10. $\quad I_{L(max)} = \dfrac{0.7 \text{ V}}{R_4}$

$$R_4 = \frac{0.7 \text{ V}}{I_{L(max)}} = \frac{0.7 \text{ mA}}{250 \text{ mA}} = \textbf{2.8 } \boldsymbol{\Omega}$$

$$P = I_{L(max)}^2 R_4 = (250 \text{ mA})^2 2.8 \ \Omega = \textbf{0.175 W}, \ \text{Use a 0.25 W.}$$

11. $\quad R_4 = \dfrac{2.8 \ \Omega}{2} = 1.4 \ \Omega$

$$I_{L(max)} = \frac{0.7 \text{ V}}{R_4} = \frac{0.7 \text{ V}}{1.4 \ \Omega} = \textbf{500 mA}$$

Section 18-3 Basic Shunt Regulators

12. Q_1 conducts more when the load current increases, assuming that the output voltage attempts to increase. When the output voltage tries to increase due to a change in load current, the attempted increase is sensed by R_3 and R_4 and a proportional voltage is applied to the op-amp's noninverting input. The resulting difference voltage increases the op-amp output, driving Q_1 more and thus increasing its collector current.

13. $\quad \Delta I_C = \dfrac{\Delta V_{R1}}{R_1} = \dfrac{1 \text{ V}}{100 \ \Omega} = \textbf{10 mA}$

14. $\quad V_{OUT} = \left(1 + \dfrac{R_3}{R_4}\right)V_{REF} = \left(1 + \dfrac{10 \text{ k}\Omega}{3.9 \text{ k}\Omega}\right)5.1 \text{ V} = \textbf{18.2 V}$

$$I_{L1} = \frac{V_{OUT}}{R_{L1}} = \frac{18.2 \text{ V}}{1 \text{ k}\Omega} = 18.2 \text{ mA}$$

$$I_{L2} = \frac{V_{OUT}}{R_{L2}} = \frac{18.2 \text{ V}}{1.2 \text{ k}\Omega} = 15.2 \text{ mA}$$

$$\Delta I_L = 15.2 \text{ mA} - 18.2 \text{ mA} = -3.0 \text{ mA}$$
$$\Delta I_S = -\Delta I_L = \textbf{3.0 mA}$$

15. $$I_{L(max)} = \frac{V_{IN}}{R_1} = \frac{25\text{ V}}{100\,\Omega} = \textbf{250 mA}$$

$$P_{R1} = I_{L(max)}^2 R_1 = (250\text{ mA})^2 100\,\Omega = \textbf{6.25 W}$$

Section 18-4 Basic Switching Regulators

16. $$V_{OUT} = \left(\frac{t_{on}}{T}\right) V_{IN}$$

$$t_{on} = T - t_{off}$$

$$T = \frac{1}{f} = \frac{1}{100\text{ Hz}} = 0.01\text{ s} = 10\text{ ms}$$

$$V_{OUT} = \left(\frac{4\text{ ms}}{10\text{ ms}}\right) 12\text{ V} = \textbf{4.8 V}$$

17. $f = 100$ Hz, $t_{off} = 6$ ms

$$T = \frac{1}{f} = \frac{1}{100\text{ Hz}} = 10\text{ ms}$$

$$t_{on} = T - t_{off} = 10\text{ ms} - 6\text{ ms} = 4\text{ ms}$$

$$\text{duty cycle} = \frac{t_{on}}{T} = \frac{4\text{ ms}}{10\text{ ms}} = 0.4$$

percent duty cycle $= 0.4 \times 100\% = \textbf{40\%}$

18. The diode D_1 becomes forward-biased when Q_1 turns off.

19. The output voltage **decreases**.

Section 18-5 Integrated Circuit Voltage Regulators

20. (a) 7806: **+6 V**
    (b) 7905.2: **−5.2 V**
    (c) 7818: **+18 V**
    (d) 7924: **−24 V**

21. $$V_{OUT} = \left(1 + \frac{R_2}{R_1}\right) V_{REF} + I_{ADJ} R_2 = \left(1 + \frac{10\text{ k}\Omega}{1.0\text{ k}\Omega}\right) 1.25\text{ V} + (50\ \mu\text{A})(10\text{ k}\Omega)$$

$$= 13.7\text{ V} + 0.5\text{ V} = \textbf{14.3 V}$$

22.
$$V_{OUT(min)} = -\left[\left(1 + \frac{R_{2(min)}}{R_1}\right)V_{REF} + I_{ADJ}R_{2(min)}\right]$$

$R_{2(min)} = 0\ \Omega$

$V_{OUT(min)} = -\left(1.25\ \text{V}(1+0) + 0\right) = \mathbf{-1.25\ V}$

$$V_{OUT(max)} = -\left[\left(1 + \frac{R_{2(max)}}{R_1}\right)V_{REF} + I_{ADJ}R_{2(max)}\right] = -\left[1.25\ \text{V}\left(1 + \frac{10\ \text{k}\Omega}{470\ \Omega}\right) + (50\ \mu\text{A})(10\ \text{k}\Omega)\right]$$

$$= -\left(1.25\ \text{V}(22.28) + 0.5\ \text{V}\right) = \mathbf{-28.4\ V}$$

23. The regulator current equals the current through $R_1 + R_2$.

$$I_{REG} \cong \frac{V_{OUT}}{R_1 + R_2} = \frac{14.3\ \text{V}}{11\ \text{k}\Omega} = \mathbf{1.3\ mA}$$

24. $V_{IN} = 18\ \text{V}$, $V_{OUT} = 12\ \text{V}$

$I_{REG(max)} = 2\ \text{mA}$, $V_{REF} = 1.25\ \text{V}$

$$R_1 = \frac{V_{REF}}{I_{REG}} = \frac{1.25\ \text{V}}{2\ \text{mA}} = \mathbf{625\ \Omega}$$

Neglecting I_{ADJ}:

$V_{R2} = 12\ \text{V} - 1.25\ \text{V} = 10.8\ \text{V}$

$$R_2 = \frac{V_{R2}}{I_{REG}} = \frac{10.8\ \text{V}}{2\ \text{mA}} = \mathbf{5.4\ k\Omega}$$

For R_1 use **620 Ω** and for R_2 use either **5600 Ω** or a 10 kΩ potentiometer for precise adjustment to 12 V.

Section 18-6 Applications of IC Voltage Regulators

25. $V_{Rext(min)} = 0.7\ \text{V}$

$$R_{ext} = \frac{0.7\ \text{V}}{I_{max}} = \frac{0.7\ \text{V}}{250\ \text{mA}} = \mathbf{2.8\ \Omega}$$

26. $V_{OUT} = +12\ \text{V}$

$$I_L = \frac{12\ \text{V}}{10\ \Omega} = 1200\ \text{mA} = 1.2\ \text{A}$$

$I_{ext} = I_L - I_{max} = 1.2\ \text{A} - 0.5\ \text{A} = 0.7\ \text{A}$

$P_{ext} = I_{ext}(V_{IN} - V_{OUT}) = 0.7\ \text{A}(15\ \text{V} - 12\ \text{V}) = 0.7\ \text{A}(3\ \text{V}) = \mathbf{2.1\ W}$

27. $V_{Rlim(min)} = 0.7\ \text{V}$

$$R_{lim(min)} = \frac{0.7\ \text{V}}{I_{ext}} = \frac{0.7\ \text{V}}{2\ \text{A}} = \mathbf{0.35\ \Omega}$$

See Figure 18-2.

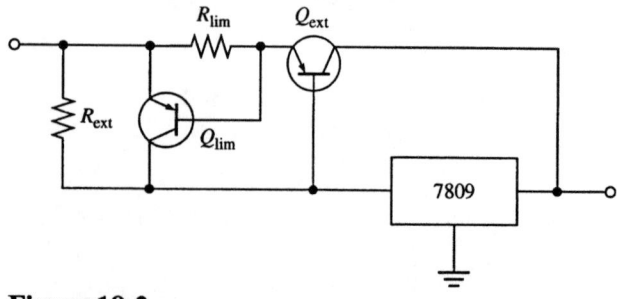

Figure 18-2

28. $R = \dfrac{1.25\,V}{500\,mA} = \mathbf{2.5\,\Omega}$

See Figure 18-3.

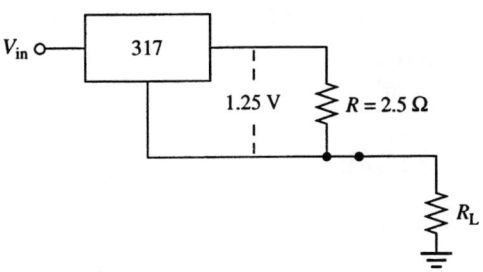

Figure 18-3

29. $R = \dfrac{8\,V}{500\,mA} = \mathbf{16\,\Omega}$

See Figure 18-4.

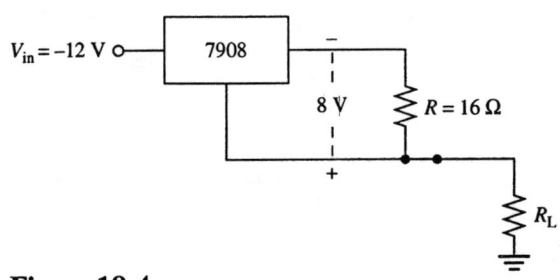

Figure 18-4

30. $V_{REF} = 1.25\,V$

The voltage divider must reduce the output voltage (12 V) down to the reference voltage (1.25 V). See Figure 18-38 in the text.

$$V_{REF} = \left(\dfrac{R_1}{R_1 + R_2}\right)V_{OUT}$$

$$\dfrac{R_1}{R_1 + R_2} = \dfrac{V_{REF}}{V_{OUT}}$$

$$R_1 = R_1(V_{REF}/V_{OUT}) + R_2(V_{REF}/V_{OUT})$$

$$R_2 = \dfrac{R_1 - R_1(V_{REF}/V_{OUT})}{(V_{REF}/V_{OUT})} = \dfrac{R_1(1 + V_{REF}/V_{OUT})}{(V_{REF}/V_{OUT})}$$

Let $R_1 = \mathbf{10\,k\Omega}$.

$$R_2 = \dfrac{10\,k\Omega(1 - 1.25\,V/12\,V)}{(1.25\,V/12\,V)} = \mathbf{86\,k\Omega}$$

Chapter 18

EWB/Multisim Troubleshooting Problems

The solutions showing instrument connections for Problems 31 through 34 are available in the Solutions folder for Chapter 18 on the CD-ROM provided with the textbook. The solutions may be accessed using the password *ED5FLOYD*. The faults in the circuit files may be accessed using the password *book* (all lowercase).

31. R_2 leaky

32. Zener diode open

33. Q_2 collector-to-emitter open

34. R_1 open

Results for System Applications

Results for System Applications

Chapter 2
The Components
Transformer: 9 V rms
Diode: 1N5400, 1N4719, or MR500
Surge resistor: 1.0 Ω
Fuse: 250 mA slow-blow
Filter Capacitor 6800 μF

Troubleshooting
Board 1: Fuse is open
Board 2: Diode open
Board 3: Third diode from top is open

Chapter 3
The Components
Regulator: 1N4733 5.1 V zener
Limiting resistor: 24 Ω
Series resistors: 36 Ω for LED, 330 kΩ for photodiode
Fuse: 250 mA slow-blow

Troubleshooting
Board 1: Photodiode defective
Board 2: Filter capacitor open
Board 3: Zener is open and not regulating

Chapter 4
The Components
Bias resistors: 1/4 W
Q_6 collector resistor: 1 W max (depends on load of time delay circuit)
Relay: 12 V, 55 Ω, 0.15 A (relay A)
Diode: 1N4002

Troubleshooting
Board 1: CE junction of Q_2 open
Board 2: CE junction of Q_3 open
Board 3: R_{12} shorted

Chapter 5
Analysis of the Temperature-to-Voltage Conversion Circuit
At $T = 46°C$: $V_{OUT} = 4.78$ V
At $T = 50°C$: $V_{OUT} = 6.54$ V
At $T = 54°C$: $V_{OUT} = 7.06$ V
The transistor is operating linearly.

The Power Supply Circuit
Resistors: $R_1 = 1.0\ \Omega$, $R_2 = 6.8\ \Omega$, $R_3 = 56\ \Omega$
Zener diodes: 1N4739, 9.1 V; 1N4733, 5.1 V. The 9.1 V zener should have a heat sink if there is no quaranteeed minimum load.

Troubleshooting
Board 1: Most likely a 9.1 V zener instead of a 5.1 V has been inserted.
Board 2: Thermistor open
Board 3: CE junction of transistor open

Chapter 6
Analysis of the Preamplifier Circuit
Input resistance: $R_{in(1)} = 17\ \Omega$
Input power: $P = 362\ \mu W$
DC voltages:
$V_{B(1)} = 19.3$ V, $V_{E(1)} = 1.23$ V, $V_{C(1)} = 9.29$ V
$V_{B(2)} = 1.88$ V, $V_{E(2)} = 1.18$ V, $V_{C(2)} = 7.54$ V
Total voltage gain: Max $A_v = 733$, Min $A_v = 145$
DC current: 2.68 mA
Resistor power ratings: All 1/8 W
Lowest frequency: 935 Hz

The Power Supply Circuit
To adapt, change to a 12 V zener regulator such as a 1N4742.

Troubleshooting
Board 1: R_6 is open, causing Q_2 to saturate.
Board 2: Signal input, no signal output. No signal at collector of Q_1, but dc voltage appears ok. Most likely fault is open C_1.
Board 3: Gain of stage 2 is approximately 4, which is much too low. C_4 is open.

Chapter 7

The schematic for the circuit board is as follows:

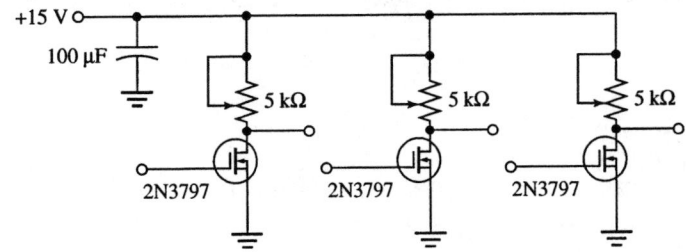

Analysis of the pH Sensor Circuits

Input resistance: $R_{in(min)} = 10 \times 10^{12}\ \Omega$
Rheostat: 4 kΩ maximum, 2.76 kΩ typical, 1.33 kΩ minimum
Output voltage range: 5.32 V to 8.52 V represent pH values from about 3.5 to about 9.5.

Troubleshooting

Board 1: Q_2 is probably open although R_2 could be shorted.
Board 2: V_{OUT} for sensor 2 is too high. The rheostat is probably miscalibrated or Q_2 is faulty.

Chapter 8
Basic MOSFET Amplifier Design

Drain-to-source voltage: $V_{DS(min)} = 3$ V, $V_{DS(max)} = 9$ V
Voltage gain: $A_{v(min)} = 2.25$, $A_{v(max)} = 4.50$

Variation in I_{DSS} from one FET to another will affect the Q-point of the circuit. Use of voltage-divider bias rather than zero-bias will lessen the dependency of the Q-point on I_{DSS}.

Since g_m varies from one device to another, the voltage gain will also vary. To minimize the influence of g_m, a swamping source resistor with a value much greater than $1/g_m$ can be used and the drain resistor adjusted accordingly.

Amplifier Performance on the Test Bench

Measurement 1: Variation in I_{DSS} for Q_1 (larger for set 2)
Measurement 2: Variation in I_{DSS} for Q_2 (larger for set 1)
Measurement 3: Variation in g_m for Q_1 (larger for set 1)
Measurement 4: Variation in g_m for Q_2 (larger for set 2)

Set 1 Q_1: $I_{DSS} = 2.53$ mA, $g_m = 2070\ \mu S$
Set 1 Q_2: $I_{DSS} = 4.12$ mA, $g_m = 2270\ \mu S$
Set 2 Q_1: $I_{DSS} = 4.87$ mA, $g_m = 1700\ \mu S$
Set 2 Q_2: $I_{DSS} = 3.95$ mA, $g_m = 2780\ \mu S$

Using FETs with maximum g_m and typical I_{DSS}, a FET amplifier with 118 stages is required to achieve the same maximum gain of the bipolar junction amplifier.

Results for System Applications

Recommendation

1. MOSFETs are not feasible replacements for the BJTs in this case.
2. Device variation in parameters make mass production impossible because circuit must be "tweaked" to match the gains, unlike BJTs.
3. Retain the BJT because 118 FET stages are required to match the gain of the two-stage BJT.

Chapter 9
Analysis of the Power Amplifier Circuit

Input resistance: $R_{in(min)} = 8\ k\Omega$
Voltage gain: 1360 (preamp and power amp combined)
Transistor power ratings: Not sufficient without the heat sink.

Troubleshooting

Board 1: The signal appears at the bases but not at the output. One of the darlington transistors is faulty.

Board 2: There is no signal at either base of the darlington transistors, but the dc voltages are ok, indicating that the bias transistor junctions are not faulty. Since there is a signal through C_1, there is no obvious fault other than an ac short to ground at both bases, which in unlikely. So, the scope measurements are faulty. Perhaps the probe is not making contact with test points 2 and 4 or something has happened to the scope between step 4 and step 5.

Chapter 10
Analysis of the Amplifier Circuit

First stage: $f_{cl(in)} = 2.31$ Hz, $f_{cl(out)} = 1.37$ Hz, $f_{cl(bypass)} = 12.7$ Hz, $f_{cl(bypass)}$ is dominant.
First stage: $f_{cu(in)} = 206$ kHz, $f_{cu(out)} = 13.7$ MHz, $f_{cu(in)}$ is dominant.
Second stage: $f_{cl(in)} = 1.37$ Hz, $f_{cl(out)} = 1.08$ Hz, $f_{cl(bypass)} = 17.9$ Hz, $f_{cl(bypass)}$ is dominant.
Second stage: $f_{cu(in)} = 450$ kHz, $f_{cu(out)} = 12$ MHz, $f_{cu(in)}$ is dominant.
Overall lower critical frequency: 17.9 Hz
Overall upper critical frequency: 206 kHz
Overall bandwidth: approximately 206 kHz

Frequency Response on the Test Bench

Lower critical frequency: Calculated $f_{cl} = 17.9$ Hz, $T = 55.9$ ms;
55.9 ms/5.5 div = 10.2 ms/div. Closest setting is 10 ms/div. The actual frequency being measured is $f_{cl} = 1/(10\ ms/div \times 5.5\ div) = 18.2$ Hz
Upper critical frequency: Calculated $f_{cu} = 206$ kHz, $T = 4.85\ \mu s$;
4.85 μs/5 div = 0.97 μs/div. Closest setting is 1 μs/div. The actual frequency being measured is $f_{cu} = 1/(1\mu s/div \times 5\ div) = 200$ kHz

Chapter 11
Analysis of the Motor Speed-Control Circuit

PUT gate voltage of 0 V, assuming forward voltage of 0 V, and the potentiometer set at 25 kΩ:

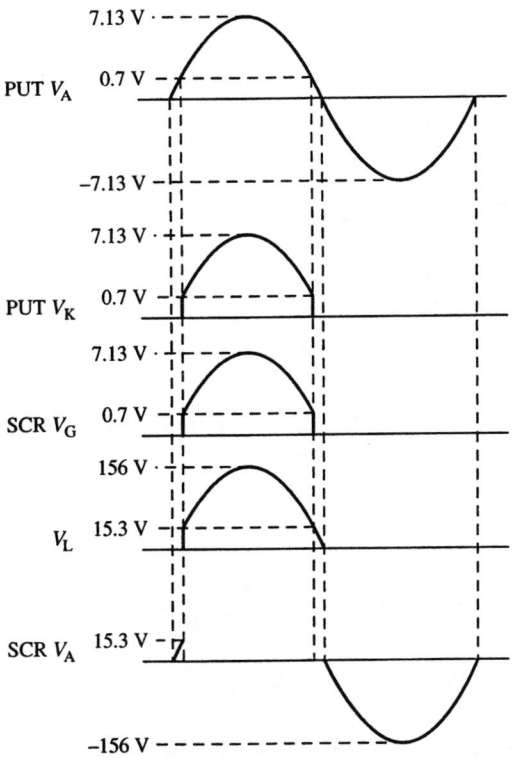

For the potentiometer set to 25 kΩ, V_A of the PUT is the same. With $V_G = 0$ V, 2 V, 4 V, 6 V, 8 V, and 10 V, the PUT conducts with $V_A = 0.7$ V, 2.7 V, 4.7 V, 6.7 V, 8.7 V, and 10.7 V respectively. Since $V_A = 7.13$ V maximum for $V_G = 8$ V and 10 V, the PUT never conducts and the SCR never fires and the load voltage is zero. The voltages across the load resistor are as follows:

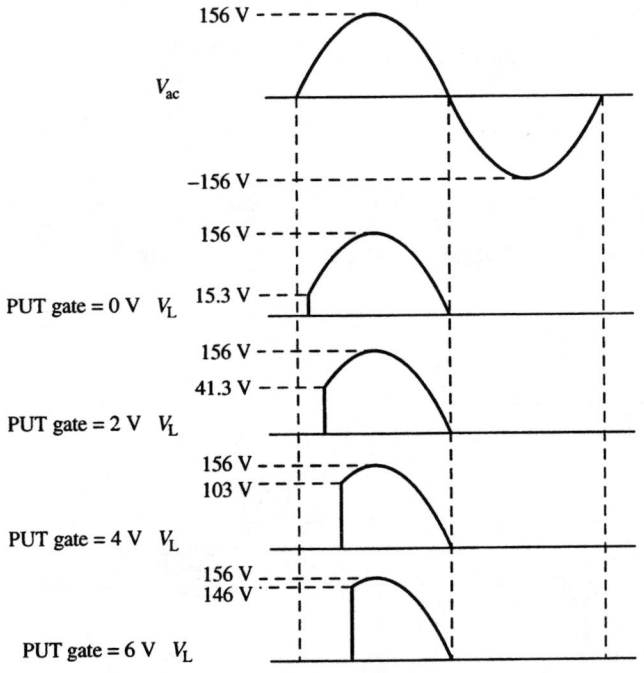

Results for System Applications

Troubleshooting

Board 1: The 50 kΩ resistor is open or the 1.2 kΩ resistor is shorted.
Board 2: The SCR is open.
Board 3: The SCR is shorted.
Board 4: The PUT is shorted.

Chapter 12
Analysis of the Audio Amplifier Circuit

Midrange voltage gain: $A_{v(mid)} = 46.8$
Lower critical frequency: $f_{cl} = 15.4$ Hz
Bandwidth: $BW \cong 15$ kHz
Maximum input: $V_{in(max)} = 470$ mV peak-to-peak
Speaker power: $P_{out(max)} = 3.78$ W

Troubleshooting

Board 1: The op-amp is faulty, improper connection at pins 3 or 6, or supply not on.
Board 2: R_5 is open or BE junction of Q_1 is open.
Board 3: R_3 is open.

Chapter 13
Analysis of the ADC Circuit

Summing amplifier gain: $A_v = -1$
Slope of integrator ramp +2 V input: $\Delta V_{out}/\Delta t = 2$ V/μs
Slope of integrator ramp –8 V input: $\Delta V_{out}/\Delta t = -8$ V/μs
Dual-slope output: Positive ramp from 0 V to +3 V in 1 μs followed by negative ramp back to 0 V in 0.375 μs.
Sampling rate: 571 kHz

Troubleshooting

Board 1: IC3 output stuck high.
Board 2: R_1 or R_2 is open.
Board 3: C_2 is shorted making IC2 a voltage follower.

Chapter 14
The Circuits

Isolation amplifier gain: $A_{v1} = \dfrac{R_3}{R_1} + 1 = \dfrac{330\,k\Omega}{86\,k\Omega} = 3.8$; $A_{v2} = \dfrac{R_5}{R_4} + 1 = \dfrac{120\,k\Omega}{100\,k\Omega} = 1.2$; $A_{v(tot)} = 4.6$

Filter bandwidth: ≈ 106 Hz
Filter gain: $A_v = 1.59$
Post amplifier gain: $A_{v(min)} = -100$, $A_{v(max)} = -150$
Amplifier gain: $A_{v(min)} = -1750$, $A_{v(max)} = -2620$
Voltage range at position pot wiper: $V_{min} = -59.7$ mV, $V_{max} = +59.7$ mV

Troubleshooting

Board 1: Several faults can product no output including R_{10} open or IC3 output faulty or open.

Board 2: R_6 or R_7 open.

Board 3: R_{10} open.

Board 4: R_{15} or R_{16} open.

Chapter 15
The Filter Circuit

Sallen-Key critical frequencies: IC1 filter, 15.9 kHz; IC2 filter, 53 kHz; IC4 filter, 18.9 kHz; IC5 filter, 15.9 kHz

Multiple FB center frequency: 19 kHz

Bandwidths: Approximately the same as the critical frequency for each filter.

Sallen-Key voltage gains: IC1 filter, 1.59; IC2 filter, 1.59; IC3 filter, 0.915; IC4 filter, 1.59; IC5 filter 1.59

Sallen-key response: $R_1/R_2 = 0.589$ (approximately Butterworth)

Chapter 16
The Function Generator Circuit

Oscillator frequencies:

×1,: minimum f = 0.73 Hz, Maximum f = 8.84 Hz

×10,: minimum f = 7.3 Hz, Maximum f = 88.4 Hz

×100,: minimum f = 73 Hz, Maximum f = 884 Hz

×1k,: minimum f = 730 Hz, Maximum f = 8.84 Hz

×10k,: minimum f = 7.3 kHz, Maximum f = 88.4 kHz

Output voltages:

Sine wave: 25.4 V pp

Square wave: 30 V pp

Triangular wave: 12.6 V pp

Troubleshooting

Unit 1: Fault is in the IC1 Wien-bridge oscillator block. IC1 output could be open or lead-lag feedback loop open.

Unit 2: Output of IC2 is open.

Unit 3: Output of IC3 open or R_7 or R_{10} open.

Unit 4: Negative feedback path of IC3 is open causing it to saturate.

Chapter 17
The PC Board

During board assembly, a "stuffing error" has resulted in a resistor where diode D_1 should be.

The Circuits

- Originate mode: $f_{orig(PLL)} \dfrac{1.2}{4R_1C_1} = \dfrac{1.2}{4(5.6\ \mathrm{k\Omega})(0.05\ \mu\mathrm{F})} = 1.07\ \mathrm{kHz}$

Answer mode: $R_1 = R_3 \parallel R_4 = 6.2\ \mathrm{k\Omega} \parallel 5.6\ \mathrm{k\Omega} = 2.94\ \mathrm{k\Omega}$ (Neglecting Q_2 sat R)

$$f_{ans(PLL)} \cong \frac{1.2}{4R_1C_1} = \frac{1.2}{4(2.94\ \mathrm{k\Omega})(0.05\ \mu\mathrm{F})} = 2.04\ \mathrm{kHz}$$

- Same calculations as above: $f_{orig(VCO)} \cong 1.07$ kHz, $f_{ans(VCO)} \cong 2.04$ kHz

- Max and min voltages are nearly equal to the supply voltage +6 V and –6 V.

- When Q_4 is off and $R_{11} = 0$ Ω and R_8 set for maximum voltage: $V_9 = +6$ V

- $T = \dfrac{1}{300\,\text{Hz}} = 3.33$ ms, $\dfrac{T}{2} = 1.67$ ms

  FSK data: 1090 Hz tone for 1.67 ms when pin 9 is low and 1270 Hz tone for 1.67 ms when pin 9 is high.

- $\Delta f = 1270$ Hz – 1070 Hz = 2225 Hz – 2025 Hz = 200 Hz

  $V = \dfrac{200\,\text{Hz}}{50\,\text{Hz/V}} = +4$ V

Troubleshooting

- No circuit power, frequency components out of tolerance preventing lock, faulty PLL or op-amp.

- Q_2, R_2, or R_3 open, Q_1 shorted, faulty PLL.

- VCO faulty, C_3 open.

- Q_3 or R_6 open, pin 9 or VCO shorted to ground, Q_4 shorted.

Chapter 18
The Power Supply Circuit

Bridge voltages at peak of input: Top corner: ≈ 17 V peak, bottom corner: ≈ -17 V peak, left corner: –16.3 V peak , right corner +16.3 peak.
PIV: 33.2 V
Regulator input voltages: 7812: +16.3 V; 7912: –16.3 V
Regulator current: 250 mA from each regulator. Heat sinks are not necessary.

Troubleshooting

Board 1: Fuse may be blown. Transformer may have an open primary of secondary winding or a shorted primary winding.
Board 2: Input or output of IC1 may be open. Pin 2 of IC1 may be open. C_1 or C_3 may be shorted.
Board 3: Input or output or pin 2 of IC2 may be open. C_2 or C_4 may be shorted.
Board 4: IC1 and IC2 may be swapped.

Summary of EWB/Multisim Circuit Files

Password for Solution Files: ED5FLOYD

Password for Fault Circuits: book

Prepared by Gary Snyder

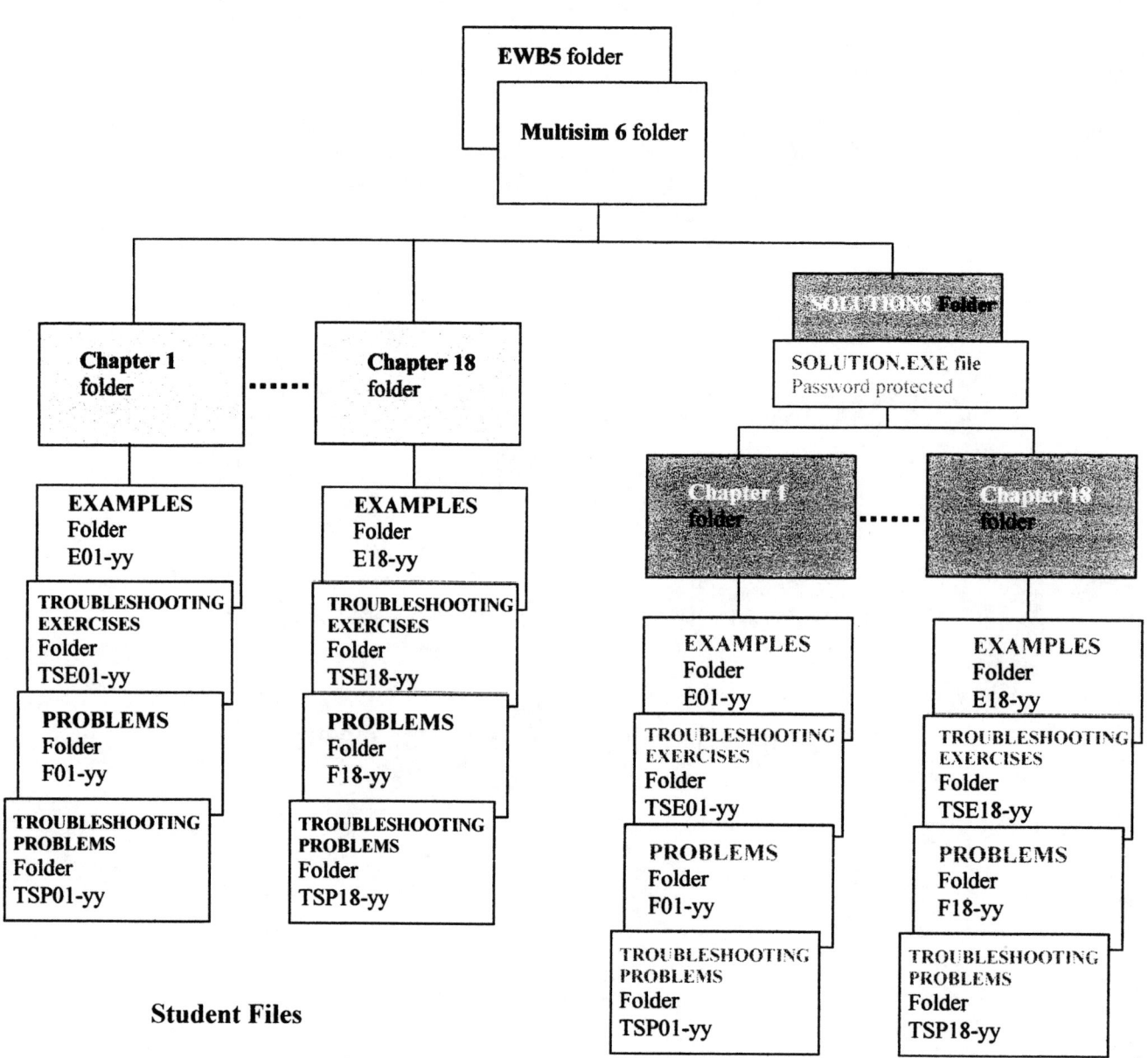

CD-ROM Organization Diagram

Summary of Circuit Files

Chapter 1:

Circuit	EWB	MultiSim
E01-01	$V_R(1) = 9.287$ V $V_D(1) = 712.8$ mV $V_R(2) = 9.98$ mV $V_D(2) = 9.99$ V	$V_R(1) = 9.287$ V $V_D(1) = 0.713$ V $V_R(2) = 9.980$ mV $V_D(2) = 9.99$ V
F01-41a	$V_R = 0.000$ µV	$V_R = 0.020$ nV
F01-41b	$V_R = 99.15$ V	$V_R = 99.151$ V
F01-41c	$V_R = 23.68$ V	$V_R = 23.681$ V
F01-41d	$V_D = 651.5$ mV	$V_D = 0.651$ V
F01-42a	$V_D = 25.00$ V	$V_D = 25.000$ V
F01-42b	$V_D = 15.00$ V	$V_D = 15.000$ V
F01-42c	$V_D = 2.500$ V	$V_D = 2.500$ V
F01-42d	$V_R = 0.0113$ µV	$V_R = 11.285$ nV
F01-43	$V_A = 25.00$ V $V_B = 24.25$ V $V_C = 8.746$ V $V_D = 8.000$ V	$V_A = 25.00$ V $V_B = 24.255$ V $V_C = 8.746$ V $V_D = 8.000$ V
TSP01-20	$V_R = 3.000$ V	$V_R = 3.000$ V
TSP01-21	$V_D = 100.0$ V	$V_D = 99.994$ V
TSP01-22	$V_D = 32.43$ V	$V_D = 32.434$ V
TSP01-23	$V_D = -0.001$ µV	$V_D = -1.000$ pV
TSP01-24	$V_D = 667.6$ mV	$V_D = 0.668$ V
TSP01-25	$V_D = 0.192$ µV	$V_D = 0.192$ nV
TSP01-26	$V_D = 2.577$ V	$V_D = 2.577$ V
TSP01-27	$V_D = 11.99$ V	$V_D = 11.994$ V
TSP01-28	$V_A = 25.00$ V $V_B = 24.25$ V $V_C = 8.000$ V $V_D = 8.000$ V	$V_A = 25.00$ V $V_B = 24.253$ V $V_C = 8.000$ V $V_D = 8.000$ V

Chapter 2:

Circuit	EWB	MultiSim
E02-02a	Half-wave $V_P = 4.2115$ V	Half-wave $V_P = 4.3$ V
E02-02b	Half-wave $V_P = 98.0893$ V	Half-wave $V_P = 99.2$ V
E02-03	Half-wave $V_P = 76.9264$ V	Half-wave $V_P = 77.0$ V
E02-05a	Full-wave $V_P = 24.2233$ V	Full-wave $V_P = 24.3$ V
E02-05b	Full-wave $V_P = 24.2233$ V	Full-wave $V_P = 24.3$ V
E02-06	Full-wave $V_P = 41.2853$ V	Full-wave $V_P = 41.0$ V
E02-07	$V_L(max) = 14.6294$ V $V_L(min) = 13.8651$ V	$V_L(max) = 14.7$ V $V_L(min) = 13.8$ V
E02-09	Half-wave $V_P(max) = 8.9581$ V $V_P(min) = 8.9581$ V	Half-wave $V_P(max) = 9.1$ V $V_P(min) = 779.1$ mV
E02-10	Clipped $V_P(max) = 5.7492$ V $V_P(min) = -5.7469$ V	Clipped $V_P(max) = 5.7$ V $V_P(min) = -5.7$ V
E02-11	Clipped $V_P(max) = 8.9729$ V $V_P(min) = -17.8942$ V	Clipped $V_P(max) = 9.0$ V $V_P(min) = -18.0$ V
E02-12	Negative Clamp $V_P(max) = 609.2934$ mV $V_P(min) = -46.7967$ V	Negative Clamp $V_P(max) = 729$ mV $V_P(min) = -45.5$ V
F02-71a	Half-wave $V_P = 4.1826$ V	Half-wave $V_P = 4.2$ V

F02-71b	Half-wave V_P = -49.0255 V	Half-wave V_P = -49.3 V
F02-72	Half-wave V_P = 78.9313 V	Half-wave V_P = 80.5 V
F02-74	Full-wave V_P = 19.4361 V	Full-wave V_P = 19.6 V
F02-75	Full-wave V_P = 29.2363 V	Full-wave V_P = 29.5 V
F02-76	V_L(max) = 47.4164 V V_L(min) = 46.6476 V	V_L(max) = 47.6 V V_L(min) = 46.6 V
F02-77	Half-wave V_P(max) = 712.1375 mV V_P(min) = -9.8960 V	Half-wave V_P(max) = 712.7 mV V_P(min) = -10.0 V
F02-81a	Clipped V_P(max) = 721.5138 mV V_P(min) = -722.2388 mV	Clipped V_P(max) = 721.9 mV V_P(min) = -722.0 mV
F02-81b	Clipped V_P(max) = 721.9223 mV V_P(min) = -722.2338 mV	Clipped V_P(max) = 722.0 mV V_P(min) = -722.0 mV
F02-84	V_{SEC} = 114.7 V_{AC} V_{REC} = ~0 V V_L = 59.91 V	V_{SEC} = 117.66 V_{AC} V_{REC} = 4.969 V V_L = 58.449 V
F02-86	Full-wave V_P = 15.4930 V	Full-wave V_P = 15.5 V
TSE02-01	V_{FUSE} = 0 V	V_{FUSE} = 0 V
TSE02-02	V_{SURGE} = 0 V	V_{SURGE} = 0 V
TSE02-03	V_L(max) = 21.1824 V V_L(min) = 20.0721 V	Not implemented
TSP02-48	Unrectified AC 9.9124 V_{PP}	Unrectified AC 10.0 V_{PP}
TSP02-49	V_L(max) = 38.0269 V V_L(min) = -48.8304 V	V_L(max) = 38.4 V V_L(min) = -49.3 V
TSP02-50	V_L = 0 V	V_L = 0 V
TSP02-51	Half-wave V_P = 18.5137 V	Half-wave V_P = 19.6 V
TSP02-52	Clipped Full-wave V_P(max) = 59.8993 V V_P(min) = Variable	Clipped Full-wave V_P(max) = 59.8 V V_P(min) = 1.6 V
TSP02-53	Full-wave V_P(max) = 48.8389 V V_P(min) = 1.8545 V	Full-wave V_P(max) = 49.1 V V_P(min) = 784.1 mV
TSP02-54	Positive Clipped V_P(max) = 678.1462 mV V_P(min) = -896.6640 mV	Positive Clipped V_P(max) = 679.1 mV V_P(min) = -909.1 mV
TSP02-55	Half-wave V_P(min) = -29.4365 V	Half-wave V_P(min) = -30.0 V
TSP02-56	Half-wave V_P(max) = 15.8707 mV V_P(min) = Variable	Half-wave V_P(max) = 16.0 V V_P(min) = 480.1 mV

Chapter 3:

Circuit	EWB	MultiSim
E03-05	I_D(1) = 4.441 µA V_D(1) = 4.860 V I_D(2) = 193.1 mA V_D(2) = 6.385 V	I_D(1) = 4.749 µA V_D(1) = 4.860 V I_D(2) = 206 mA V_D(2) = 5.137 V
E03-06	I_D = 1.329 mA V_R = 23.45 mA V_D = 11.93 V	I_D = 1.330 mA V_R = 24 mA V_D = 11.93 V
E03-08	Clipped V_P(max)(1) = 5.6034 V V_P(min)(1) = -3.7857 V V_P(max)(2) = 6.7324 V V_P(min)(2) = -15.5693 V	Clipped V_P(max)(1) = 5.6 V V_P(min)(1) = -3.8 V V_P(max)(2) = 6.7 V V_P(min)(2) = -15.5 V

F03-61	$I_R(1) = 150.4$ mA $V_R(1) = 4.692$ V $I_R(1) = 44.9$ mA $V_R(1) = 5.776$ V	$I_R(1) = 150$ mA $V_R(1) = 4.692$ V $I_R(1) = 40$ mA $V_R(1) = 5.116$ V
F03-64	$I_D = 34.20$ mA	$I_D = 34$ mA
F03-68	$V_{OUT} = 12.0272$ V_{DC}	$V_{OUT} = 11.002$ V_{DC}
TSE03-01	$V_{OUT} = 22.91$ V_{DC}	$V_{OUT} =$
TSE03-02	$V_C = 0$ V_{DC} $V_{OUT} = 0$ V_{DC}	$V_C = 0$ V_{DC} $V_{OUT} = 0.000$ V_{DC}
TSE03-03	$V_D = 15.3620$ V_{DC} with ripple $V_{OUT} = 15.31$ V_{DC}	$V_D = 15.0$ V_{DC} with ripple $V_{OUT} = 15.0 V_{DC}$
TSE03-04	$V_D = 0$ V Blown fuse	$V_D = 0$ V Blown fuse
TSP03-45	$V_{OUT} = 8.000$ V_{DC}	$V_{OUT} = 8.000$ V_{DC}
TSP03-46	Spikey Output $V_{OUT} = 12.0800$ V $V_{SPIKE} = 2.1937$ V	Spikey Output $V_{OUT} = 12.0$ V $V_{SPIKE} = 9.0$ V
TSP03-47	$V_R = 30.66$ V_{DC} $V_{OUT} = 0.093$ μV_{DC}	$V_R > 26$ V_{DC} $V_{OUT} = 0.079$ nV_{DC}
TSP03-48	$V_R = 23.44$ V	$V_R = 22.243$ V

Chapter 4:

Circuit	EWB	MultiSim
E04-02	$I_B = 411.9$ μA $I_C = 61.69$ mA $I_E = 62.50$ mA $V_{CB} = 2.940$ V $V_{CE} = 3.821$ V	$I_B = 412$ μA $I_C = 62$ mA $I_E = 62$ mA $V_{CB} = 2.94$ V $V_{CE} = 3.821$ V
E04-04	$I_B = 216.7$ μA $I_C = 9.838$ mA LED blinks	$I_B = 217$ μA $I_C = 9.838$ mA LED blinks
E04-10	$I_C(1) = 15.76$ mA $V_{CE}(1) = 4.129$ V $I_C(2) = 14.88$ mA $V_{CE}(2) = 4.375$ V	$I_C(1) = 16$ mA $V_{CE}(1) = 2.952$ V $I_C(2) = 13$ mA $V_{CE}(2) = 3.709$ V
F04-30	$V_C = 8.986$ V $V_B = 0.612$ V	$V_C = 8.986$ V $V_B = 0.612$ V
F04-46	$I_B = 667.2$ μA $I_C = 32.29$ mA $I_E = 32.96$ mA	$I_B = 667$ μA $I_C = 32$ mA $I_E = 33$ mA
F04-47a	$V_{BC} = -4.608$ V $V_{BE} = 976.8$ mV $V_{CE} = 5.485$ V	$V_{BC} = -4.608$ V $V_{BE} = 877$ mV $V_{CE} = 5.458$ V
F04-47b	$V_{BC} = 3.254$ V $V_{BE} = -833.8$ mV $V_{CE} = -4.088$ V	$V_{BC} = 3.254$ V $V_{BE} = -0.834$ mV $V_{CE} = -4.088$ V
F04-48	$I_B = 24.42$ μA $I_C = 1.197$ mA $I_E = 1.221$ mA	$I_B = 24$ μA $I_C = 1.197$ mA $I_E = 1.221$ mA
F04-49	$V_B(1) = 10.00$ V $V_C(1) = 20.00$ V $V_E(1) = 9.228$ V $V_B(2) = -4.00$ V $V_C(2) = -12.00$ V $V_E(2) = -3.216$ V	$V_B(1) = 10.000$ V $V_C(1) = 20.000$ V $V_E(1) = 9.228$ V $V_B(2) = -4.000$ V $V_C(2) = -12.000$ V $V_E(2) = -3.216$ V
F04-50	$V_C = 221.6$ mV	$V_C = 222$ mV

F04-51	$V_B = 838.6$ mV $V_C = 533.8$ mV	$V_B = 839$ mV $V_C = 534$ mV
TSE04-01	$V_B = 778.5$ mV $V_C = 4.917$ V	$V_B = 779$ mV $V_C = 4.917$ V
TSE04-02	$V_B = 680.0$ mV $V_C = 5.838$ mV	$V_B = 680$ mV $V_C = 5.838$ mV
TSE04-03	$V_B = 2.841$ V $V_C = 8.995$ V	$V_B = 2.841$ V $V_C = 8.995$ V
TSP04-47	$V_{RB} = 2.647$ V	$V_{RB} = 2.471$ V
TSP04-48	$V_{RC} = 14.98$ V	$V_{RC} = 14.982$ V
TSP04-49	$V_{CE} = -849.4$ mV	$V_{CE} = -0.849$ mV
TSP04-50	$V_{CE} = 10.00$ V	$V_{CE} = 10.0$ V
TSP04-51	$V_B = 10.00$ V $V_C = 20.00$ V $I_C = 91.09$ mA	$V_B = 10.00$ V $V_C = 20.00$ V $I_C = 91$ mA
TSP0452	$I_C = 5.455$ mA	$I_C = 5.456$ mA
TSP04-53	$I_B = 0.000$ μA $V_C = 4.999$ V	$I_B = 0.444$ pA $V_C = 4.999$ V
TSP04-54	$I_B = 4.350$ μA $I_C = 0.000$ μA	$I_B = 4.350$ μA $I_C = -0.021$ pA

Chapter 5:

Circuit	EWB	MultiSim
E05-01	$V_{BE} = 869.1$ mV $V_{CE} = 7.187$ V $I_C = 38.85$ mA	$V_{BE} = 869$ mV $V_{CE} = 7.187$ V $I_C = 39$ mA
E05-03	$V_{BE} = 816.0$ mV $V_{CE} = 2.775$ V $I_C = 4.615$ mA	$V_{BE} = 814$ mV $V_{CE} = 2.775$ V $I_C = 4.615$ mA
E05-04	$V_{BE} = -794.1$ mV $V_{CE} = -3.082$ V $I_C = 2.155$ mA	$V_{BE} = -794$ mV $V_{CE} = -3.082$ V $I_C = 2.155$ mA
E05-06a	$V_{BE} = 832.4$ mV $V_{CE} = 6.685$ V $I_C = 9.492$ mA	$V_{BE} = 832$ mV $V_{CE} = 6.685$ V $I_C = 9.492$ mA
E05-06b	$V_{BE} = 836.6$ mV $V_{CE} = 5.749$ V $I_C = 11.16$ mA	$V_{BE} = 837$ mV $V_{CE} = 5.749$ V $I_C = 11$ mA
E05-08	$V_{BE} = 769.0$ mV $V_{CE} = 1.731$ V $I_C = 826.9$ μA	$V_{BE} = 769$ mV $V_{CE} = 1.731$ V $I_C = 827$ μA
F05-37	$V_{CE} = 10.77$ V $I_C = 922.9$ μA	$V_{CE} = 10.771$ V $I_C = 923$ μA
F05-38	$V_{CE} = 6.001$ V $I_C = 5.126$ mA	$V_{CE} = 6.001$ V $I_C = 5.126$ mA
F05-40	$V_B = 2.047$ V $V_C = 6.237$ V $V_E = 1.267$ V	$V_B = 2.047$ V $V_C = 6.237$ V $V_E = 1.267$ V
F05-41	$V_B = -1.666$ V $V_C = -9.197$ V $V_E = -880.61$ mV	$V_B = -1.666$ V $V_C = -9.197$ V $V_E = -0.881$ V
F05-44	$V_{BE} = -845.8$ mV $V_{CE} = -7.182$ V $I_C = 15.93$ mA	$V_{BE} = -846$ mV $V_{CE} = -7.182$ V $I_C = 16$ mA

F05-45	V_B = 774.4 mV V_C = 1.169 V V_E = 1.017 mA	V_B = 774 mV V_C = 1.169 V V_E = 1.017 mA
TSE05-01	V_B = 0.059 μV V_C = 10.00 V V_E = 0.005 μV	V_B = 0.047 μV V_C = 10.000 V V_E = 4.700 nV
TSE05-02	V_B = 3.197 V V_C = 10.00 V V_E = 0.002 μV	V_B = 3.197 V V_C = 10.000 V V_E = 0.000 V
TSE05-03	V_B = 3.145 V V_C = 5.061 V V_E = 2.329 V	V_B = 3.145 V V_C = 5.061 V V_E = 2.329 V
TSE05-04	V_B = 3.197 V V_C = 10.00 V V_E = 2.695 V	V_B = 3.197 V V_C = 10.000 V V_E = 2.695 V
TSP05-51	V_B = 668.8 mV V_C = 17.9 mV	V_B = 669 mV V_C = 18 mV
TSP05-52	I_B = 0.000 μA	I_B = -0.444 pA
TSP05-53	V_B = 3.664 V	V_B = 3.664 V
TSP05-54	V_C = -2.846 V	V_C = -2.846 V
TSP05-55	V_C = -10.00 V V_E = 9.203 V	V_C = -10.00 V V_E = 9.203 V
TSP05-56	V_B = 2.999 V	V_B = 2.999 V

Chapter 6:

Circuit	EWB	MultiSim
E06-08	V_C = 5.529 V V_b = 25.8546 mV$_{PP}$ V_c = 220.6865 mV$_{PP}$ DC values off, gain is OK	V_C = 5.469 V V_b = 26.1 mV$_{PP}$ V_c = 221.9 mV$_{PP}$ DC values off, gain is OK
E06-09	V_b = 2.8045 mV$_{PP}$ V_c = 2.7548 mV$_{PP}$ DC values off, gain is OK	V_b = 2.8 mV$_{PP}$ V_c = 2.8 mV$_{PP}$ DC values off, gain is OK
E06-11	V_b = 13.8475 mV$_{PP}$ V_c = 917.7385 mV$_{PP}$	V_b = 14.0 mV$_{PP}$ V_c = 930.5 mV$_{PP}$
F06-45	V_B = 2.572 V$_{DC}$ V_b = 99.99 mV$_{AC}$ V_{OUT} = ~300 μV$_{DC}$ V_{out} = 214.5 mV$_{AC}$	V_B = 2.570 V$_{DC}$ V_b = 99 mV$_{AC}$ V_{OUT} = ~0 V$_{DC}$ V_{out} = 216 mV$_{AC}$
F06-46	V_B = 2.439 V$_{DC}$ V_b = 98.18 mV$_{AC}$ V_{OUT} = 1.239 mV$_{DC}$ V_{out} = 5.705 V$_{AC}$	Not implemented
F06-47	V_B = 1.594 V$_{DC}$ V_b = 100.0 mV$_{AC}$ V_{OUT} = ~800 μV$_{DC}$ V_{out} = 395 mV$_{AC}$	V_B = 1.593 V$_{DC}$ V_b = 101 mV$_{AC}$ V_{OUT} = ~0 mV$_{DC}$ V_{out} = 347 mV$_{AC}$
F06-48	V_B = 1.727 V$_{DC}$ V_b = 1.000 V$_{AC}$ V_{OUT} = ~80 mV$_{DC}$ V_{out} = 885.1 mV$_{AC}$	V_B = 1.741 V$_{DC}$ V_b = 1.01 V$_{AC}$ V_{OUT} = 88 mV$_{DC}$ V_{out} = 881 mV$_{AC}$

F06-51	$V_B(1) = 2.491$ V $V_C(1) = 9.527$ V $V_E(1) = 1.737$ V $V_b(1) = 50.00$ mV $V_B(2) = 670.6$ mV $V_C(2) = 7.983$ V $V_{OUT}(2) = -128.5$ mV $V_{out}(2) = 6.195$ V	Not implemented
F06-53	$V_{in} = 99.9$ mV $V_{out} = 3.13$ V	$V_{in} = 0.100$ mV $V_{out} = 3.28$ V
TSE06-01	$V_B(1) = 1.680$ V $V_C(1) = 5.768$ V $V_E(1) = 908.4$ mV $V_b(1) = 100.0$ μV $V_c(1) = 5.094$ mV $V_e(1) = 0.483$ μV $V_B(2) = 1.679$ V $V_C(2) = 5.678$ V $V_E(2) = 907.0$ mV $V_b(2) = 5.094$ mV $V_c(2) = 836.7$ mV $V_e(2) = 21.15$ μV $V_{OUT} = {\sim}85$ mV $V_{out} = 836.7$ mV	$V_B(1) = 1.680$ V $V_C(1) = 5.772$ V $V_E(1) = 908$ mV $V_b(1) = 0.101$ mV $V_c(1) = 5.131$ mV $V_e(1) = 0.474$ μV $V_B(2) = 1.680$ V $V_C(2) = 5.737$ V $V_E(2) = 0.909$ V $V_b(2) = 5.132$ mV $V_c(2) = 0.833$ mV $V_e(2) = 0.015$ mV $V_{OUT} = 0.033$ V $V_{out} = 832$ mV
TSE06-02	$V_B(1) = 1.680$ V $V_C(1) = 5.770$ V $V_E(1) = 908.4$ mV $V_b(1) = 100.0$ μV $V_c(1) = 16.35$ mV $V_e(1) = 0.420$ μV $V_B(2) = 1.680$ V $V_C(2) = 5.679$ V $V_E(2) = 908.4$ mV $V_b(2) = 0.571$ μV $V_c(2) = 32.46$ μV $V_e(2) = 0.769$ μV $V_{OUT} = {\sim}3.338$ mV $V_{out} = 32.77$ μV	$V_B(1) = 1.680$ V $V_C(1) = 5.772$ V $V_E(1) = 0.908$ mV $V_b(1) = 0.101$ mV $V_c(1) = 0.016$ V $V_e(1) = 0.470$ μV $V_B(2) = 1.680$ V $V_C(2) = 5.772$ V $V_E(2) = 0.908$ V $V_b(2) = 7.423$ fV $V_c(2) = 0.022$ pV $V_e(2) = 2.869$ fV $V_{OUT} = 1.841$ pV $V_{out} = 3.462$ pV
TSE06-03	$V_B(1) = 1.680$ V $V_C(1) = 5.770$ V $V_E(1) = 908.4$ mV $V_b(1) = 100.0$ μV $V_c(1) = 10.12$ mV $V_e(1) = 0.570$ μV $V_B(2) = 1.680$ V $V_C(2) = 5.773$ V $V_E(2) = 908.1$ mV $V_b(2) = 10.12$ mV $V_c(2) = 45.80$ mV $V_e(2) = 9.844$ mV $V_{OUT} = 1.128$ mV $V_{out} = 45.80$ mV	$V_B(1) = 1.680$ V $V_C(1) = 5.772$ V $V_E(1) = 908$ mV $V_b(1) = 0.101$ mV $V_c(1) = 0.010$ V $V_e(1) = 0.471$ μV $V_B(2) = 1.680$ V $V_C(2) = 5.772$ V $V_E(2) = 0.908$ V $V_b(2) = 0.010$ V $V_c(2) = 0.046$ mV $V_e(2) = 9.867$ mV $V_{OUT} = -0.013$ mV $V_{out} = 0.046$ V

TSE06-04	$V_B(1) = 1.680$ V $V_C(1) = 5.772$ V $V_E(1) = 908.5$ mV $V_b(1) = 100.0$ μV $V_c(1) = 10.41$ mV $V_e(1) = 0.109$ μV $V_B(2) = 1.754$ V $V_C(2) = 10.00$ V $V_E(2) = 0.002$ μV $V_b(2) = 10.41$ mV $V_c(2) = 0.000$ μV $V_e(2) = 0.000$ μV $V_{OUT} = -0.000$ μV $V_{out} = 0.000$ μV	$V_B(1) = 1.680$ V $V_C(1) = 5.772$ V $V_E(1) = 908$ mV $V_b(1) = 0.101$ mV $V_c(1) = 0.010$ V $V_e(1) = 0.467$ μV $V_B(2) = 1.754$ V $V_C(2) = 9.999$ V $V_E(2) = 0.000$ V $V_b(2) = 0.010$ V $V_c(2) = 0.047$ pV $V_e(2) = 0.000$ V $V_{OUT} = 0.012$ nV $V_{out} = 0.016$ nV
TSP06-54	$V_b = 99.90$ mV $V_c = 214.5$ mV $V_{out} = 5.361$ μV	$V_b = 0.100$ V $V_c = 0.215$ V $V_{out} = 0.000$ V
TSP06-55	$V_b = 99.02$ mV $I_E = 0.000$ μA	$V_b = 0.100$ V $I_E = 1.8$ fA
TSP06-56	$V_b = 100.0$ mV $V_{out} = 926.6$ mV	$V_b = 0.099$ V $V_{out} = 0.928$ V
TSP06-57	$V_{in} = 100.0$ mV $V_b = 0.000$ μV $V_{out} = 0.000$ μV	$V_{in} = 0.100$ V $V_b = 0.011$ pV $V_{out} = 0.010$ pV
TSP06-58	$V_b = 100.0$ mV $V_c = 119.9$ mV	$V_b = 0.100$ V $V_c = 0.114$ V
TSP06-59	$V_c(1) = 2.778$ V $V_b(2) = 0.129$ μV	$V_c(1) = 2.764$ V $V_b(2) = 0.037$ pV

Chapter 7:

Circuit	EWB	MultiSim
E07-06 Related Exercise	$I_D = 8.378$ mA $V_D = 5.053$ V $V_{GS} = -3.116$ $V_S = 3.147$ V	$I_D = 8.078$ mA $V_D = 5.053$ V $V_{GS} = -3.116$ $V_S = 3.147$ V
E07-09 Related Exercise	$I_D = 4.826$ mA $V_D = 7.762$ V $V_{GS} = -2.700$	$I_D = 4.827$ mA $V_D = 7.760$ V $V_{GS} = -2.700$
E07-12 Related Exercise	$I_D = 1.282$ mA $V_D = 7.129$ V $V_{GS} = -2.020$ V	$I_D = 1.281$ mA $V_D = 7.129$ V $V_{GS} = -2.020$ V
F07-58a	$V_{GS} = -996.7$ mV $V_{DS} = 6.262$ V $I_D = 1.007$ mA	$V_{GS} = -0.997$ V $V_{DS} = 6.262$ V $I_D = 1.007$ mA
F07-58b	$V_{GS} = -496.9$ mV $V_{DS} = 6.139$ V $I_D = 5.020$ mA	$V_{GS} = -0.497$ V $V_{DS} = 6.139$ V $I_D = 5.020$ mA
F07-58c	$V_{GS} = -1.408$ V $V_{DS} = 6.922$ V $I_D = 3.025$ mA	$V_{GS} = -1.408$ V $V_{DS} = 6.922$ V $I_D = 3.025$ mA
F07-61	$I_D = 2.854$ mA $V_{GS} = -856.0$ mV	$I_D = 2.854$ mA $V_{GS} = -0.856$ V
F07-62	$I_D = 3.356$ mA $V_{GS} = 1.190$ V	$I_D = 3.356$ mA $V_{GS} = 1.190$ V
F07-63	$I_D = 857.1$ μA $V_{GS} = -1.184$ V	$I_D = 0.857$ mA $V_{GS} = -1.186$ V

F07-64	$I_D = 1.917$ mA $V_{GS} = -1.508$ V	$I_D = 1.917$ mA $V_{GS} = -1.508$ V
F07-67a	$I_S = 8.000$ mA $V_{GS} = 4.000$ V	$I_S = 8.000$ mA $V_{GS} = 4.000$ V
F07-67b	$I_D = 8.000$ mA $V_{GS} = 5.400$ V	$I_D = 8.000$ mA $V_{GS} = 5.400$ V
F07-67c	$I_D = -8.000$ mA $V_{GS} = -4.520$ V	$I_D = -8.000$ mA $V_{GS} = -4.520$ V
F07-68	$I_D = 904.2$ µA $V_{GS} = 3.098$ V	$I_D = 0.904$ mA $V_{GS} = 3.098$ V
F07-71	$V_{DS} = 10.94$ V $V_{GS} = -380.6$ mV	$V_{DS} = 10.940$ V $V_{GS} = -0.381$ V
TSE07-01	$V_{GS} = -80.14$ mV $V_D = 14.63$ V $V_S = 81.09$ mV $I_D = 367.7$ uA	$V_{GS} = -0.080$ V $V_D = 14.631$ V $V_S = 0.081$ V $I_D = 0.368$ mA
TSE07-02	$V_{GS} = -0.001$ uV $V_D = 0.010$ uV $V_S = 0.001$ uV $I_D = 0.000$ uA	$V_{GS} = 0.000$ V $V_D = 0.000$ V $V_S = 0.000$ V $I_D = 0.000$ A
TSE07-03	$V_{GS} = -1.994$ V $V_D = 15.00$ V $V_S = 2.014$ V $I_D = 0.000$ uA	$V_{GS} = -1.994$ V $V_D = 14.999$ V $V_S = 2.014$ V $I_D = -1.776$ uA
TSP07-66	$V_D = 30.93$ mV $V_S = 0.003$ µV $V_G = 0.345$ µV	$V_D = 0.031$ V $V_S = 2.547$ pV $V_G = 0.345$ µV
TSP07-67	$V_D = 6.000$ V $V_S = 906.3$ mV $V_G = 62.97$ µV	$V_D = 6.000$ V $V_S = 0.906$ V $V_G = 0.063$ mV
TSP07-68	$V_D = -2.988$V $V_S = -1.303$ V $V_G = -0.000$ µV	$V_D = -2.988$V $V_S = -1.303$ V $V_G = -0.004$ aV
TSP07-69	$V_D = 7.166$ V $V_S = 1.287$ V $V_G = 23.08$ µV	$V_D = 7.166$ V $V_S = 1.287$ V $V_G = 0.018$ mV
TSP07-70	$V_D = 12.00$ V $V_S = 0.015$ µV $V_G = 4.737$ V	$V_D = 12.000$ V $V_S = 0.000$ V $V_G = 4.737$ V
TSP07-71	$V_D = 0.001$ µV $V_G = -0.000$ µV	$V_D = 0.000$ V $V_G = 0.000$ V
TSP07-72	$V_D = 10.00$ V $V_G = 0.000$ µV	$V_D = 10.000$ V $V_G = 1.000$ fV
TSP07-73	$V_D = 4.307$ V $V_S = 4.307$ V $V_G = 0.000$ µV	$V_D = 4.307$ V $V_S = 4.307$ V $V_G = 0.000$ V
TSP07-74	$V_D = 8.352$ V $V_S = 8.311$ V $V_G = 9.000$ V	$V_D = 8.352$ V $V_S = 8.311$ V $V_G = 9.000$ V

Chapter 8:

Circuit	EWB	MultiSim
E08-04	$V_D = 5.510$ V_{DC} $V_d = 1.066$ V_{rms}	$V_D = 5.490$ V_{DC} $V_d = 1.067$ V_{rms}
E08-07	$V_D = 8.397$ V_{DC} $V_d = 328.6$ mV_{rms} $V_g = 49.99$ mV_{rms}	$V_D = 8.397$ V_{DC} $V_d = 0.329$ V_{rms} $V_g = 0.050$ V_{rms}

E08-09	$I_S = 2.636$ mA$_{DC}$ $V_D = 6.307$ V$_{DC}$ $V_1 = 1.713$ V$_{rms}$	$I_S = 2.638$ mA$_{DC}$ $V_D = 6.305$ V$_{DC}$ $V_1 = 1.711$ V$_{rms}$
E08-10	$V_{GS} = -568.4$ mV$_{DC}$ $V_{in} = 10.00$ mV$_{rms}$ $V_{out} = 8.725$ mV$_{rms}$	$V_{GS} = -0.568$ V$_{DC}$ $V_{in} = 0.010$ V$_{rms}$ $V_{out} = 8.732$ mV$_{rms}$
E08-11	$V_{in} = 10.00$ mV$_{rms}$ $V_{out} = 101.1$ mV$_{rms}$	$V_{in} = 0.010$ V$_{rms}$ $V_{out} = 0.101$ V$_{rms}$
F08-35	$I_D = 2.833$ mA$_{DC}$ $V_{DS} = 4.916$ V$_{DC}$ $V_S = 2.833$ V$_{DC}$	$I_D = 2.834$ mA$_{DC}$ $V_{DS} = 4.914$ V$_{DC}$ $V_S = 2.834$ V$_{DC}$
F08-36a	$I_D = 1.844$ mA$_{DC}$ $V_{in} = 50.00$ mV$_{rms}$ $V_{out} = 215.4$ mV$_{rms}$	$I_D = 1.843$ mA$_{DC}$ $V_{in} = 0.050$ V$_{rms}$ $V_{out} = 0.216$ V$_{rms}$
F08-36b	$I_D = 1.016$ mA$_{DC}$ $V_{in} = 50.00$ mV$_{rms}$ $V_{out} = 496.5$ mV$_{rms}$	$I_D = 1.016$ mA$_{DC}$ $V_{in} = 0.050$ V$_{rms}$ $V_{out} = 0.497$ V$_{rms}$
F08-37	$I_D = 5.847$ mA$_{DC}$ $V_{in} = 50.00$ mV$_{rms}$ $V_{out} = 141.5$ mV$_{rms}$	$I_D = 5.847$ mA$_{DC}$ $V_{in} = 0.050$ V$_{rms}$ $V_{out} = 0.142$ V$_{rms}$
F08-38	$I_D = 4.463$ mA$_{DC}$ $V_{DS} = 3.065$V$_{DC}$ $V_G = -1.458$ V$_{DC}$	$I_D = 4.463$ mA$_{DC}$ $V_{DS} = 3.065$V$_{DC}$ $V_G = -1.458$ V$_{DC}$
F08-39	$V_D = 17.15$ V$_{DC}$ $V_G = 5.484$ V$_{DC}$ $I_S = 2.849$ mA$_{DC}$	$V_D = 17.151$ V$_{DC}$ $V_G = 5.484$ V$_{DC}$ $I_S = 2.849$ mA$_{DC}$
F08-41	$V_D = 15.00$ mA$_{DC}$ $V_D = 9.000$ V$_{DC}$ $V_d = 48.00$ mV$_{rms}$ $V_{in} = 10.00$ mV$_{rms}$	$V_D = 0.015$ A$_{DC}$ $V_D = 9.000$ V$_{DC}$ $V_d = 0.048$ V$_{rms}$ $V_{in} = 0.010$ V$_{rms}$
F08-44a	$I_D = 279.4$ μA$_{DC}$ $V_{in} = 50.00$ mV$_{rms}$ $V_{out} = 45.26$ mV$_{rms}$	$I_D = 0.280$ mA$_{DC}$ $V_{in} = 0.050$ V$_{rms}$ $V_{out} = 0.045$ V$_{rms}$
F08-44b	$I_D = 6.615$ mA$_{DC}$ $V_{in} = 50.00$ mV$_{rms}$ $V_{out} = 14.01$ mV$_{rms}$	$I_D = 6.615$ mA$_{DC}$ $V_{in} = 0.050$ V$_{rms}$ $V_{out} = 0.014$ V$_{rms}$
TSE08-01	$V_{in} = 10.00$ mV$_{rms}$ $I_D(1) = 3.126$ mA$_{DC}$ $V_D(1) = 7.313$ V$_{DC}$ $V_G(2) = -227.9$ μV$_{DC}$ $V_g(2) = 75.00$ mV$_{rms}$ $I_D(2) = 3.132$ mA$_{DC}$ $V_{out}(2) = 562.3$ mV$_{rms}$	$V_{in} = 0.010$ V$_{rms}$ $I_D(1) = 3.125$ mA$_{DC}$ $V_D(1) = 7.312$ V$_{DC}$ $V_G(2) = -0.416$ mV$_{DC}$ $V_g(2) = 0.075$ V$_{rms}$ $I_D(2) = 3.134$ mA$_{DC}$ $V_{out}(2) = 0.563$ V$_{rms}$
TSE08-02	$V_{in} = 10.00$ mV$_{rms}$ $I_D(1) = 6.092$ mA$_{DC}$ $V_D(1) = 2.863$ V$_{DC}$ $V_G(2) = 2.863$ V$_{DC}$ $V_g(2) = 433.5$ μV$_{rms}$ $I_D(2) = 6.115$ mA$_{DC}$ $V_{out}(2) = 128.6$ μV$_{rms}$	$V_{in} = 0.010$ V$_{rms}$ $I_D(1) = 6.092$ mA$_{DC}$ $V_D(1) = 2.863$ V$_{DC}$ $V_G(2) = 2.863$ V$_{DC}$ $V_g(2) = 0.434$ mV$_{rms}$ $I_D(2) = 6.115$ mA$_{DC}$ $V_{out}(2) = 0.128$ mV$_{rms}$
TSE08-03	$V_{in} = 10.00$ mV$_{rms}$ $I_D(1) = 0.000$ μA$_{DC}$ $V_D(1) = 12.00$ V$_{DC}$ $V_G(2) = 67.36$ μV$_{DC}$ $V_g(2) = 0.000$ μV$_{rms}$ $I_D(2) = 3.125$ mA$_{DC}$ $V_{out}(2) = 0.000$ μV$_{rms}$	$V_{in} = 0.010$ V$_{rms}$ $I_D(1) = 1.776$ μA$_{DC}$ $V_D(1) = 12.001$ V$_{DC}$ $V_G(2) = 0.067$ mV$_{DC}$ $V_g(2) = 0.020$ nV$_{rms}$ $I_D(2) = 3.125$ mA$_{DC}$ $V_{out}(2) = 0.441$ μV$_{rms}$

TSE08-04	$V_{in} = 10.00$ mV$_{rms}$ $I_D(1) = 3.125$ mA$_{DC}$ $V_D(1) = 7.313$ V$_{DC}$ $V_G(2) = {<}500$ μV$_{DC}$ $V_g(2) = 75.00$ mV$_{rms}$ $I_D(2) = 0.000$ μA$_{DC}$ $V_{out}(2) = 0.000$ μV$_{rms}$	$V_{in} = 0.010$ V$_{rms}$ $I_D(1) = 3.126$ mA$_{DC}$ $V_D(1) = 7.312$ V$_{DC}$ $V_G(2) = {<}500$ μV$_{DC}$ $V_g(2) = 0.075$ V$_{rms}$ $I_D(2) = -2.35$ aA$_{DC}$ $V_{out}(2) = 0.026$ nV$_{rms}$
TSP08-46	$I_D = 4.800$ mA$_{DC}$ $V_{DS} = 0.005$ μV$_{DC}$ $V_S = 4.800$ V$_{DC}$	$I_D = 4.800$ mA$_{DC}$ $V_{DS} = 4.801$ pV$_{DC}$ $V_S = 4.800$ V$_{DC}$
TSP08-47	$I_D = 1.842$ mA$_{DC}$ $V_S = 34.02$ mV$_{rms}$ $V_{in} = 50.00$ mV$_{rms}$ $V_{out} = 69.14$ mV$_{rms}$	$I_D = 1.842$ mA$_{DC}$ $V_S = 0.034$ V$_{rms}$ $V_{in} = 0.050$ V$_{rms}$ $V_{out} = 0.069$ V$_{rms}$
TSP08-48	$I_D = 1.000$ mA$_{DC}$ $V_G = 0.008$ μV$_{rms}$ $V_{in} = 50.00$ mV$_{rms}$ $V_{out} = 0.084$ μV$_{rms}$	$I_D = 1.000$ mA$_{DC}$ $V_G = 0.000$ V$_{rms}$ $V_{in} = 0.050$ V$_{rms}$ $V_{out} = 0.021$ nV$_{rms}$
TSP08-49	$I_D = 12.70$ mA$_{DC}$ $V_{GS} < 200$ μV$_{DC}$ $V_{in} = 50.00$ mV$_{rms}$ $V_{out} = 208.5$ mV$_{rms}$	$I_D = 0.013$ A$_{DC}$ $V_{GS} < 0.3$ mV$_{DC}$ $V_{in} = 0.050$ V$_{rms}$ $V_{out} = 0.209$ V$_{rms}$
TSP08-50	$I_D = 0.009$ μA$_{DC}$ $V_{DS} = 9.000$ V$_{DC}$ $V_{GS} = 26.89$ μV$_{DC}$	$I_D = 9.008$ nA$_{DC}$ $V_{DS} = 9.000$ V$_{DC}$ $V_{GS} = -2.941$ μV$_{DC}$
TSP08-51	$V_{R1} = 20.00$ V$_{DC}$ $V_G = 136.0$ μV$_{DC}$ $V_D = 20.00$ V$_{DC}$ $I_D = 0.000$ μA$_{DC}$	$V_{R1} = 20.00$ V$_{DC}$ $V_G = 0.136$ mV$_{DC}$ $V_D = 20.00$ V$_{DC}$ $I_D = 0.028$ nA$_{DC}$
TSP08-52	$V_{RD} = 24.00$ V$_{DC}$ $V_{in} = 10.00$ mV$_{rms}$ $I_D = 0.240$ μA$_{DC}$ $V_D = 50.00$ μV$_{DC}$ $V_d = 2.291$ μV$_{rms}$ $V_{out} = 2.291$ μV$_{rms}$	$V_{RD} = 24.00$ V$_{DC}$ $V_{in} = 0.010$ V$_{rms}$ $I_D = 0.240$ μA$_{DC}$ $V_D = 0.050$ mV$_{DC}$ $V_d = 0.080$ μV$_{rms}$ $V_{out} = 0.080$ μV$_{rms}$
TSP08-53	$I_D = 9.876$ mA$_{DC}$ $V_{DS} = 3.186$ V$_{DC}$ $V_{GS} = 17.99$ V$_{DC}$ $V_{out} = 23.65$ mV$_{rms}$	$I_D = 9.876$ mA$_{DC}$ $V_{DS} = 3.186$ V$_{DC}$ $V_{GS} = 17.992$ V$_{DC}$ $V_{out} = 0.024$ V$_{rms}$
TSP08-54	$I_D = 279.5$ μA$_{DC}$ $V_B = 46.67$ mV$_{rms}$ $V_{in} = 10.00$ mV$_{rms}$ $V_{out} = 0.000$ μV$_{rms}$	$I_D = 0.280$ mA$_{DC}$ $V_B = 0.047$ V$_{rms}$ $V_{in} = 0.010$ V$_{rms}$ $V_{out} = 0.000$ V$_{rms}$

Chapter 9:

Circuit	EWB	MultiSim
E09-03 Lower than 40 V$_{PP}$	$V_{out} = 35.5$ V$_{PP}$	$V_{out} = 35.5$ V$_{PP}$ (clipped)
E09-04 Lower than 20 V$_{PP}$	$V_{out} = 13.35$ V$_{PP}$	$V_{out} = 13.6$ V$_{PP}$
F09-41	$V_{CE} = 6.270$ V $I_C = 60.36$ mA	$V_{CE} = 6.263$ V $I_C = 0.060$ mA
F09-43	$V_{out} = 6.522$ V$_{PP}$ for $V_{in} = 100$ mV$_{rms}$	$V_{out} = 6.3$ V$_{PP}$ for $V_{in} = 100$ mV$_{rms}$
F09-44	$V_{out} = 13.5329$ V$_{PP}$	$V_{out} = 13.6$ V$_{PP}$
F09-45	$V_{out} = 13.6346$ V$_{PP}$	$V_{out} = 13.8$ V$_{PP}$

F09-46	$V_{out} = 21.4134\ V_{PP}$ $I_{out} = 224.4\ mArms$	$V_{out} = 21.3\ V_{PP}$ $I_{out} = 225\ mA$
TSE09-01	$V_B = 3.360\ V_{DC}$ with output clipped on bottom	$V_B = 3.360\ V_{DC}$ with output clipped on bottom
TSE09-02	$V_B = 839.2\ mV_{DC}$ $V_{out}(max) = 2.2982\ V_P$ $V_{out}(min) = -1.9019\ V_P$	$V_B = 0.839\ V_{DC}$ $V_{out}(max) = 2.2\ V_P$ $V_{out}(min) = -1.8\ V_P$
TSE09-03	$V_B = 1.8256\ V_{DC}$ with nonlinear distortion	$V_B = 1.826\ V_{DC}$ with nonlinear distortion
TSP09-35	$I_C = 60.30\ mA_{DC}$ $V_{CE} = 6.278\ V_{DC}$ $V_D = 0.061\ \mu V_{rms}$	$I_C = 0.060\ A_{DC}$ $V_{CE} = 6.278\ V_{DC}$ $V_D = 0.019\ pV_{rms}$
TSP09-36	$V_B = 4.214\ V_{DC}$ $V_{RE2} = 3.702\ V_{DC}$ V_{out} is negative pulses	$V_B = 4.208\ V_{DC}$ $V_{RE2} = 3.767\ V_{DC}$ V_{out} is negative pulses
TSP09-37	$V_{out} = -6.75\ V_P$ half-wave output	$V_{out} = -6.8\ V_P$ half-wave output
TSP09-38	$V_{D2} = 0.007\ \mu V_{DC}$ $V_{out} = 12.87\ V_{PP}$	$V_{D2} = 6.886\ pV_{DC}$ $V_{out} = 13.0\ V_{PP}$
TSP09-39	V_{out} is positive half-wave output	V_{out} is positive half-wave output

Chapter 10:

Circuit	EWB	MultiSim
E10-06 Ideal = 78.5 Hz	$f_C = 79.6\ Hz$	$f_C = 66.1\ Hz$
E10-07	$f_C = 16.2\ Hz$	$f_C = 16\ Hz$
E10-08	$f_C = 17.1\ Hz$	$f_C = 17\ Hz$
E10-10 Ideal = 1.62 MHz	$f_C = 1.77\ MHz$	$f_C = 1.8\ MHz$
F10-50	$f_C(1) = 3.1\ kHz$ $f_C(2) = 24.9\ MHz$	$f_C(1) = 3.1\ kHz$ $f_C(2) = 26\ kHz$
F10-51	$f_C = 9.23\ kHz$	$f_C = 95\ kHz$
F10-54	$f_C = 3.16\ kHz$	$f_C = 2.95\ kHz$
TSP10-45	$V_{RC} = 19.77\ V_{DC}$	$V_{RC} = 19.765\ V_{DC}$
TSP10-46	$V_d = 205\ mV_{PP}$ $V_{out} = 0\ V_{rms}$	$V_d = 204.1\ mV_{PP}$ $V_{out} = 0.0\ V_{rms}$
TSP10-47	$V_B = 2.591\ V_{DC}$	$V_B = 2.610\ V_{DC}$
TSP10-48	$V_{RD} = 10\ V_{DC}$ $I_D = 17.86\ mA$	$V_{RD} = 10.00\ V_{DC}$ $I_D = 0.018\ A$

Chapter 11:

Circuit	EWB	MultiSim
E11-02	$I = 109.1\ mA$	Not implemented
E11-03	$I_{SCR} = 23.18\ mA$ Expected SCR operation	$I_{SCR} = 0.023\ A$ Expected SCR operation
E11-04	Sine wave with missing piece from 90° to 180°	Not implemented
F11-61	$I = 0.250\ uA$	Not implemented
F11-62	Expected SCR operation	Expected SCR operation
F11-64	Expected diac operation	Not implemented
TSP11-31	Diode always on	Not implemented
TSP11-32	SCR never fires	SCR never fires
TSP11-33	$V_{R1} = 0.249\ \mu V_{rms}$ V_{out} is half-wave ouput	$VR1 = 0.100\ nV$ V_{out} is half-wave output

Chapter 12:

Circuit	EWB	MultiSim
E12-03	$V_{in} = 100.0$ mV$_{rms}$ $V_{out} = 2.228$ V$_{rms}$	$V_{in} = 0.100$ V$_{rms}$ $V_{out} = 2.228$ V$_{rms}$
E12-04	$V_{in} = 100.0$ mV$_{rms}$ $V_{out} = 10.00$ V$_{rms}$	$V_{in} = 0.100$ V$_{rms}$ $V_{out} = 10.002$ V$_{rms}$
E12-05	$V_{in} = 100.0$ mV$_{rms}$ $V_{out} = 2.300$ V$_{rms}$	$V_{in} = 0.100$ V$_{rms}$ $V_{out} = 2.302$ V$_{rms}$
E12-07	$V_{in} = 10.0$ mV$_{rms}$ $V_{out} = 10.00$ V$_{rms}$	$V_{in} = 0.010$ V$_{rms}$ $V_{out} = 10.004$ V$_{rms}$
E12-12	$BW(1) = 41.6$ kHz $BW(2) = 62.7$ kHz	Not implemented
F12-53	$V_{in} = 10.0$ mV$_{rms}$ $V_{out} = 3.741$ V$_{rms}$	$V_{in} = 0.010$ V$_{rms}$ $V_{out} = 3.741$ V$_{rms}$
F12-54a	$V_{in} = 10.0$ mV$_{rms}$ $V_{out} = 110.0$ mV$_{rms}$	$V_{in} = 0.010$ V$_{rms}$ $V_{out} = 0.110$ V$_{rms}$
F12-54b	$V_{in} = 10.0$ mV$_{rms}$ $V_{out} = 1.009$ V$_{rms}$	$V_{in} = 0.010$ V$_{rms}$ $V_{out} = 1.010$ V$_{rms}$
F12-54c	$V_{in} = 10.0$ mV$_{rms}$ $V_{out} = 478.0$ mV$_{rms}$	$V_{in} = 0.010$ V$_{rms}$ $V_{out} = 0.478$ V$_{rms}$
F12-54d	$V_{in} = 10.0$ mV$_{rms}$ $V_{out} = 230.0$ mV$_{rms}$	$V_{in} = 0.010$ V$_{rms}$ $V_{out} = 0.230$ V$_{rms}$
F12-56a	$V_{in} = 1.000$ V$_{rms}$ $V_{out} = 1.000$ V$_{rms}$	$V_{in} = 1.000$ V$_{rms}$ $V_{out} = 1.000$ V$_{rms}$
F12-56b	$V_{in} = 1.000$ V$_{rms}$ $V_{out} = 1.000$ V$_{rms}$	$V_{in} = 1.000$ V$_{rms}$ $V_{out} = 1.000$ V$_{rms}$
F12-56c	$V_{in} = 10.00$ mV$_{rms}$ $V_{out} = 222.8$ mV$_{rms}$	$V_{in} = 0.010$ V$_{rms}$ $V_{out} = 0.223$ V$_{rms}$
F12-56d	$V_{in} = 1.000$ V$_{rms}$ $V_{out} = 10.00$ V$_{rms}$	$V_{in} = 1.000$ V$_{rms}$ $V_{out} = 9.998$ V$_{rms}$
F12-57	$V_{in} = 1.000$ V$_{rms}$ $I_S = 30.31$ µA$_{rms}$ $V_{out} = 10.00$ V$_{rms}$ $I_f = 30.31$ µA$_{rms}$	$V_{in} = 1.000$ V$_{rms}$ $I_S = 0.030$ mA$_{rms}$ $V_{out} = 10.00$ V$_{rms}$ $I_f = 0.030$ mA$_{rms}$
F12-58a	$V_{in} = 10.00$ mV$_{rms}$ $I_S = 0.000$ µA$_{rms}$ $V_{out} = 2.2468$ V$_{rms}$ $I_f = 4.017$ µA$_{rms}$	$V_{in} = 0.010$ V$_{rms}$ $I_S = 0.100$ nA$_{rms}$ $V_{out} = 2.252$ V$_{rms}$ $I_f = 4.027$ µA$_{rms}$
F12-58b	$V_{in} = 10.00$ mV$_{rms}$ $I_S = 0.000$ µA$_{rms}$ $V_{out} = 323.2$ mV$_{rms}$ $I_f = 6.670$ µA$_{rms}$	$V_{in} = 0.010$ V$_{rms}$ $I_S = 0.100$ nA$_{rms}$ $V_{out} = 0.324$ mV$_{rms}$ $I_f = 6.685$ µA$_{rms}$
F12-58c	$V_{in} = 10.00$ mV$_{rms}$ $I_S = 0.000$ µA$_{rms}$ $V_{out} = 188.5$ mV$_{rms}$ $I_f = 0.180$ µA$_{rms}$	$V_{in} = 0.010$ V$_{rms}$ $I_S = 0.100$ nA$_{rms}$ $V_{out} = 0.189$ mV$_{rms}$ $I_f = 0.181$ µA$_{rms}$
F12-60a	$V_{in} = 10.00$ mV$_{rms}$ $I_S = 1.000$ µA$_{rms}$ $V_{out} = 150.0$ mV$_{rms}$ $I_f = 1.001$ µA$_{rms}$	$V_{in} = 0.010$ V$_{rms}$ $I_S = 1.004$ µA$_{rms}$ $V_{out} = 0.151$ V$_{rms}$ $I_f = 1.005$ µA$_{rms}$
F12-60b	$V_{in} = 10.00$ mV$_{rms}$ $I_S = 0.100$ µA$_{rms}$ $V_{out} = 998.7$ V$_{rms}$ $I_f = 0.110$ µA$_{rms}$	$V_{in} = 0.010$ V$_{rms}$ $I_S = 0.101$ µA$_{rms}$ $V_{out} = 1.004$ V$_{rms}$ $I_f = 0.110$ µA$_{rms}$

F12-60c	$V_{in} = 10.00$ mV$_{rms}$ $I_S = 21.27$ μA$_{rms}$ $V_{out} = 212.8$ mV$_{rms}$ $I_f = 21.27$ μA$_{rms}$	$V_{in} = 0.010$ mV$_{rms}$ $I_S = 0.021$ mA$_{rms}$ $V_{out} = 0.213$ V$_{rms}$ $I_f = 0.021$ mA$_{rms}$
TSE12-01	$V_{in} = 100.0$ mV$_{rms}$ $V_{out} = 2.228$ mV$_{rms}$	$V_{in} = 0.100$ V$_{rms}$ $V_{out} = 2.230$ V$_{rms}$
TSE12-02	$V_{in} = 0.069$ μV$_{rms}$ V_{out} is railed	$V_{in} = 0.047$ μV$_{rms}$ V_{out} is railed
TSE12-03	$V_{in} = 100.0$ mV$_{rms}$ $V_{out} = 10.00$ V$_{rms}$	$V_{in} = 0.100$ V$_{rms}$ $V_{out} = 10.004$ V$_{rms}$
TSE12-04	$V_{in} = 100.0$ mV$_{rms}$ $V_{out} = 0.006$ μV$_{rms}$	$V_{in} = 0.100$ V$_{rms}$ $V_{out} = 0.000$ V$_{rms}$
TSP12-57	$V_{in} = 10.00$ mV$_{rms}$ V_{out} is railed	$V_{in} = 0.010$ V$_{rms}$ V_{out} is railed
TSP12-58	$V_{in} = 1.0$ V$_{rms}$ $V_{out} = 1.0$ V$_{rms}$	$V_{in} = 1.0$ V$_{rms}$ $V_{out} = 1.0$ V$_{rms}$
TSP12-59	$V_{in} = 10$ mV$_{rms}$ $V_{out} = 10$ mV$_{rms}$	$V_{in} = 0.010$ V$_{rms}$ $V_{out} = 0.010$ V$_{rms}$
TSP12-60	V_{out} is railed $V_{Ri} = 0.000$ V$_{rms}$	V_{out} is railed $V_{Ri} = 64.3$ pV$_{rms}$
TSP12-61	$V_{in} = 10.00$ mV$_{rms}$ $V_{out} \approx 10.00$ mV$_{rms}$	$V_{in} = 0.010$ V$_{rms}$ $V_{out} \approx 0.010$ V$_{rms}$
TSP12-62	$V_{in} = 1.0$ V$_{rms}$ $V_{out} \approx 0.5$ V$_{rms}$	$V_{in} = 1.0$ V$_{rms}$ $V_{out} \approx 0.5$ V$_{rms}$
TSP12-63	$V_{in} = 5.0$ V$_{rms}$ $V_{out} \approx 5$ mV$_{rms}$	$V_{in} = 5.0$ V$_{rms}$ $V_{out} \approx 5.0$ mV$_{rms}$
TSP12-64	$V_{in} = 1.0$ mV$_{rms}$ $V_{out} \approx 10$ V$_{rms}$	$V_{in} = 1$ mV$_{rms}$ $V_{out} \approx 10$ V$_{rms}$
TSP12-65	$V_{in} = 1.0$ V$_{rms}$ V_{out} is railed	$V_{in} = 1$ V$_{rms}$ V_{out} is railed
TSP12-66	$V_{in} = 1.0$ V$_{rms}$ $V_{out} = 0$ V	$V_{in} = 1.0$ V$_{rms}$ $V_{out} = 0$ V
TSP12-67	$V_{in} = 1.0$ V$_{rms}$ V_{out} is railed	$V_{in} = 1.0$ V$_{rms}$ V_{out} is railed
TSP12-68	$V_{in} = 1.0$ V$_{rms}$ $V_{out} \approx 1.0$ V$_{rms}$	$V_{in} = 1.0$ V$_{rms}$ $V_{out} \approx 1.01$ V$_{rms}$
TSP12-69	$V_{in} = 10$ mV$_{rms}$ V_{out} is railed	$V_{in} = 10$ mV$_{rms}$ V_{out} is railed
TSP12-70	$V_{in} = 1.0$ V$_{rms}$ $V_{out} = 0$ V	$V_{in} = 1.0$ V$_{rms}$ $V_{out} = 1.0$ pV$_{rms}$
TSP12-71	$V_{in} = 1.0$ V$_{rms}$ $V_{out} = 0$ V	$V_{in} = 1.0$ V$_{rms}$ $V_{out} = 0$ V
TSP12-72	$V_{in} = 10$ mV$_{rms}$ $V_{out} \approx 1.2$ V$_{rms}$	$V_{in} = 10$ mV$_{rms}$ $V_{out} \approx 1.2$ V$_{rms}$

Chapter 13:

Circuit	EWB	MultiSim
E13-01 Ideal = 1.63 V	$V_{UTP} = 1.76$ V $V_{LTP} = 1.66$ V	$V_{UTP} = 1.7$ V $V_{LTP} = 1.5$ V
E13-02 Ideal = ±2.5 V	$V_{LTP} = -2.75$ V $V_{UTP} = 2.50$ V	$V_{LTP} = -2.5$ V $V_{UTP} = 2.7$ V
E13-03 Ideal = ±2.54 V	$V_{LTP} = -2.61$ V $V_{UTP} = 2.55$ V $V_{out} = \pm 8$ V$_P$	$V_{LTP} = -2.3$ V $V_{UTP} = 2.3$ V $V_{out} = \pm 7.4$ V$_P$
E13-05	$V_{OUT} = -12.00$ V	$V_{OUT} = -12.00$ V
E13-06	$V_{OUT} = -6.999$ V	$V_{OUT} = -7.000$ V

E13-07	V_{OUT} = -2.5000 V	V_{OUT} = -2.5000 V
E13-08	V1 = 3.000 V V2 = 2.000 V V3 = 8.000 V V_{OUT} = -8.838 V	V1 = 3.000 V V2 = 2.000 V V3 = 8.000 V V_{OUT} = -8.838 V
E13-10	Integrator ouput $\Delta V/\Delta t$ = -5 V/100 µs	Integrator ouput $\Delta V/\Delta t$ = -5 V/100 µs
F13-52	V_{LTP} = -2.93 V V_{UTP} = +2.90 V	V_{LTP} = -3.1 V V_{UTP} = +3.0 V
F13-54a	V_{LTP} = -4.0544 V V_{UTP} = 4.0812 V	V_{LTP} = -4.1 V V_{UTP} = 4.0 V
F13-54b	V_{LTP} = -3.212 V V_{UTP} = 3.2052 V	V_{LTP} = -3.6 V V_{UTP} = 3.7 V
F13-55	V_{LTP} = -1.05 V V_{UTP} = 1.05 V V_{out} = ±6.34 V_P	V_{LTP} = -1.2 V V_{UTP} = 1.2 V V_{out} = -4.3 V_P/+4.8 V_P
F13-56a	V_{OUT} = -2.50 V	V_{OUT} = -2.50 V
F13-56b	V_{OUT} = -3.520 V	V_{OUT} = -3.520 V
F13-57	V_{OUT} = -14.00 V	V_{OUT} = -14.00 V
F13-58	V_{OUT} = -3.572 V	V_{OUT} = -3.572 V
F13-59	Integrator output $\Delta V/\Delta t$ = -4.42 V/100 µs	Integrator output $\Delta V/\Delta t$ = -4.5 V/100 µs
F13-60	V_{out} = 200 mV_{PP} square wave	Vout = 200 mV_{PP} square wave
TSE13-01	V(-) = 2.000 V V_{OUT} is railed	V(-) = 2.000 V V_{OUT} is railed
TSE13-02	V_{IN} = 3V, 2V, 8V V(-) = 6.682 V V_{OUT} = 6.682 V	V_{IN} = 3V, 2V, 8V V(-) = 6.682 V V_{OUT} = 6.682 V
TSE13-03	V_{in} = 0V to 5V square wave V_{out} = 0 V	V_{in} = 0V to 5V square wave V_{out} = 0 V
TSE13-04	Vin = 20 V_{PP} triangle wave V(-) = 0 V	Vin = 20 V_{PP} triangle wave V(-) = 0 V
TSE13-05	V_{out}(min) = -1.07 V V_{out}(max) = +7.02 V	V_{out}(min) = -834.4 V V_{out}(max) = +6.9 V
TSE13-06	Not implemented	0V ouptut
TSE13-07	V_{LTP} = -2.61 V V_{UTP} = 2.55 V V_{out} = ±8 V_P	V_{LTP} = -2.3 V V_{UTP} = 2.5 V V_{out} = -7/7 V_P/+7.9 V_P
TSE13-08	V_{in} = 1 V, 0.5 V, 0.2V, 0.1 V V(-) = 450 mV V_{out} is railed negative	V_{in} = 1 V, 0.5 V, 0.2V, 0.1 V V(-) = 0.450 V V_{out} is railed negative
TSE13-09	V_{in} = 1 V, 0.5 V, 0.2V, 0.1 V V(-) = 500 mV V_{out} is railed negative	V_{in} = 1 V, 0.5 V, 0.2V, 0.1 V V(-) = 0.500 V V_{out} is railed negative
TSP13-30	$V_{LTP} \approx 0$ V $V_{UTP} \approx 0$ V	V_{LTP} = -121.0 mV V_{UTP} = -10.5 mV
TSP13-31	$V_{LTP} \approx 0$ V $V_{UTP} \approx 0$ V V_{out} = ±8 V_P	V_{LTP} = -30.2 mV V_{UTP} = -1.0 mV V_{out} = ±8.1 V_P
TSP13-32	V_{in} = 2.0 V_P V_{out} = 2.0 V_P	V_{in} = 2.0 V_P V_{out} = 2.0 V_P
TSP13-33	V_{out} (min) = -709 mV V_{out}(max) = +5.62 V	V_{out} (min) = -913.9 mV V_{out}(max) = +5.5 V
TSP13-34	V_{OUT} = -1.500 V	V_{OUT} = -1.500 V
TSP13-35	V(-) = 1.000 V V_{out} is railed negative	V(-) = 1.000 V V_{out} is railed negative

TSP13-36	V_{OUT} = -12.72 mV	V_{OUT} = -0.013 V
TSP13-37	V(-) = 2.433 V	V(-) = 2.432 V
	V_{out} is railed negative	V_{out} is railed negative
TSP13-38	V_{out} = 0 V	V_{out} = 2.804 V
TSP13-39	V_{out} = 0 V	V_{out} = 0.0 V

Chapter 14:

Circuit	EWB	MultiSim
E14-07	V_{OUT} = -155 mV	V_{OUT} = -160.787 mV
Ideal = 150 mV		
F14-40	V_{out} = 2.010 Vrms	V_{out} = 2.013 Vrms
F14-47	V_{OUT} = -162.4 mV	V_{OUT} = -162.385 mV
F14-49a	I_L = 4.7242 mA	I_L = 4.624 mA
F14-49b	I_L = 1.1765 mA	I_L = 1.176 mA
TSP14-34	V_{out} = 21.96 V_{rms}	V_{out} = 22.003 V_{rms}
TSP14-35	V(-) = 0.0000 μV	V(-) = -0.000 V
TSP14-36	V(-) = 201.7 mV	V(-) = 207.077 mV
TSP14-37	I_L = 6.000 mA	I_L = 6.000 mA
TSP14-38	I_L = 594.1 μA	I_L = 594.058 μA

Chapter 15:

Circuit	EWB	MultiSim
E15-03	$f_C \approx$ 7.8 kHz	$f_C \approx$ 7.7 kHz
Ideal = 7.69 kHz		
E15-06	$f_C(1) \approx$ 650 Hz	$f_C(1) \approx$ 634 Hz
	$f_C(2) \approx$ 830 Hz	$f_C(2) \approx$ 854 Hz
E15-07	$f_C(1) \approx$ 7.1 kHz	$f_C(1) \approx$ 7.1 kHz
	$f_C(2) \approx$ 7.3 kHz	$f_C(2) \approx$ 7.3 kHz
E15-08	$f_C \approx$ 60.3 Hz	$f_C \approx$ 60.1 Hz
F15-32a	$f_C \approx$ 11.2 kHz	$f_C \approx$ 11.2 kHz
F15-32b	$f_C \approx$ 162 kHz	$f_C \approx$ 162 kHz
F15-32c	$f_C \approx$ 49 kHz	$f_C \approx$ 49 kHz
F15-34	$f_C(1) \approx$ 176 Hz	$f_C(1) \approx$ 174 Hz
	$f_C(2) \approx$ 200 Hz	$f_C(2) \approx$ 200 Hz
F15-35	$f_C \approx$ 1.28 kHz	$f_C \approx$ 1.27 kHz
F15-36b	$f_C(1) \approx$ 405 Hz	$f_C(1) \approx$ 402 Hz
	$f_C(2) \approx$ 500 Hz	$f_C(2) \approx$ 500 Hz
F15-36c	$f_{PEAK} \approx$ 15.99 kHz	$f_{PEAK} \approx$ 15.8 kHz
F15-37	$f_{NOTCH} \approx$ 1.325 kHz	$f_{NOTCH} \approx$ 1.316 kHz
TSP15-23	I_{R4} = 0.000 μA$_{rms}$	I_{R4} = 0.000 μA$_{rms}$
	V_{R4} = 432.5 mV$_{rms}$	V_{R4} = 432.5 mV$_{rms}$
TSP15-24	IR3 = 0.000 μA$_{rms}$	IR3 = 0.001 aA$_{rms}$
TSP15-25	V(+)2 = 0.001 μV$_{rms}$	V(+)2 = 0.0322 pV$_{rms}$
TSP15-26	$f_C \approx$ 270 Hz	$f_C \approx$ 270 Hz
TSP15-27	$f_C \approx$ 2.48 kHz	$f_C \approx$ 2.45 kHz
TSP15-28	V(+)1 = 1.477 μV$_{rms}$	V(+)1 = 2.955 pV$_{rms}$
	I_{R2} = 1.475 mV$_{rms}$	I_{R2} = 1.479 mV$_{rms}$
TSP15-29	V_S = 100 mV$_{rms}$	V_S = 0.100 V$_{rms}$
	V on end of R1 = 0 V	V on end of R1 = 0 V
TSP15-30	V_{C2} = 100 mV$_{rms}$	V_{C2} = 0.100 V$_{rms}$
	I_{C2} = 0.000 μA$_{rms}$	I_{C2} = 0.017 μA$_{rms}$
TSP15-31	$V_{out}(2)$ = 36 mV$_{PP}$	$V_{out}(2)$ = 36.7 mV$_{PP}$
	V(-)3 = 0 V	V(-)3 = 0 V

Chapter 16:

Circuit	EWB	MultiSim
E16-01	$V_{out} \approx 2$ V_{PP} @ 1.51 kHz	$V_{out} \approx 2.2$ V_{PP} @ 1.45 kHz
E16-02	$V_{out} \approx 1.05$ V_{PP} @ 6.43 kHz	$V_{out} \approx 1.06$ V_{PP} @ 6.56 kHz
E16-04 Ideal = 8.25 kHz	$V_{out} \approx 12.5$ V_{PP} @ 7.6 kHz triangle wave	Not implemented
F16-50	$V_{out} \approx 2.16$ V_{PP} @ 11.8 kHz	$V_{out} \approx 2.2$ V_{PP} @ 9.11 kHz
F16-51	$V_{out} \approx 1.03$ V_{PP} @ 688 Hz	$V_{out} \approx 13.4$ V_{PP} @ 694 Hz
F16-52a	$V_{out} \approx 580$ mV_{PP} @ 217 kHz	$V_{out} \approx 700$ mV_{PP} @ 87.7 kHz Unstable
F16-52b	$V_{out} \approx 4.34$ V_{PP} @ 60.0 kHz	$V_{out} \approx 4.2$ V_{PP} @ 59.5 kHz
F16-54	$V_{out} \approx 12.3$ V_{PP} @ 1.64 kHz	$V_{out} \approx 12.0$ V_{PP} @ 1.53 kHz
F16-56	$t_H = 141.3$ μs $t_L = 107.6$ μs $f = 4.02$ kHz	$t_H = 141.2$ μs $t_L = 108.9$ μs $f = 4.00$ kHz
TSP16-23	$R_{DS} = 0.0000$ Ω	$R_{DS} = 0.000$ Ω
TSP16-24	V_{C3} open from oscilloscope trace	V_{C3} open from oscilloscope trace
TSP16-25	$V_{CE} = 0.000$ μV_{DC}	$V_{CE} < 1$ pV_{DC}
TSP16-26	$V_{R1} = 8.442$ V_{DC}	$V_{R1} = 8.442$ V_{DC}
TSP16-27	R2 is open	R2 = 999.999 GΩ
TSP16-28	$t_H = 112.3$ μs $t_L = 108.4$ μs	$t_H = 109.4$ μs $t_L = 111.7$ μs

Chapter 18:

Circuit	EWB	MultiSim
E18-03 Ideal = 10.2 V	$V_{OUT} = 10.32$ V	$V_{OUT} = 10.342$ V
E18-05	$V_{OUT} = 10.32$ V	$V_{OUT} = 10.340$ V
F18-45	$V_{OUT} = 10.62$ V	$V_{OUT} = 10.625$ V
F18-46	$V_{OUT} = 8.505$ V	$V_{OUT} = 8.757$ V
F18-47	$V_{R2} = 352.7$ mV $I_{R4} = 125.8$ mA $I_{Q2} = 0.207$ μA $I_L = 125.1$ mA $V_{OUT} = 9.383$ V	$V_{R2} = 0.354$ V $I_{R4} = 0.126$ A $I_{Q2} < 1$ μA $I_L = 0.126$ mA $V_{OUT} = 9.424$ V
F18-48	$I_L = 35.45$ mA	$I_L = 0.037$ mA
TSP18-31	$V_{R3} = 2.471$ V $V_{OUT} = 2.496$ V	$V_{R3} = 2.497$ V $V_{OUT} = 2.472$ V
TSP18-32	$V_Z = 11.88$ V $V_{OUT} = 12.00$ V	$V_Z = 11.881$ V $V_{OUT} = 11.992$ V
TSP18-33	$V_{R2} = 352.2$ mV $I_{R4} = 125.8$ mA $I_{Q2} = 0.0000$ μA $I_L = 125.1$ mA $V_{OUT} = 9.383$ V	$V_{R2} = 0.353$ V $I_{R4} = 0.126$ A $I_{Q2} < 2$ μA $I_L = 0.126$ A $V_{OUT} = 9.419$ V
TSP18-34	$V_{R1} = 24.99$ V $I_L = 24.12$ μA	$V_{R1} = 24.99$ V $I_L = 0.019$ mA

Test Item File

Prepared by Kenneth Lawell

Chapter 1:   Introduction to Semiconductors

MULTIPLE CHOICE

1. A molecule is the smallest particle of an element that retains the characteristics of that element.
   a) true
   b) false

2. A forward-biased diode of a conducting germanium diode has a potential of about 0.7 V across it.
   a) true
   b) false

3. Silicon doped with impurities is used in the manufacture of semiconductor devices.
   a) true
   b) false

4. Reverse bias permits full current through a PN junction.
   a) true
   b) false

5. Semiconductor material of the P-type has few free electrons.
   a) true
   b) false

6. The dc voltages for a device to operate properly is called:
   a) rectification
   b) amplification
   c) bias
   d) a PN junction

7. The majority carriers are the holes in a(n):
   a) N-type semiconductor
   b) P-type semiconductor
   c) PN junction semiconductor
   d) none of the above

8. Semiconductor materials are those with:
   a) conductive properties that are in between those of a conductor or an insulator
   b) conductive properties that are very good
   c) no conductive properties
   d) a or b

9. A current flows across the junction of a forward-biased diode. This current is called:
   a) forward-bias current
   b) reverse breakdown current
   c) conventional current
   d) reverse leakage current

10. A large current that flows in the opposite direction across a PN junction is called:
    a) forward-bias current
    b) reverse breakdown current
    c) conventional current
    d) reverse leakage current

11. A small current that flows when a diode is reverse biased is called:
    a) forward-bias current
    b) reverse breakdown current
    c) conventional current
    d) reverse-leakage current

12. As the forward current through a forward-biased diode decreases, the voltage across the diode:
    a) increases
    b) decreases
    c) is relatively constant
    d) increases and then decreases

13. Which statement best describes a semiconductor?
    a) A material with many free electrons.
    b) A material doped to have some free electrons.
    c) A material with few free electrons.
    d) None of these.

14. As the forward current through a silicon diode decreases, the internal resistance of the diode will:
    a) increase
    b) decrease
    c) remain the same
    d) either b or c

15. A silicon diode measures a high value of resistance with the meter leads in both positions. The trouble, if any, is:
    a) the diode is open
    b) the diode is shorted to ground
    c) the diode is internally shorted
    d) the diode is ok

16. A silicon diode is reverse biased. The voltage measured to ground from the anode is _____, and the voltage to ground from the anode is _____.
    a) 16 V, 15.3 V
    b) -16 V, -16.7 V
    c) 0.2 V, -0.5 V
    d) 15.3 V, 16 V

17. The forward voltage across a conducting silicon diode is about:
    a) 1.3 V
    b) 0.3 V
    c) 0.7 V
    d) -0.3 V

18. To change ac to pulsating dc, the best type of diode to use might be:
    a) a Shockley diode
    b) a Zener diode
    c) a rectifier diode
    d) a photodiode

19. An unknown type diode is in a circuit. The voltage measured across it was found to be 0.3 V. The diode is:
    a) a silicon diode
    b) a germanium diode
    c) a transistor
    d) none of the above

20. A reverse-biased diode has the _____ connected to the positive side of the source, and the _____ connected towards the negative side of the source.
    a) cathode, anode
    b) cathode, base
    c) base, anode
    d) anode, cathode

21. A silicon diode is forward biased. You measure the voltage to ground from the anode at _____ V, and the voltage from the cathode to ground at _____ V.
    a) 16, 32
    b) 2.3, 1.6
    c) 1.6, 2.3
    d) 0.3, 0

22. The boundary between p-type material and n-type material is called:
    a) a diode
    b) a reverse-biased diode
    c) a PN junction
    d) a forward-biased diode

23. The Atomic number of an atom refers to the:
    a) number of protons in the nucleus
    b) number of electrons in a charged atom
    c) net electrical charge of the atom
    d) number of neutrons in the nucleus

24. Electrons orbiting the nucleus of an atom are grouped into energy bands known as:
    a) orbits
    b) tracks
    c) shells
    d) tunnels

25. Valence electrons have the _____ energy level of all the electrons in orbit around the nucleus of a given atom.
    a) lowest
    b) highest
    c) same
    d) none of the above

26. The difference in energy levels that exists between the valence band and the conduction band is called:
    a) co-valent gap
    b) semi-conductor region
    c) Then-nal energy gap
    d) energy gap

27. The valence electron of a copper atom experiences what kind of attraction toward the nucleus?
    a) None
    b) Weak
    c) Strong
    d) Impossible to say

28. Which of the following cannot actually move?
    a) Holes
    b) Free electrons
    c) Ions
    d) Majority carriers

29. Reverse bias is a condition that essentially _____ current through the diode.
    a) prevents
    b) allows
    c) increases
    d) blocks

30. The knee voltage of a diode is approximately equal to the:
    a) applied voltage
    b) barrier potential
    c) breakdown voltage
    d) forward voltage

31. How is a non-conducting diode biased?
    a) Forward
    b) Inverse
    c) Poorly
    d) Reverse

32. What kind of a device is a diode?
    a) Bilateral
    b) Linear
    c) Nonlinear
    d) Unipolar

33. How much forward diode voltage is there with the ideal-diode approximation?
    a) 0 V
    b) 0.7 V
    c) More than 0.7 V
    d) 1 V

34. The dynamic resistance r'_d of a forward biased PN junction diode is smallest:
    a) below the knee
    b) above the knee
    c) in the breakdown region
    d) in cutoff

35. If the positive lead of an ohmmeter is placed on the cathode and the negative lead is placed on the anode, which of the following readings would indicate a defective diode?
    a) 0Ω
    b) $\infty\Omega$
    c) 50Ω
    d) $1 K\Omega$

Chapter 1: Introduction to Semiconductors

1. Answer: b Difficulty: 2

2. Answer: b Difficulty: 2

3. Answer: a Difficulty: 2

4. Answer: b Difficulty: 2

5. Answer: a Difficulty: 2

6. Answer: c Difficulty: 2

7. Answer: a Difficulty: 2

8. Answer: a Difficulty: 2

9. Answer: a Difficulty: 2

10. Answer: b Difficulty: 2

11. Answer: d Difficulty: 2

12. Answer: c Difficulty: 2

13. Answer: b Difficulty: 2

14. Answer: a Difficulty: 2

15. Answer: a Difficulty: 2

16. Answer: d Difficulty: 3

17. Answer: c Difficulty: 2

18. Answer: c Difficulty: 2

19. Answer: b Difficulty: 2

20. Answer: a Difficulty: 3

21. Answer: b Difficulty: 3

22. Answer: c Difficulty: 2

23. Answer: a Difficulty: 1 Section: 1

24. Answer: c Difficulty: 2 Section: 1

25. Answer: b Difficulty: 2 Section: 1

26. Answer: d Difficulty: 3 Section: 2

27. Answer: b Difficulty: 2 Section: 1

28. Answer: a Difficulty: 2 Section: 7

29. Answer: a Difficulty: 2 Section: 7

30. Answer: b Difficulty: 2 Section: 8

31. Answer: d Difficulty: 2 Section: 7

32. Answer: c Difficulty: 1 Section: 8

33. Answer: a Difficulty: 1 Section: 9

34. Answer: a Difficulty: 3 Section: 8

35. Answer: a Difficulty: 3 Section: 10

Chapter 2:   Diode Applications

MULTIPLE CHOICE

1. A diode conducts currents when forward biased and blocks current when reverse biased.
   a) true
   b) false

2. The larger the ripple voltage, the better the filter.
   a) true
   b) false

3. Clamping circuits use capacitors and diodes to add a dc level to a waveform.
   a) true
   b) false

4. The diode in a half-wave rectifier conducts for _____ of the input cycle.
   a) 0°
   b) 45°
   c) 90°
   d) 180°

5. A full-wave bridge rectifier uses _____ diode(s) in a bridge circuit.
   a) 1
   b) 2
   c) 3
   d) 4

6. A silicon diode is connected in series with 10 kΩ resistor and a 12 V battery. If the cathode of the diode is connected to the positive terminal of the battery, the voltage from the anode to the negative terminal of the battery is:
   a) 0 V
   b) 0.7 V
   c) 11.3 V
   d) 12 V

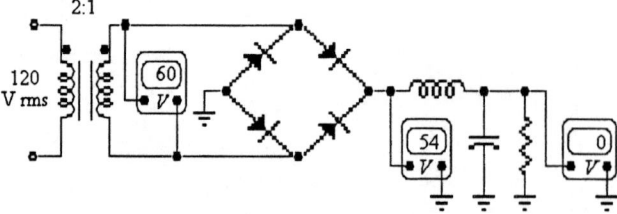

Figure 2-1

194

7. Refer to Figure 2-1. If the voltmeter across the transformer secondary reads 0 V, the probable trouble, if any, would be:
   a) one of the diodes is open
   b) the filter capacitor is shorted
   c) the transformer secondary is open
   d) the inductor is open
   e) everything is normal

8. Refer to Figure 2-1. In servicing this power supply, you notice that the ripple voltage is higher than normal and that the ripple frequency has changed to 60 Hz. The probable trouble is:
   a) the filter capacitor has opened
   b) the inductor has opened
   c) a diode has shorted
   d) a diode has opened

(a) (b) (c) (d)

Figure 2-2

9. Refer to Figure 2-2 (a). This oscilloscope trace indicates the output from:
   a) a half-wave filtered rectifier
   b) a full-wave rectifier with no filter and an open diode
   c) a full-wave filtered rectifier
   d) a full-wave filtered rectifier with an open diode

10. Refer to Figure 2-2 (b). The trace on this oscilloscope indicates the output from:
    a) a half-wave rectifier with no filter
    b) a full-wave rectifier with no filter
    c) a full-wave filtered rectifier
    d) a full-wave filtered rectifier with an open diode

11. Refer to Figure 2-2 (c). This is the output from:
    a) a half-wave rectifier with no filter
    b) a full-wave rectifier with no filter and an open diode
    c) a full-wave filtered rectifier
    d) a full-wave filtered rectifier with an open diode

12. Refer to Figure 2-2 (d). This trace shows the output from:
    a) a half-wave rectifier with no filter
    b) a full-wave rectifier with no filter and an open diode
    c) a full-wave filtered rectifier
    d) a full-wave filtered rectifier with an open diode

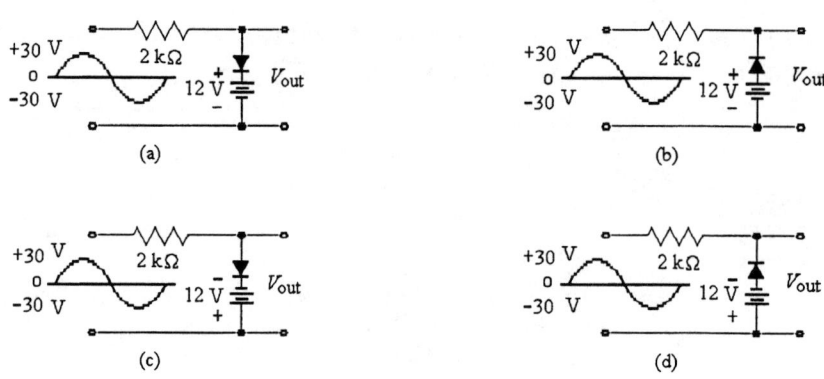

Figure 2-3

13. Refer to Figure 2-3. These circuits are known as:
a) amplifiers
b) clippers
c) clampers
d) rectifiers

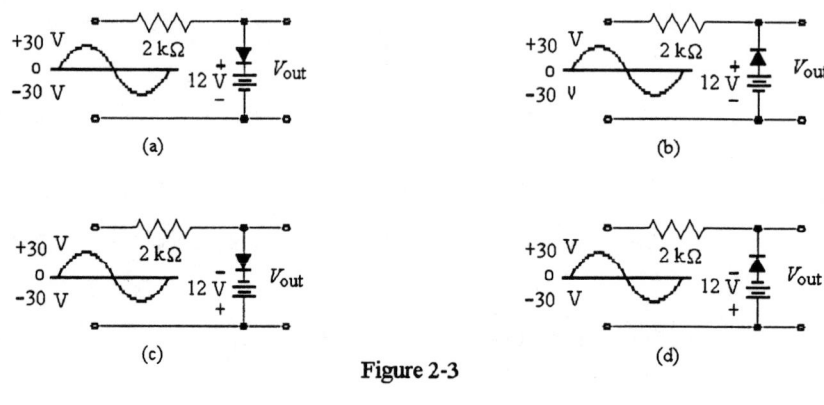

Figure 2-3

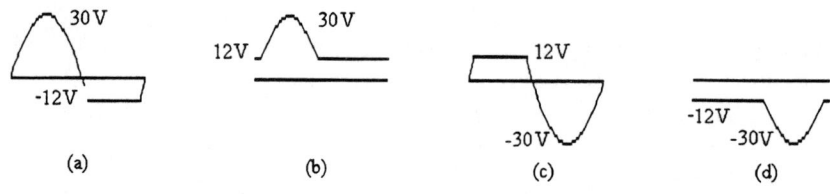

Figure 2-4

14. Which of the circuits in Figure 2-3 will produce the signal in Figure 2-4?
a) (a)
b) (b)
c) (c)
d) (d)

15. Which of the circuits in Figure 2-3 will produce the signal in Figure 2-4 (b)?
a) (a)
b) (b)
c) (c)
d) (d)

16. Which of the circuits in Figure 2-3 will produce the signal in Figure 2-4 (c)?
    a) (a)
    b) (b)
    c) (c)
    d) (d)

17. Which of the circuits in Figure 2-3 will produce the signal in Figure 2-4 (d)?
    a) (a)
    b) (b)
    c) (c)
    d) (d)

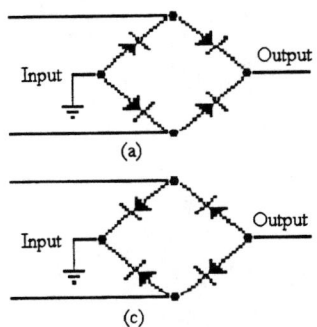
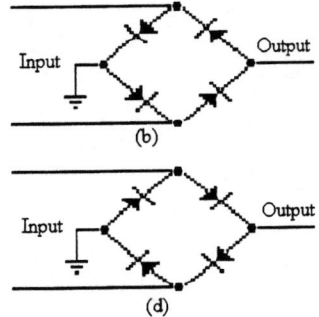

Figure 2-5

18. Refer to Figure 2-5 (c). This rectifier arrangement:
    a) will produce a positive output voltage
    b) will produce a negative output voltage
    c) is incorrectly connected
    d) a or c

19. Refer to Figure 2-5 (d). This rectifier arrangement:
    a) will produce a positive output voltage
    b) will produce a negative output voltage
    c) is incorrectly connected
    d) none of the above

20. A silicon diode has a voltage to ground of 117 V from the anode. The voltage to ground from the cathode is 117.7 V. The diode is:
    a) open
    b) shorted
    c) forward biased
    d) reverse biased

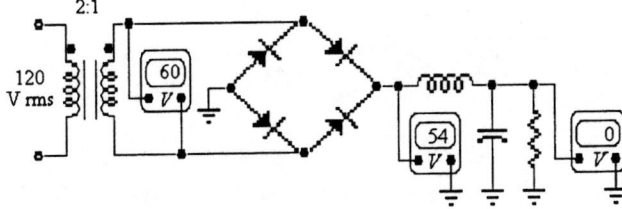

Figure 2-1

21. Refer to Figure 2-1. The probable trouble, if any, indicated by these voltages:
    a) is one of the diodes is open
    b) is a diode is shorted
    c) is an open transformer secondary
    d) is the filter capacitor is shorted
    e) is no trouble exists

22. Refer to Figure 2-1. If the voltmeter across the transformer reads 0 V, the probable trouble, if any, would be:
    a) one of the diodes is open
    b) is an open transformer secondary
    c) is the filter capacitor is shorted
    d) no trouble exists

Figure 2-2

23. Refer to Figure 2-2. Which oscilloscope trace indicates the output from a full-wave rectifier with an open diode?
    a) (a)
    b) (b)
    c) (c)
    d) (d)

24. The ripple frequency of a bridge rectifier is:
    a) the same as the input frequency
    b) double the input frequency
    c) four times the input frequency
    d) cannot be determined

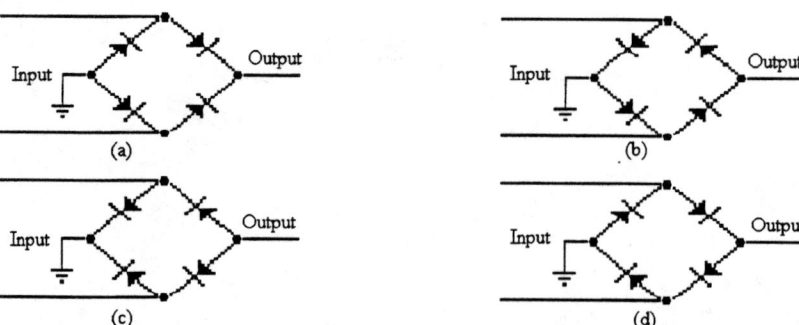

Figure 2-5

198

25. Refer to Figure 2-5. Which diode arrangement is correct to supply a positive output voltage?
    a) (a)
    b) (b)
    c) (c)
    d) (d)

26. With a half-wave rectified voltage across the load resistor, load current flows for what part of a cycle?
    a) 0 degrees
    b) 90 degrees
    c) 180 degrees
    d) 360 degrees

27. When a 60 Hz sinusoidal signal voltage is applied to the input of a half-wave rectifier, the output frequency is:
    a) 120 Hz
    b) 60 Hz
    c) 30 Hz
    d) 90 Hz

28. The average value of the half-wave rectified output voltage is approximately _____ of Vp.
    a) 31.8%
    b) 63.6%
    c) 70.7%
    d) 100%

29. Using a practical diode as a model, what would $V_{p(out)}$ equal if $V_{p(in)}$ was 10 VAC?
    a) 10 VAC
    b) 9.3 VAC
    c) 10.7 VAC
    d) 10.3 VAC

30. One of the advantages of using transformer coupling in a half-wave rectifier is that it allows the ac source to be directly connected to the load.
    a) true
    b) false

31. If input frequency is 60 Hz, the output frequency of a bridge rectifier is:
    a) 30 Hz
    b) 60 Hz
    c) 120 Hz
    d) 240 Hz

32. To obtain an output voltage with a peak equal to the input peak (minus .7V), what type of transformer and turns ratio is needed?
    a) Step-down/turns ratio = 2
    b) Step-down/turns ratio = 4
    c) Step-up/turns ratio = 2
    d) Step-up/turns ratio = 4

33. The dc current through each diode in a bridge rectifier equals:
    a) twice the dc load current
    b) half the dc load current
    c) the load current
    d) one-forth the dc load current

34. The peak inverse voltage across a nonconducting diode is a bridge rectifier that equals approximately:
    a) half the peak secondary voltage
    b) twice the peak secondary voltage
    c) the peak value of the secondary voltage
    d) four times the peak value of the secondary voltage

35. The PIV rating of a diode in a full-wave bridge rectifier is more than that required for a full-wave center-tapped configuration.
    a) true
    b) false

36. The ideal dc output voltage of a capacitor-input filter equals the:
    a) rms value of the rectified voltage
    b) peak value of the rectified voltage
    c) average value of the rectified voltage
    d) peak-to-peak value of the secondary voltage

37. A filtered full-wave rectifier voltage has a smaller ripple than does a half-wave rectifier voltage for the same load resistance and capacitor values because:
    a) shorter time between peaks
    b) longer time between peaks
    c) the larger the ripple, the better the filtering action
    d) none of the above

38. If the output of a voltage regulator varies from 20 to 19.8 V when the line voltage varies over its specified range, the source regulation is:
    a) 0%
    b) 1%
    c) 2%
    d) 5%

39. Thermal shutdown occurs in an IC regulator if:
    a) power dissipation is too high
    b) internal temperature is too high
    c) current through the device is too high
    d) all the above occur

40. The efficiency of a voltage regulator is high when:
    a) input power is low
    b) output power is high
    c) little power is wasted
    d) input power is high

41. An increase of line voltage into a power supply usually produces:
    a) a decrease in load resistance
    b) an increase in load voltage
    c) a decrease in efficiency
    d) less power dissipation in the rectifier diodes

42. A diode clamper will:
    a) clip off a portion of the input signal
    b) eliminate the positive or negative alternation of a signal
    c) add an ac voltage to a signal
    d) add a dc voltage to a signal

43. Voltage multipliers use _____ action to increase peak rectified voltages without the necessity of increasing the input transformer voltage rating.
    a) clipping
    b) clamping
    c) charging
    d) cropping

44. Which of the following diode information **is not** provided by a manufacturer's datasheet?
    a) Frequency response
    b) PIV ratings
    c) Mechanical data
    d) Temperature parameters

45. The complete trouble-shooting process contains how many steps?
    a) 4
    b) 5
    c) 6
    d) 7

1. Answer: a   Difficulty: 2

2. Answer: b   Difficulty: 2

3. Answer: a   Difficulty: 2

4. Answer: d   Difficulty: 2

5. Answer: d   Difficulty: 2

6. Answer: a   Difficulty: 3

7. Answer: c   Difficulty: 3

8. Answer: d   Difficulty: 3

9. Answer: b   Difficulty: 3

10. Answer: a   Difficulty: 3

11. Answer: c   Difficulty: 3

12. Answer: d   Difficulty: 3

13. Answer: b   Difficulty: 2

14. Answer: d   Difficulty: 2

15. Answer: b   Difficulty: 2

16. Answer: a   Difficulty: 2

17. Answer: c   Difficulty: 2

18. Answer: b   Difficulty: 2

19. Answer: c   Difficulty: 2

20. Answer: d   Difficulty: 2

21. Answer: d   Difficulty: 3

22. Answer: c   Difficulty: 3

23. Answer: d   Difficulty: 3

24. Answer: b   Difficulty: 2

25. Answer: a   Difficulty: 2

26. Answer: c Difficulty: 2 Section: 1

27. Answer: b Difficulty: 1 Section: 1

28. Answer: a Difficulty: 2 Section: 1

29. Answer: b Difficulty: 3 Section: 1

30. Answer: b Difficulty: 2 Section: 1

31. Answer: c Difficulty: 1 Section: 2

32. Answer: c Difficulty: 4 Section: 2

33. Answer: c Difficulty: 3 Section: 2

34. Answer: c Difficulty: 4 Section: 2

35. Answer: b Difficulty: 2 Section: 2

36. Answer: b Difficulty: 3 Section: 3

37. Answer: a Difficulty: 3 Section: 3

38. Answer: b Difficulty: 2 Section: 3

39. Answer: b Difficulty: 1 Section: 3

40. Answer: c Difficulty: 2 Section: 3

41. Answer: b Difficulty: 2 Section: 3

42. Answer: d Difficulty: 3 Section: 4

43. Answer: b Difficulty: 3 Section: 5

44. Answer: a Difficulty: 4 Section: 6

45. Answer: c Difficulty: 1 Section: 7

Chapter 3:   Special-Purpose Diodes

MULTIPLE CHOICE

1. The regulating ability of a Zener diode depends upon its ability to operate in a breakdown condition.
   a) true
   b) false

2. Dark Current is the amount of thermally generated forward current in a photodiode in the absence of light.
   a) true
   b) false

3. A _____ diode maintains a constant voltage across it when operating in the breakdown condition.
   a) silicon
   b) germanium
   c) Zener
   d) none of the above

4. A tunnel diode has _____ characteristic(s).
   a) an extremely narrow depletion region
   b) a negative resistance
   c) no breakdown effect
   d) all of the above

5. Typically, the maximum V_F for an LED is between:
   a) 0 V and 1 V
   b) 1 V and 1.2 V
   c) 1.2 V and 3.2 V
   d) 3.2 V and 4 V

6. A 5.1 V Zener has a resistance of 8 Ω. The actual voltage across its terminals when the current is 20 mA is:
   a) 5.1 V
   b) 100 mV
   c) 5.26 V
   d) 4.94 V

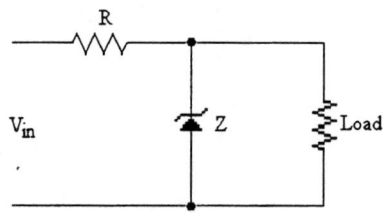

Figure 3-1

7. Refer to Figure 3-1. If V_{in} increases, V_R will:
   a) increase
   b) decrease
   c) remain the same
   d) cannot be determined

8. Refer to Figure 3-1. If V_{RL} increases, I_Z will:
   a) increase
   b) decrease
   c) remain the same
   d) cannot be determined

9. Refer to Figure 3-1. Measurements show that V_{RL} has increased. Which of the following faults, if any, could have caused this problem?
   a) R opens
   b) The Zener shorts
   c) V_{in} has decreased
   d) The Zener opens

10. Refer to Figure 3-1. If V_{RL} attempts to decrease, I_R will:
    a) increase
    b) decrease
    c) remain the same
    d) cannot be determined

11. Refer to Figure 3-1. If the load current increases, I_R will _____ and I_Z will _____.
    a) remain the same, increase
    b) decrease, remain the same
    c) increase, remain the same
    d) remain the same, decrease

12. Refer to Figure 3-1. If V_{in} decreases, I_R will:
    a) increase
    b) decrease
    c) remain the same
    d) cannot be determined

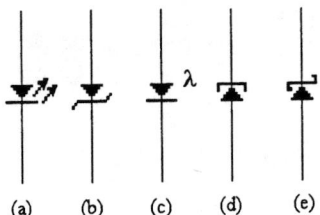

(a)   (b)   (c)   (d)   (e)

Figure 3-2

13. Refer to Figure 3-2 (a). The symbol is for:
    a) a Zener diode
    b) an LED
    c) a Schottky diode
    d) a photodiode
    e) a tunnel diode

14. Refer to Figure 3-2 (b). The symbol is for:
    a) a Zener diode
    b) an LED
    c) a Schottky diode
    d) a photodiode
    e) a tunnel diode

15. Refer to Figure 3-2 (c). The symbol is for:
    a) a zener diode
    b) an LED
    c) a Schottky diode
    d) a photodiode
    e) a tunnel diode

16. Refer to Figure 3-2 (d). The symbol is for:
    a) a Zener diode
    b) an LED
    c) a Schottky diode
    d) a photodiode
    e) a tunnel diode

17. Refer to Figure 3-2 (e). The symbol is for:
    a) a Zener diode
    b) an LED
    c) a Schottky diode
    d) a photodiode
    e) a tunnel diode

18. A varactor is a diode that:
    a) varies its resistance with temperature
    b) changes its capacitance with voltage
    c) emits light when forward biased
    d) switches very fast
    e) exhibits an increase in reverse current with light intensity

19. A Schottky diode is a diode that:
    a) varies its resistance with temperature
    b) changes its capacitance with voltage
    c) emits light when forward biased
    d) switches very fast
    e) exhibits an increase in reverse current with light intensity

20. A photodiode is a diode that:
    a) varies its resistance with temperature
    b) changes its capacitance with voltage
    c) emits light when forward biased
    d) switches very fast
    e) exhibits an increase in reverse current with light intensity

21. An LED is being tested by placing it in a forward bias position across a 5 V dc supply. The correct conclusion would be:
    a) nothing is wrong with the LED, go ahead and use it
    b) your test was correct, but the LED was bad
    c) your test was incorrect, and the LED is now bad
    d) there is no way to test the LED. Put in a new one

22. A diode with a negative-resistance characteristic is needed. A correct selection might be:
    a) a tunnel diode
    b) a Gunn diode
    c) a varactor diode
    d) a Schottky diode

23. A 6.2 V Zener is rated at 1 watt. The maximum safe current the Zener can carry is:
    a) 1.61 A
    b) 161 mA
    c) 16.1 mA
    d) 1.61 mA

24. An LED is forward biased. The diode should be on, but no light is showing. A possible problem might be:
    a) the diode is open
    b) the series resistor is too small
    c) none, the diode should be off if forward biased
    d) the power supply voltage is too high

25. The best type of diodes to use in a turning circuit is:
    a) an LED
    b) a Schottky diode
    c) a Gunn diode
    d) a varactor

26. What is true about the breakdown voltage in a Zener diode?
    a) It decreases when current increases
    b) It destroys the diode
    c) It equals the current times the resistance
    d) It is approximately constant

27. Two types of reverse breakdown in a Zener diode are:
    a) avalanche and Zener
    b) avalanche and reverse
    c) avalanche and forward
    d) charge and discharge

28. If the load current increases in a Zener regulator:
    a) the series current increases
    b) the series current remains the same
    c) the Zener current increases
    d) both b and c above

29. For Zener diodes, the temperature coefficient is:
    a) always positive
    b) always negative
    c) negative for breakdown voltages less than 5 V and positive for breakdown voltages greater than 6 V
    d) always zero

30. Data sheets for Zener diodes usually specify the Zener voltage at a particular test current designated:
    a) I_S
    b) I_{ZK}
    c) I_{ZM}
    d) I_{ZT}

31. When the source voltage increases in a Zener regulator, which of these currents remains approximately constant?
    a) Series current
    b) Zener current
    c) Load current
    d) Total current

32. If the load resistance decreases in a Zener regulator, the Zener current:
    a) decreases
    b) stays the same
    c) increases
    d) equals the source voltage divided by the series resistance

33. If the load resistance decreases in a Zener regulator, the series current:
    a) decreases
    b) stays the same
    c) Increases
    d) equals the source voltage divided by the series resistance

34. The varactor is usually:
    a) forward biased
    b) reverse biased
    c) unbiased
    d) operated in the breakdown region

35. The capacitance of a varactor diode:
    a) remains constant as the bias voltage varies
    b) decreases as the reverse bias voltage increases
    c) increases as the reverse bias voltage increases
    d) is usually 1000 µF or more

36. A photodiode is normally:
    a) reverse biased
    b) forward biased
    c) not biased
    d) used to regulate voltage

37. When the light increases, the reverse minority carrier current in a photodiode:
    a) decreases
    b) increases
    c) is unaffected
    d) reverses direction

38. A blown-fuse indicator uses a:
    a) Zener diode
    b) constant-current diode
    c) light-emitting diode
    d) back diode

39. To display the digit 8 in a seven-segment indicator:
    a) C must be lighted
    b) G must be off
    c) F must be on
    d) all segments must be on

40. Typically the forward voltage on an LED is between:
    a) 1.2 to 3.2 V
    b) 0.7 to 1.1 V
    c) 1.5V to 3.7 V
    d) 1 to 6 V

41. A Schottky diode:
    a) has a forward voltage drop of about 2 V
    b) has no limit on maximum current
    c) has no charge storage
    d) cannot operate properly at high frequencies

42. The PIN diode, when reverse biased acts like a nearly constant
    _____.
    a) resistance
    b) capacitance
    c) voltage source
    d) current source

43. Which of the following has a negative-resistance region?
    a) Tunnel diode
    b) Step-recovery diode
    c) Schottky diode
    d) Optocoupler

44. When Laser diodes are operating above their threshold level of current, they produce:
    a) incoherent light
    b) coherent light
    c) high frequency
    d) none of the above

45. When the reverse voltage increases, the capacitance:
    a) decreases
    b) stays the same
    c) increases
    d) has more bandwidth

1. Answer: a Difficulty: 2

2. Answer: b Difficulty: 2

3. Answer: c Difficulty: 2

4. Answer: b Difficulty: 2

5. Answer: c Difficulty: 2

6. Answer: a Difficulty: 2

7. Answer: a Difficulty: 3

8. Answer: a Difficulty: 3

9. Answer: d Difficulty: 3

10. Answer: c Difficulty: 2

11. Answer: b Difficulty: 3

12. Answer: b Difficulty: 2

13. Answer: b Difficulty: 2

14. Answer: a Difficulty: 2

15. Answer: d Difficulty: 2

16. Answer: e Difficulty: 2

17. Answer: c Difficulty: 2

18. Answer: b Difficulty: 2

19. Answer: d Difficulty: 2

20. Answer: e Difficulty: 2

21. Answer: c Difficulty: 3

22. Answer: a Difficulty: 2

23. Answer: b Difficulty: 2

24. Answer: a Difficulty: 3

25. Answer: d Difficulty: 2

26. Answer: d Difficulty: 2 Section: 1

27. Answer: a Difficulty: 2 Section: 1

28. Answer: b Difficulty: 3 Section: 1

29. Answer: c Difficulty: 2 Section: 1

30. Answer: d Difficulty: 1 Section: 1

31. Answer: c Difficulty: 3 Section: 2

32. Answer: a Difficulty: 2 Section: 2

33. Answer: b Difficulty: 2 Section: 2

34. Answer: b Difficulty: 2 Section: 3

35. Answer: b Difficulty: 3 Section: 3

36. Answer: c Difficulty: 2 Section: 4

37. Answer: b Difficulty: 1 Section: 4

38. Answer: d Difficulty: 1 Section: 4

39. Answer: d Difficulty: 2 Section: 4

40. Answer: a Difficulty: 2 Section: 4

41. Answer: c Difficulty: 3 Section: 5

42. Answer: b Difficulty: 3 Section: 5

43. Answer: a Difficulty: 2 Section: 5

44. Answer: a Difficulty: 3 Section: 5

45. Answer: a Difficulty: 3 Section: 3

Chapter 4:   Bipolar Junction Transistors (BJTs)

MULTIPLE CHOICE

1. BJT transistors have two PN junctions.
   a) true
   b) false

2. A BJT transistor has the base-emitter junction reverse biased for proper operation.
   a) true
   b) false

3. The ratio I_E/I_C is β_{dc}.
   a) true
   b) false

4. Proper operation of a BJT requires that the base-collector junction should be reverse biased.
   a) true
   b) false

5. The formula for I_C is, $I_C = I_E - I_B$.
   a) true
   b) false

6. A BJT has an I_B of 75 μA and a β_{dc} of 100.   The value of I_C is:
   a) 175 μA
   b) 75 mA
   c) 10 mA
   d) 7.5 mA

7. A certain transistor has an $I_C = 12$ mA and an $I_B = 125$ μA. β_{dc} is:
   a) 150
   b) 15
   c) 96
   d) 12

8. Normal operation of an NPN BJT requires the base to be _____ with respect to the emitter, and _____ with respect to the collector.
   a) positive, negative
   b) positive, positive
   c) negative, positive
   d) negative, negative

9. A transistor amplifier has an input voltage of 67 mV and an output voltage of 2.48 V.   The voltage gain is:
   a) 67
   b) 37
   c) 27
   d) 17

10. A 22 mV signal is applied to the base of a properly biased transistor that has an $r_e = 7\ \Omega$ and an $R_C = 12\ k\Omega$. The output voltage at the collector is:
    a) 22 mV
    b) 17.1 V
    c) 7 V
    d) 3.77 V

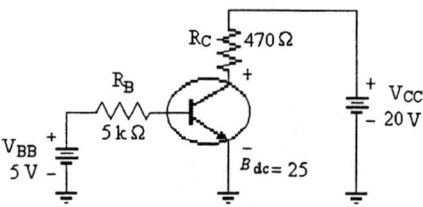

Figure 4-1

11. Refer to Figure 4-1. This circuit is operating:
    a) in cutoff
    b) in saturation
    c) normally
    d) incorrectly because the bias voltages are wrong

12. Refer to Figure 4-1. The value of I_B is:
    a) 8.6 mA
    b) 860 μA
    c) 1 mA
    d) 0.7 μA

13. Refer to Figure 4-1. If the value of V_{BB} were increased to 10 V, the transistor would be:
    a) cut off
    b) saturated
    c) operating ok
    d) cannot be determined

14. Refer to Figure 4-1. If this transistor is operating in saturation, minimum value of $I_{C(sat)}$ flowing is:
    a) 9.4 mA
    b) 4.26 mA
    c) 28.6 mA
    d) 42.6 mA

15. Refer to Figure 4-1. Assume that this circuit is operating in cutoff. The measurement, if any, that would confirm this assumption is:
    a) $V_{BE} = 0.7$ V
    b) $V_{CE} = 8$ V
    c) $V_{CE} = 20$ V
    d) $V_{CC} = 20$ V
    e) none of these

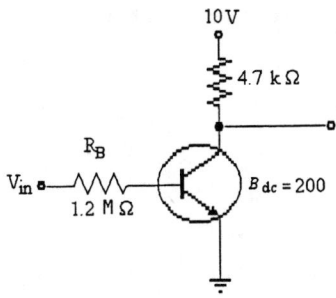

Figure 4-2

16. Refer to Figure 4-2. The value of I_C at cutoff is:
   a) 0 mA
   b) 2.13 mA
   c) 10.65 μA
   d) 10 mA

17. Refer to Figure 4-2. If the value of the collector resistor is increased to 6.8 kΩ, the new value of $I_{C(sat)}$ is:
   a) 2.13 mA
   b) .68 mA
   c) 1.47 mA
   d) 0 mA

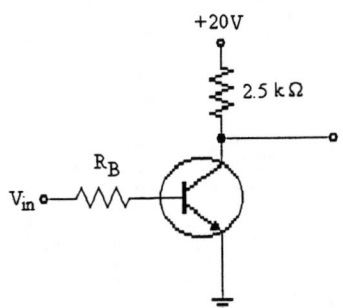

Figure 4-3

18. Refer to Figure 4-3. If the collector resistor value is changed to 4.7 kΩ and $\beta_{dc} = 200$, $I_C(sat)$ would be:
   a) 4.26 mA
   b) 8 mA
   c) 4.26 μA
   d) 8.426 mA

19. Refer to Figure 4-3. If the measure voltage from the collector to ground was 0 V, the transistor is operating in:
   a) saturation
   b) cutoff
   c) normal
   d) not enough data

20. Refer to Figure 4-3. This circuit is saturated. To get the circuit to operate close to its linear range:
    a) R_B should be decreased
    b) R_C should be decreased
    c) V_{in} should be increased
    d) R_B should be increased

21. A 35 mV signal is applied to the base of a properly biased transistor with an $r_e = 8\ \Omega$ and $R_C = 1\ k\Omega$. The output signal voltage at the collector is:
    a) 3.5 V
    b) 28.57 V
    c) 4.375 V
    d) 4.375 mV

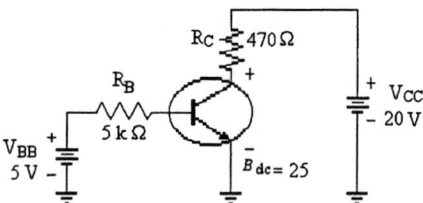

Figure 4-1

22. Refer to Figure 4-1. The value of V_{CE} is:
    a) 9.9 V
    b) 9.2 V
    c) 0.7 V
    d) 19.3 V

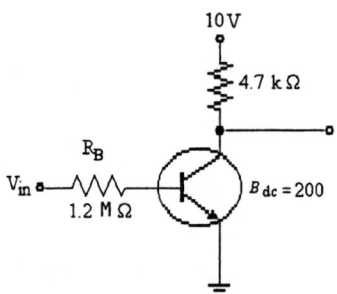

Figure 4-2

23. Refer to Figure 4-2. The minimum value of I_B that will produce saturation is:
    a) 0.25 mA
    b) 5.325 µA
    c) 1.065 µA
    d) 10.65 µA

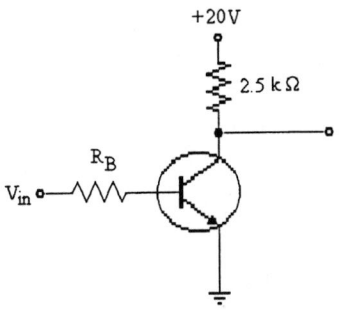

Figure 4-3

24. Refer to Figure 4-3. The voltage V_{CE} was measured and found to be 20 V. The transistor is operating in:
    a) saturation
    b) cutoff
    c) normal
    d) not enough data

25. Refer to Figure 4-3. If V_{CE} is measured and is equal to nearly zero, the transistor is operating in:
    a) cutoff
    b) normally
    c) saturation
    d) cannot be determined

26. In an NPN transistor, the majority carriers in the base are:
    a) free electrons
    b) holes
    c) neither
    d) both

27. The base of an NPN transistor is thin and:
    a) heavily doped
    b) lightly doped
    c) metallic
    d) doped by a pentavalent material

28. In a transistor, the relation of the three transistor currents is:
    a) $I_C = I_E + E_C$
    b) $I_C = I_B - 2I_E$
    c) $I_E = I_C + I_B$
    d) $I_C = I_E + I_B$

29. A transistor has a β DC of 250 and a base current, I_B, of 20 μA. The collector current, I_C, equals:
    a) 500 μA
    b) 5 mA
    c) 50 mA
    d) 5 A

30. In a transistor, collector current is controlled by:
    a) collector voltage
    b) base current
    c) collector resistance
    d) all of the above

31. Most of the electrons in the base of an NPN transistor flow:
    a) out of the base lead
    b) into the collector
    c) into the emitter
    d) into the base supply

32. When a transistor is operated in the active region, changes in the collector voltage V_{CC}:
    a) produce changes in collector current
    b) produce changes in base voltage
    c) have little or no effect on collector current
    d) produce changes in emitter voltage

33. A bipolar junction transistor has ____ regions of operation.
    a) 1
    b) 2
    c) 3
    d) 4

34. Which region in a transistor has to dissipate the most heat?
    a) Emitter
    b) Base
    c) Collector
    d) Anode

35. The symbol h_{FE} is the same as:
    a) βDC
    b) αDC
    c) hj-fj
    d) βac

36. V_{CE} approximately equals _____ when a transistor switch is in saturation.
    a) V_C
    b) V_B
    c) 0.2 V
    d) 0.7 V

37. When a transistor switch is on, the collector current is limited by
    _____.
    a) the base current
    b) the load resistance
    c) the base voltage
    d) the base resistance

38. The signal output voltage (V_{out}) is a function of the _____.
   a) current flowing base to collector
   b) voltage drop emitter to base
   c) power being dissipated in the collector
   d) changing collector current (I_C) flowing through the collector resistor R_C

39. The signal voltage gain of an amplifier, A_V, is defined as:
   a) $A_V = \dfrac{V_{in}}{V_{out}}$
   b) $A_V = I_c \times R_c$
   c) $A_V = \dfrac{R_c}{r'_e}$
   d) $A_V = \dfrac{R_c}{R_L}$

40. When transistors are used in digital circuits they usually operate in the:
   a) active region
   b) breakdown region
   c) saturation and cutoff regions
   d) linear region

41. When trouble-shooting a Bipolar Junction Transistor using an ohmmeter, and one of the junctions reads low in both directions, the junction is shorted and the transistor is bad. If one of the junctions reads high in both directions, the junction is shorted and the transistor is good?
   a) true
   b) false

42. The transistor provides the control function of opening or closing a _____.
   a) voltage path
   b) current path
   c) power path
   d) ground path

43. When a transistor switch is on, the collector current is limited by _____.
   a) the base current
   b) the load resistance
   c) the base voltage
   d) the base resistance

44. A transistor output characteristic curve is a graph showing:
   a) emitter current (I_E) versus collector/emitter voltage (V_{CE}) with (I_B) base current held constant.
   b) collector current (I_C) versus collector/emitter voltage (V_{CE}) with (I_B) base current held constant.
   c) collector current (I_C) versus collector/emitter voltage (V_C) with (I_B) base current held constant.
   d) collector current (I_C) versus collector/emitter voltage (V_{CC}) with (I_B) base current held constant.

1. Answer: a Difficulty: 2

2. Answer: b Difficulty: 2

3. Answer: b Difficulty: 2

4. Answer: a Difficulty: 2

5. Answer: a Difficulty: 2

6. Answer: d Difficulty: 2

7. Answer: c Difficulty: 2

8. Answer: a Difficulty: 2

9. Answer: b Difficulty: 2

10. Answer: d Difficulty: 2

11. Answer: c Difficulty: 3

12. Answer: b Difficulty: 2

13. Answer: b Difficulty: 3

14. Answer: d Difficulty: 3

15. Answer: c Difficulty: 3

16. Answer: a Difficulty: 2

17. Answer: c Difficulty: 2

18. Answer: a Difficulty: 2

19. Answer: a Difficulty: 2

20. Answer: d Difficulty: 3

21. Answer: c Difficulty: 2

22. Answer: a Difficulty: 2

23. Answer: d Difficulty: 2

24. Answer: b Difficulty: 2

25. Answer: c Difficulty: 3

26. Answer: b Difficulty: 1 Section: 1

27. Answer: b Difficulty: 2 Section: 2

28. Answer: c Difficulty: 2 Section: 2

29. Answer: b Difficulty: 2 Section: 3

30. Answer: b Difficulty: 2 Section: 3

31. Answer: b Difficulty: 2 Section: 3

32. Answer: c Difficulty: 3 Section: 3

33. Answer: b Difficulty: 2 Section: 3

34. Answer: c Difficulty: 2 Section: 3

35. Answer: a Difficulty: 2 Section: 3

36. Answer: c Difficulty: 2 Section: 3

37. Answer: b Difficulty: 2 Section: 3

38. Answer: d Difficulty: 3 Section: 4

39. Answer: c Difficulty: 2 Section: 4

40. Answer: c Difficulty: 1 Section: 5

41. Answer: b Difficulty: 3 Section: 7

42. Answer: b Difficulty: 2 Section: 3

43. Answer: b Difficulty: 2 Section: 5

44. Answer: b Difficulty: 3 Section: 3

Chapter 5: Transistor Bias Circuits

MULTIPLE CHOICE

1. Biasing a BJT amplifier means setting the dc voltages with the correct bias for proper operation.
   a) true
   b) false

2. A transistor operating in saturation has very little current flowing.
   a) true
   b) false

3. The base of fixed-bias circuit arrangement provides good stability because the Q-point does not vary with temperature.
   a) true
   b) false

4. Negative feedback in the collector-feedback circuit provides a more stable operation.
   a) true
   b) false

5. The correct formula for finding the dc current gain is $\beta_{dc} = I_C/I_B$.
   a) true
   b) false

6. A certain transistor in a fixed-bias circuit has these values, $I_B = 50\ \mu A$, $\beta_{dc} = 125$, $V_{CC} = 18\ V$, and $R_C = 1.2\ k\Omega$. V_C is:
   a) 0 V
   b) 7.5 V
   c) 10.5 V
   d) 18 V

7. An indication of cutoff is that:
   a) $I_C = I_{C(sat)}$
   b) $V_{CE} = 0\ V$
   c) $V_{BE} = 0.7\ V$
   d) $V_{CE} = V_{CC}$

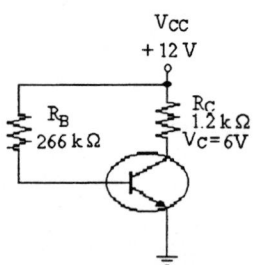

Figure 5-1

8. Refer to Figure 5-1. This transistor is biased for _____ operation.
   a) saturation
   b) linear
   c) cutoff
   d) a or c

9. Refer to Figure 5-1. The voltage on the base of this silicon transistor is:
   a) 0.3 V
   b) 0 V
   c) 12 V
   d) 11.3 V
   e) 0.7 V

10. Refer to Figure 5-1. If β_{dc} = 100, the minimum value of I_B that would cause this transistor to saturate is:
    a) 100 μA
    b) 50 μA
    c) 1 mA
    d) 0.1 mA

11. Refer to Figure 5-1. If V_C is increased to 9 V, the change that is correct to do is to:
    a) increase the value of R_B
    b) replace the transistor with one with a higher β_{dc}
    c) decrease the value of R_B
    d) increase the value of R_C

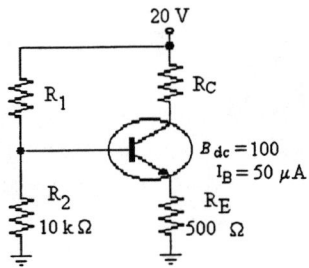

Figure 5-2

12. Refer to Figure 5-2. The value of R_C that will produce a value of V_C = 10 V is:
    a) 2.2 kΩ
    b) 2 kΩ
    c) 1 kΩ
    d) 500 Ω

13. Refer to Figure 5-2. If the transistor were replaced with a transistor whose β_{dc} = 200, the change that might occur is:
    a) V_C would increase to near 20 V
    b) V_C would decrease to near 0 V
    c) I_B would increase significantly
    d) V_C would change a small amount

14. Refer to Figure 5-2. If V_C = 10 V, the minimum value of I_B that would cause saturation is:
    a) 10 mA
    b) 8 mA
    c) 80 μA
    d) 100 μA

223

15. Refer to Figure 5-2. The purpose for R_1 and R_2 is:
    a) to form an upper limit for the base voltage
    b) to stabilize the operating point with negative feedback
    c) to develop the output voltage
    d) to maintain V_{BE} at 0.7 V

16. Refer to Figure 5-2. The purpose of R_C is:
    a) to form an upper limit for the base voltage
    b) to stabilize the operating point with negative feedback
    c) to develop the output voltage
    d) to maintain V_{BE} at 0.7 V

17. Refer to Figure 5-2. The purpose of R_E is:
    a) to form an upper limit for the base voltage
    b) to stabilize the operating point with negative feedback
    c) to develop the output voltage
    d) to maintain V_{BE} at 0.7 V

18. Two important easily measured values that determine if a transistor amplifier is operating correctly are:
    a) β_{dc} and I_B
    b) I_C and V_C
    c) V_C and V_{BE}
    d) V_{BE} and I_E

19. Saturation and cutoff are operating conditions that are very useful when operating the transistor:
    a) as a linear amplifier
    b) as a switch
    c) as a current amplifier
    d) none of the above

20. For linear operation, it is usual to set the Q-point so that:
    a) $V_{CE} \partial V_{CC}$
    b) $V_{CE} \partial V_E$
    c) $V_{CE} \partial V_{CC}/4$
    d) $V_{CE} \partial V_{CC}/2$

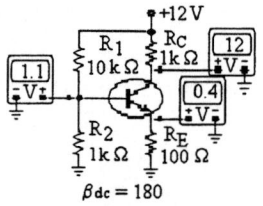

Figure 5-3 (a)

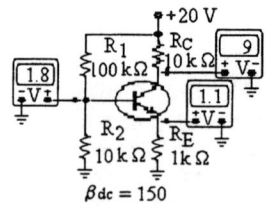

Figure 5-3 (b)

21. Refer to Figure 5-3 (a). The most probable cause of trouble, if any, from these voltage measurements would be:
    a) the base-emitter junction is open
    b) R_E is open
    c) a short from collector to emitter
    d) no problems

22. Refer to Figure 5-3 (b). The most probable cause of trouble, if any, from these voltage measurements is:
    a) the base-emitter junction is open
    b) R_E is open
    c) a short from collector to emitter
    d) no problems

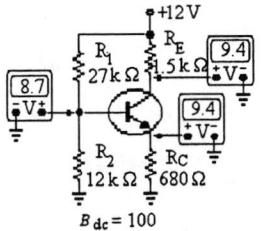 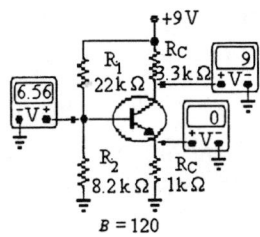

Figure 5-3 (c)   Figure 5-3 (d)

23. Refer to Figure 5-3 (c). The most probable cause of trouble, if any, from these voltage measurements is:
    a) the base-emitter junction is open
    b) R_E is open
    c) a short from collector to emitter
    d) no problems

24. Refer to Figure 5-3 (d). The most probable cause of trouble, if any, from these voltage measurements is:
    a) the base-emitter junction is open
    b) R_E is open
    c) a short from collector to emitter
    d) no problems

25. The most suitable biasing technique used is the:
    a) base-bias
    b) emitter-bias
    c) voltage-divider bias
    d) collector-bias

26. Improper biasing can cause distortion in transistor circuits:
    a) input signal
    b) output signal
    c) input/output signal
    d) frequency response

27. On a dc load line, the area between saturation and cutoff is called the:
    a) saturation zone
    b) depletion region
    c) linear region
    d) breakdown region

28. Three different Q points are shown on a dc load line. The upper Q point represents the:
    a) minimum current gain
    b) intermediate current gain
    c) maximum current gain
    d) cutoff point

29. If a transistor operates at the middle of the dc load line, a decrease in the current gain will move the Q point:
    a) off the load line
    b) nowhere
    c) up
    d) down

30. The input resistance, R_{in}, of a voltage-divider biased NPN transistor is _____ by a factor of βeta.
    a. stepped-up
    b. stepped-down
    c. not affected
    d. none of the above

31. Voltage-divider bias provides:
    a) an unstable Q point
    b) a stable Q point
    c) A Q point that easily varies with changes in the transistor's current gain
    d) both a and c above

32. For transistors using voltage-divider bias, the base current should be:
    a) much larger than the current through the voltage divider
    b) about one-half the collector current
    c) much smaller than the current through the voltage divider
    d) βeta times larger than the collector current

33. With voltage-divider bias, the base voltage is:
    a) less than the base supply voltage
    b) equal to the base supply voltage
    c) greater than the base supply voltage
    d) greater than the collector supply voltage

34. Base bias provides:
    a) a very stable Q point
    b) a very unstable Q point
    c) no current gain
    d) zero current in the base and collector circuits

35. A circuit with a fixed emitter current is called:
    a) base-bias
    b) emitter-bias
    c) transistor-bias
    d) two-supply bias

36. For emitter bias, changes in current gain:
    a) do not affect the Q point
    b) severely affect the Q point
    c) do not occur in the transistor
    d) affect the collector voltage

37. For collector feedback bias, the Q point is set near the center of the load line by making:
    a) $R_B = \beta_{DC} R_C$
    b) $R_B = 2\beta_{DC} R_C$
    c) $R_B = \dfrac{R_C}{B_{DC}}$
    d) $R_C = \beta_{DC} R_B$

38. The Q-point of a Two Supply Emitter-Bias circuit is not affected by:
    a) V_{CC}
    b) collector resistance
    c) emitter resistance
    d) current gain

39. When measuring the resistance between the collector and emitter with an ohmmeter, the reading should be:
    a) low in both directions
    b) high in both directions
    c) high in one direction and low in the other
    d) zero both ways

40. The emitter resistor in a voltage-divider bias circuit is shorted. The collector voltage will equal approximately:
    a) V_{CC}
    b) 0 V
    c) one-half V_{CC}
    d) none of the above

41. If the base-emitter junction opens in a voltage-divider bias circuit, the emitter voltage will measure:
    a) 0 V
    b) 0.7 V less than the base
    c) 0.7 V more than the base
    d) a voltage nearly equal to V_{CC}

42. If the collector resistor decreases to zero in a base-biased circuit, the load line will become:
    a) horizontal
    b) vertical
    c) useless
    d) flat

43. The first step in analyzing emitter-based circuits is to find the:
    a) base current
    b) emitter voltage
    c) emitter current
    d) collector current

44. If the current gain is unknown in an emitter-biased circuit, you cannot calculate the:
    a) emitter voltage
    b) emitter current
    c) collector current
    d) base current

45. If the emitter resistor is open, the collector voltage is:
    a) low
    b) high
    c) unchanged
    d) unknown

1. Answer: a Difficulty: 2

2. Answer: b Difficulty: 2

3. Answer: b Difficulty: 2

4. Answer: a Difficulty: 2

5. Answer: a Difficulty: 2

6. Answer: c Difficulty: 2

7. Answer: d Difficulty: 2

8. Answer: b Difficulty: 2

9. Answer: e Difficulty: 2

10. Answer: a Difficulty: 2

11. Answer: a Difficulty: 3

12. Answer: b Difficulty: 3

13. Answer: d Difficulty: 3

14. Answer: c Difficulty: 3

15. Answer: a Difficulty: 3

16. Answer: c Difficulty: 2

17. Answer: b Difficulty: 2

18. Answer: c Difficulty: 2

19. Answer: b Difficulty: 2

20. Answer: d Difficulty: 2

21. Answer: b Difficulty: 3

22. Answer: d Difficulty: 3

23. Answer: c Difficulty: 3

24. Answer: a Difficulty: 3

25. Answer: c Difficulty: 2

26. Answer: b Difficulty: 2 Section: 1

27. Answer: c Difficulty: 3 Section: 1

28. Answer: c Difficulty: 2 Section: 1

29. Answer: d Difficulty: 2 Section: 1

30. Answer: a Difficulty: 3 Section: 3

31. Answer: b Difficulty: 1 Section: 2

32. Answer: c Difficulty: 3 Section: 2

33. Answer: a Difficulty: 1 Section: 2

34. Answer: b Difficulty: 2 Section: 3

35. Answer: b Difficulty: 2 Section: 3

36. Answer: a Difficulty: 3 Section: 3

37. Answer: a Difficulty: 4 Section: 3

38. Answer: d Difficulty: 3 Section: 3

39. Answer: b Difficulty: 2 Section: 4

40. Answer: a Difficulty: 2 Section: 4

41. Answer: a Difficulty: 2 Section: 4

42. Answer: b Difficulty: 3 Section: 4

43. Answer: b Difficulty: 2 Section: 3

44. Answer: d Difficulty: 2 Section: 4

45. Answer: b Difficulty: 2 Section: 4

Chapter 6: BJT Amplifiers

MULTIPLE CHOICE

1. A common-emitter amplifier has very high input impedance, high voltage gain, and high current gain.
   a) true
   b) false

2. A high input impedance amplifier could be a Darlington pair.
   a) true
   b) false

3. A common-collector amplifier is also known as an emitter follower.
   a) true
   b) false

4. The total voltage gain, expressed as a ratio, of a multistage amplifier is the sum of the individual voltage gains.
   a) true
   b) false

5. A common-base amplifier has a high current gain.
   a) true
   b) false

6. A certain transistor has a dc emitter current of 25 mA. The value of r_e is:
   a) 25 Ω.
   b) 2.5 Ω.
   c) 1.2 Ω.
   d) 1 Ω.

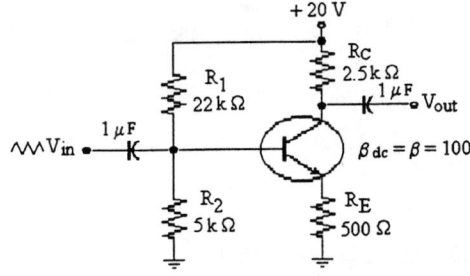

Figure 6-1

7. Refer to Figure 6-1. The value of V_C is:
   a) 20 V
   b) 10 V
   c) 5 V
   d) 0 V

231

8. Refer to Figure 6-1.   If an emitter-bypass capacitor was added, the voltage gain:
   a) would not change
   b) would decrease
   c) would increase
   d) would decrease to zero

9. Refer to Figure 6-1.   If R_2 opened, V_{CE} would be:
   a) 0 V
   b) 20 V
   c) 10 V
   d) 4.8 V

10. Refer to Figure 6-1.   If R_2 opened, the value of I_C would be:
    a) 6 mA
    b) 6.67 mA
    c) 8 mA
    d) 10 mA

11. Refer to Figure 6-1.   If R_C opened, V_E would:
    a) increase
    b) decrease
    c) remain the same
    d) be undetermined

12. Refer to Figure 6-1.   If the emitter collector shorted, the voltage V_C would be:
    a) 0 V
    b) 20 V
    c) 16.67 V
    d) 3.33 V

13. Refer to Figure 6-1.   If the collector opened internally, the voltage on the collector would:
    a) increase
    b) decrease
    c) remain the same
    d) be undetermined

14. Refer to Figure 6-1.   If $V_E = 0$, the trouble might be that:
    a) R_E is open
    b) R_C is open
    c) R_2 is open
    d) R_1 is open

15. Refer to Figure 6-1.   If an emitter-bypass capacitor was installed, the value of R_{in} would be:
    a) 50 Ω
    b) 175 Ω
    c) 378 Ω
    d) 500 Ω

16. Refer to Figure 6-1. If an emitter-bypass capacitor was installed, the new A_V would be:
    a) 4.96
    b) 125
    c) 398
    d) 600

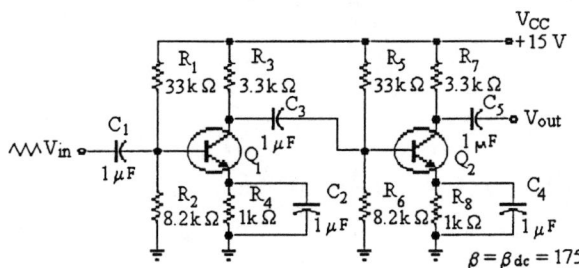

Figure 6-2

17. Refer to Figure 6-2. If $A_{V1} = 75$ and $A_{V2} = 95$, A_{VT} would be:
    a) 75
    b) 95
    c) 1275
    d) 7125

18. Refer to Figure 6-2. When checking this amplifier, V_{out} was below normal. The trouble might be:
    a) an open C_3
    b) an open C_4
    c) C_4 is shorted
    d) C_1 is open

19. Refer to Figure 6-2. If V_{B2} was higher than normal. The problem, if any, could be:
    a) C_3 is shorted
    b) R_3 is open
    c) BE_1 is open
    d) C_2 is open

20. Refer to Figure 6-2. In servicing this amplifier V_{out} was found less than normal. The problem could be caused by:
    a) an open C_3
    b) an open C_2
    c) an open base-emitter of Q_2
    d) a shorted C_2

21. Refer to Figure 6-2. The output signal from the first stage of this amplifier is 0 V. The trouble could be caused by:
    a) an open C_4
    b) an open C_2
    c) an open base-emitter of Q_2
    d) a shorted C_4

22. The best selection for a high input impedance amplifier is a:
    a) low gain common-emitter
    b) common-base
    c) common-collector
    d) high gain common-emitter

23. The characteristic that is not of a common-base amplifier is:
    a) high input impedance
    b) current gain of 1
    c) medium voltage gain
    d) high output impedance

24. The characteristic that is not of an emitter-follower is:
    a) voltage gain of 1
    b) low input impedance
    c) low output impedance
    d) medium current gain

25. The best choice for a very high power amplifier is a(n):
    a) common-collector
    b) common-base
    c) common-emitter
    d) emitter-follower

26. For transistors:
    a) the dc and ac current gains are the same
    b) the dc current gain is zero
    c) the dc and ac current gains are usually different
    d) amplification of signal voltage is not possible

27. The ac resistance of the emitter diode r_e' equals:

    a) $\dfrac{25 \text{ mV}}{I_E}$

    b) $25 \text{ mV} \times I_C$

    c) $\dfrac{25 \text{ mV}}{I_B}$

    d) $\dfrac{25 \text{ mV}}{I_C}$

28. In general, coupling capacitors can be considered:
    a) open for signal voltage and a short for dc
    b) short for signal voltage and an open for dc
    c) lossy
    d) short for signal voltage and a short for dc

29. The primary reason an ac load line differs from a dc load line is:
    a) the effective ac collector resistance is greater than the dc collector resistance
    b) the effective ac collector resistance is less than the dc collector resistance
    c) changes in current are non-linear for small-signal amplifier operation
    d) the ac load line is not as steep as the dc load line

30. The h-parameter, h_{fe}, is the same as _____ of the transistor.
    a) dc Beta
    b) ac Beta
    c) maximum collector current
    d) minimum hold current

31. The capacitor that produces an ac ground is called a(n):
    a) bypass capacitor
    b) coupling capacitor
    c) dc open
    d) ac open

32. Reducing all dc sources to zero is one of the steps in getting the:
    a) dc equivalent circuit
    b) ac equivalent circuit
    c) complete amplifier circuit
    d) voltage-divider biased circuit

33. The input resistance, $R_{in(base)}$, of a common-emitter amplifier, consists of _____.
    a) $r_b \parallel \beta r_e$
    b) $\beta_{ac} \beta r_e'$
    c) $r_e \parallel \beta r_e'$
    d) $R_G \parallel r_c \parallel \beta r_e'$

34. The three factors that must be taken into account when determining the actual signal voltage at the base of a small signal bipolar amplifier are:
    a) source resistance, emitter resistance, and input resistance
    b) source resistance, bias resistance, and input resistance
    c) source resistance, collector resistance, internal resistance
    d) source resistance, bias resistance, and load resistance

35. The value of output resistance in a common-emitter amplifier, R_{out}, consists of:
    a) R_C
    b) $R_L + R_C$
    c) $\beta \parallel R_C$
    d) $R_L \parallel R_C$

36. The voltage gain of an amplifier is defined as:
    a) the ac input voltage divided by the ac output voltage
    b) the ac collector current divided by the ac base current
    c) the ac output collector voltage divided by the ac input base voltage
    d) the ac collector current divided by the ac emitter current

37. Removing a bypass capacitor from a fully bypassed, common-emitter amplifier circuit will _____ voltage gain and _____ input resistance.
    a) increase, decrease
    b) decrease, increase
    c) decrease, decrease
    d) increase, increase

38. The voltage gain of a common-emitter amplifier, A_V, is defined as:
    a) $A_V = \dfrac{V_b}{V_c}$
    b) $A_V = I_C \times R_C$
    c) $A_V = \dfrac{I_e R_C}{I_e r_e'}$
    d) $A_V = \dfrac{R_C}{r_e}$

39. For a bypass capacitor to work properly, the:
    a) X_C should be ten times smaller than R_E at the minimum operating frequency
    b) X_C should equal R_E
    c) X_C should be ten times greater than R_E at the minimum operating frequency
    d) X_C should be twice the value of the R_E

40. A bypass capacitor is placed across the emitter resistor in a voltage-divider biased common-emitter amplifier circuit. This will:
    a) place the emitter at ac ground
    b) shift the Q point on the dc load line
    c) reduce the emitter's dc voltage to zero
    d) all of the above

41. Removing the emitter bypass capacitor from a common-emitter amplifier:
    a) increases R_{in} and decreases A_V, voltage gain
    b) decreases R_{in} and increases A_V, voltage gain
    c) does not affect R_{in}
    d) increases the distortion

42. Increasing the resistance of the load resistor R_L, in an RC coupled common-emitter amplifier will have what effect on voltage gain?
    a) does not affect the voltage gain
    b) decreases the voltage gain
    c) increases the voltage gain
    d) none of the above

43. Leaving some of the emitter resistance unbypassed in a common-emitter amplifier will:
    a) reduce distortion
    b) stabilize the voltage gain
    c) increase the input impedance
    d) all of the above

44. In a swamped amplifier, the effects of the emitter diode (r_e') become:

    a) important to voltage gain
    b) critical to input impedance
    c) significant to the analysis
    d) unimportant

45. To reduce the distortion of an amplified signal, you can increase the:
    a) collector resistance
    b) emitter feedback resistance
    c) generator resistance
    d) load resistance

46. An emitter follower has a voltage gain that is:
    a) much less than one
    b) approximately equal to one
    c) greater than one
    d) zero

47. The total ac emitter resistance of an emitter follower equals:
    a) r_e'

    b) r_e
    c) $R_e + r_e'$

    d) R_E

48. The input resistance of the base of an emitter follower is usually:
    a) low
    b) high
    c) shorted to ground
    d) open

49. Often a common-collector will be the last stage before the load; the main function(s) of this stage is to:
    a) provide voltage gain
    b) buffer the voltage amplifiers from the low resistance load and provide impedance matching for maximum power transfer
    c) provide phase inversion
    d) provide a high frequency path to improve the frequency response

50. Output resistance in a common-collector amplifier circuit is stepped down by a factor of:
    a) alpha α
    b) Beta β
    c) $R_E \parallel R_L$
    d) $r_e' + r_e$

51. If two transistors are connected as a Darlington pair and each transistor has a βeta of 175, what would the overall current gain of the pair equal:
    a) 30,625
    b) 3,625
    c) 10,000
    d) 5,000

52. The characteristic of a common-base amplifier that is most useful is:
    a) power amplification
    b) voltage amplification
    c) low output resistance
    d) phase inversion

53. In a two-stage amplifier, the input resistance of the second stage:
    a) does not affect the voltage gain of the first stage
    b) affects the voltage gain of the first stage
    c) is in parallel with the collector resistor, RC, of the first stage
    d) both b and c above

54. In a two-stage amplifier, the voltage gain of the first stage is 80 and the voltage gain of the second stage is 50. How much is the overall voltage gain?
    a) 72
    b) 130
    c) 4,000
    d) 400

55. If a CE stage is direct coupled to an emitter-follower, how many coupling capacitors are there between the two stages?
    a) 0
    b) 1
    c) 2
    d) 3

1. Answer: b Difficulty: 2

2. Answer: a Difficulty: 2

3. Answer: a Difficulty: 2

4. Answer: b Difficulty: 2

5. Answer: b Difficulty: 2

6. Answer: d Difficulty: 2

7. Answer: c Difficulty: 2

8. Answer: c Difficulty: 2

9. Answer: a Difficulty: 3

10. Answer: b Difficulty: 3

11. Answer: b Difficulty: 2

12. Answer: d Difficulty: 2

13. Answer: a Difficulty: 3

14. Answer: d Difficulty: 2

15. Answer: c Difficulty: 2

16. Answer: d Difficulty: 2

17. Answer: d Difficulty: 2

18. Answer: b Difficulty: 3

19. Answer: a Difficulty: 3

20. Answer: b Difficulty: 2

21. Answer: c Difficulty: 3

22. Answer: c Difficulty: 2

23. Answer: a Difficulty: 2

24. Answer: b Difficulty: 2

25. Answer: c Difficulty: 2

26. Answer: c Difficulty: 1 Section: 1

27. Answer: a Difficulty: 2 Section: 2

28. Answer: a Difficulty: 2 Section: 1

29. Answer: a Difficulty: 3 Section: 1

30. Answer: b Difficulty: 2 Section: 2

31. Answer: a Difficulty: 2 Section: 3

32. Answer: b Difficulty: 2 Section: 3

33. Answer: b Difficulty: 3 Section: 3

34. Answer: b Difficulty: 3 Section: 3

35. Answer: a Difficulty: 2 Section: 3

36. Answer: c Difficulty: 2 Section: 3

37. Answer: b Difficulty: 3 Section: 3

38. Answer: c Difficulty: 3 Section: 3

39. Answer: a Difficulty: 2 Section: 3

40. Answer: a Difficulty: 2 Section: 3

41. Answer: a Difficulty: 3 Section: 3

42. Answer: c Difficulty: 3 Section: 3

43. Answer: d Difficulty: 2 Section: 3

44. Answer: d Difficulty: 2 Section: 3

45. Answer: b Difficulty: 3 Section: 3

46. Answer: b Difficulty: 1 Section: 4

47. Answer: c Difficulty: 2 Section: 4

48. Answer: b Difficulty: 2 Section: 4

49. Answer: b Difficulty: 2 Section: 4

50. Answer: b Difficulty: 3 Section: 4

51. Answer: b Difficulty: 1 Section: 4

52. Answer: c Difficulty: 2 Section: 5

53. Answer: d Difficulty: 2 Section: 6

54. Answer: d Difficulty: 1 Section: 6

55. Answer: a Difficulty: 2 Section: 6

Chapter 7:   Field-Effect Transistors (FETs)

MULTIPLE CHOICE

1. An FET has three terminals, source, drain, and gate.
   a) true
   b) false

2. The JFET operates with a forward-biased gate-source PN junction.
   a) true
   b) false

3. An E-MOSFET can be used as a switch.
   a) true
   b) false

4. A D-MOFSET can operate with both positive and negative values of V_{GS}.
   a) true
   b) false

5. Special care is required in handling a MOSFET.
   a) true
   b) false

6. An N-channel JFET has a $V_D = 8$ V, $V_{GS} = -5$ V. The value of V_{DS} is:
   a) 3 V
   b) 8 V
   c) -5 V
   d) -3 V

7. Field effect transistors are also known as:
   a) one-charge carrier
   b) two-charge carrier
   c) three-charge carrier
   d) none of the above

8. The FET that has no physical channel is the:
   a) D MOSFET
   b) E MOSFET
   c) JFET
   d) none of the above

9. An FET that has no I_{DSS} parameter is the:
   a) JFET
   b) DE MOSFET
   c) V MOSFET
   d) E MOSFET

Figure 7-1

10. Refer to Figure 7-1 (a). This symbol identifies:
    a) a P-channel E MOSFET
    b) an N-channel D MOSFET
    c) a P-channel D MOSFET
    d) an N-channel E MOSFET

11. Refer to Figure 7-1 (b). This symbol identifies:
    a) a P-channel E MOSFET
    b) an N-channel D MOSFET
    c) a P-channel D MOSFET
    d) an N-channel E MOSFET

12. Refer to Figure 7-1 (c). This symbol identifies:
    a) a P-channel E MOSFET
    b) an N-channel D MOSFET
    c) a P-channel D MOSFET
    d) an N-channel E MOSFET

13. Refer to Figure 7-1 (d). This symbol identifies:
    a) a P-channel E MOSFET
    b) an N-channel D MOSFET
    c) a P-channel D MOSFET
    d) an N-channel E MOSFET

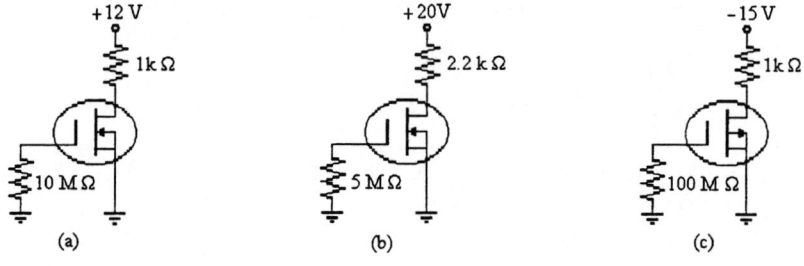

Figure 7-2

14. Refer to Figure 7-2 (a). If I_D = 4 mA, the value of V_{DS} is:
    a) 12 V
    b) 8 V
    c) 4 V
    d) 0 V

243

15. Refer to Figure 7-2 (b). If I_D = 4 mA, the value of V_{GS} is:
    a) 20 V
    b) 11.2 V
    c) 8.8 V
    d) 0 V

16. Refer to Figure 7-2 (c). If I_D = 4 mA, the value of V_{DS} is:
    a) -11 V
    b) -14 V
    c) -15 V
    d) 0 V

17. A JFET manufacturers data sheet specifies $V_{GS(off)}$ = -8 V and I_{DSS} = 6 mA. The value of I_D when V_{GS} = -4 V would be:
    a) 6 ma
    b) 1.25 mA
    c) 1.5 mA
    d) 4 mA

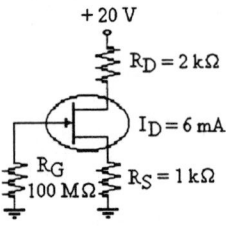

+ 20 V

$R_D = 2\,k\Omega$

$I_D = 6\,mA$

R_G
100 MΩ $R_S = 1\,k\Omega$

Figure 7-3

18. Refer to Figure 7-3. The value of the voltage drop across R_D is:
    a) 20 V
    b) 12 V
    c) 6 V
    d) 3 V

19. Refer to Figure 7-3. This amplifier is biased for:
    a) linear operation
    b) pinch-off operation
    c) saturation
    d) operation as a switch

20. Refer to Figure 7-3. In this circuit, V_{GS} is biased correctly for proper operation. This means that V_{GS} is:
    a) positive
    b) negative
    c) either negative or positive
    d) 0 V

21. Refer to Figure 7-3. Calculate the value of V_D.
    a) 20 V
    b) 8 V
    c) 6 V
    d) 2 V

22. Refer to Figure 7-3. Calculate the value of V_{DS}.
    a) 0 V
    b) 2 V
    c) 4 V
    d) -2 V

23. For proper operation, an N-channel E-MOSFET should be biased so that V_{GS} is:
    a) either positive or negative
    b) negative
    c) positive
    d) -4 V

24. A good application for a V-MOSFET would be:
    a) as a power amplifier
    b) as a low power amplifier
    c) as a low input impedance device
    d) as a substitute for a diode

25. A V MOSFET device operates in:
    a) the depletion mode
    b) the enhancement mode
    c) a JFET mode
    d) in either enhancement or depletion mode

26. The gate-source junction of a JFET is:
    a) normally not biased
    b) normally forward biased
    c) normally reverse biased
    d) a low resistance path for dc current when reverse biased

27. The channel width in a JFET is controlled by:
    a) varying gate voltage
    b) varying drain voltage
    c) increasing forward bias on the gate-source junction
    d) increasing reverse bias on the drain-source junction

28. When operated in the ohmic area, a JFET acts like a(n):
    a) small resistor
    b) voltage source
    c) current source
    d) insulator

29. V_{DS} equals pinchoff voltage divided by the:
    a) rain current
    b) gate current
    c) ideal drain current
    d) drain current for zero gate voltage

30. $I_{D(ss)}$ can be defined as:
    a) the minimum possible drain current
    b) the maximum possible current with the drain shorted to the source
    c) the maximum current drain-to-source with a shorted gate
    d) the maximum drain current with the source shorted

31. The pinchoff voltage has the same magnitude as the:
    a) gate voltage
    b) drain-source voltage
    c) gate-source voltage
    d) gate-source cutoff voltage

32. JFETs are often called:
    a) one-way switches
    b) two-way switches
    c) bipolar devices
    d) square-law devices

33. The transconductance curve of a JFET is a graph of:
    a) I_S versus V_{DS}
    b) I_C versus V_{CE}
    c) I_D versus V_{GS}
    d) $I_D \times R_{DS}$

34. For a JFET, maximum drain current flows when:
    a) V_{GS} equals $V_{GS(off)}$
    b) V_{DS} is zero
    c) the drain and source are interchanged
    d) V_{GS} is zero

35. The transconductance curve of a JFET is:
    a) hyperbolic
    b) linear
    c) nonlinear
    d) symmetrical

36. JFET data sheets specify input resistance by giving the values for V_{GS} and I_{DSS}.
    a) true
    b) false

37. A _____ in V_{DS} will produce a _____ change in I_D.
    a) small, large
    b) large, small
    c) large, small
    d) small, small

38. To get a negative gate-source voltage in a self-biased JFET circuit, you must use a:
    a) voltage divider
    b) source resistor
    c) ground
    d) negative gate supply voltage

39. Under no signal conditions midpoint bias allows the maximum amount of drain current swing between I_{DSS} and zero.
    a) true
    b) false

40. The easiest way to bias a JFET in the ohmic region is with:
    a) voltage-divider bias
    b) self-bias
    c) gate bias
    d) source bias

41. One advantage of voltage-divider bias is that the dependency of drain current I_D, on the range of Q-Points is:
    a) increased
    b) reduced
    c) not affected
    d) none of the above

42. The depletion-mode MOSFET can:
    a) operate with only positive gate voltages
    b) operate with only negative gate voltages
    c) not operate in the ohmic region
    d) operate with positive as well as negative gate voltages

43. An N-channel E-MOSFET conducts when it has:
    a) $V_{GS} > V_P$
    b) a thin layer of positive charges in the substrate region near the SiO_2 layer
    c) $V_{DS} > 0$
    d) a thin layer of negative charges in the substrate region near the SiO_2 layer

44. Power FET's, _____ devices that utilize a vertical internal construction, permit a wider channel and greater current capability.
    a) switching JFET
    b) enhancement MOSFET
    c) depletion MOSFET
    d) linear FET

45. For an enhancement-mode MOSFET, the minimum V_{GS} required to produce drain current is called the:
    a) threshold voltage, designated $V_{GS(th)}$
    b) blocking voltage, designated V_B
    c) breakover voltage
    d) I_{Dss}

46. Special handling precautions should be taken when working with MOSFETs. Which of the following is **not one** of these precautions?
    a) All test equipment should be grounded.
    b) MOSFET devices should have their leads shorted together for shipment and storage.
    c) Never remove or insert MOSFET devices with the power on.
    d) Workers handling MOSFET devices should not have grounding straps attached to their wrists.

47. The simplest method to bias a D-MOSFET is to:
    a) set $V_{GS} = +4$
    b) set $V_{GS} = -4$
    c) set $V_{GS} = 0$
    d) select the correct value R_D

48. The type of bias most often used with E-MOSFET circuits is:
    a) drain-feedback
    b) constant current
    c) voltage-divider
    d) both a & c

1. Answer: a   Difficulty: 2

2. Answer: b   Difficulty: 2

3. Answer: a   Difficulty: 2

4. Answer: a   Difficulty: 2

5. Answer: a   Difficulty: 2

6. Answer: a   Difficulty: 2

7. Answer: a   Difficulty: 2

8. Answer: b   Difficulty: 2

9. Answer: d   Difficulty: 2

10. Answer: b   Difficulty: 2

11. Answer: c   Difficulty: 2

12. Answer: d   Difficulty: 2

13. Answer: a   Difficulty: 2

14. Answer: b   Difficulty: 2

15. Answer: d   Difficulty: 2

16. Answer: a   Difficulty: 3

17. Answer: c   Difficulty: 3

18. Answer: b   Difficulty: 2

19. Answer: a   Difficulty: 2

20. Answer: b   Difficulty: 3

21. Answer: b   Difficulty: 2

22. Answer: b   Difficulty: 2

23. Answer: c   Difficulty: 2

24. Answer: a   Difficulty: 2

25. Answer: b   Difficulty: 2

26. Answer: c Difficulty: 2 Section: 1

27. Answer: a Difficulty: 2 Section: 1

28. Answer: a Difficulty: 2 Section: 2

29. Answer: d Difficulty: 3 Section: 2

30. Answer: c Difficulty: 2 Section: 2

31. Answer: d Difficulty: 3 Section: 2

32. Answer: d Difficulty: 2 Section: 2

33. Answer: c Difficulty: 2 Section: 2

34. Answer: d Difficulty: 2 Section: 2

35. Answer: c Difficulty: 2 Section: 2

36. Answer: b Difficulty: 2 Section: 2

37. Answer: b Difficulty: 3 Section: 2

38. Answer: b Difficulty: 3 Section: 3

39. Answer: b Difficulty: 2 Section: 3

40. Answer: a Difficulty: 3 Section: 3

41. Answer: b Difficulty: 2 Section: 3

42. Answer: d Difficulty: 2 Section: 4

43. Answer: d Difficulty: 3 Section: 4

44. Answer: b Difficulty: 2 Section: 4

45. Answer: a Difficulty: 2 Section: 5

46. Answer: c Difficulty: 2 Section: 5

47. Answer: c Difficulty: 3 Section: 6

48. Answer: d Difficulty: 2 Section: 6

Chapter 8: FET Amplifiers

MULTIPLE CHOICE

1. The formula for the voltage gain of a common-source amplifier is R_D/g_m.
   a) true
   b) false

2. Load resistance added to the output of an amplifier increases the voltage gain.
   a) true
   b) false

3. The addition of a source bypass capacitor will increase the voltage gain.
   a) true
   b) false

4. In an amplifier using a JFET, the gate current is 0.
   a) true
   b) false

5. A common-source amplifier has a _____ phase shift between the input and the output.
   a) 45°
   b) 90°
   c) 180°
   d) 360°

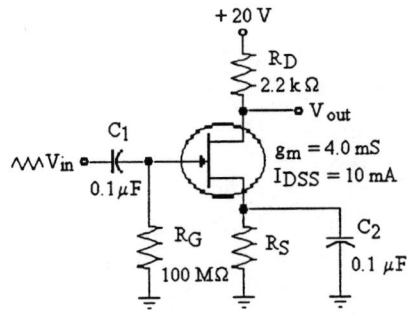

Figure 8-1

6. Refer to Figure 8-1. Assuming midpoint biasing, if V_{GS} = -4 V, the value of R_S that will provide this value is:
   a) 600 Ω
   b) 1.2 kΩ
   c) 80 Ω
   d) 800 Ω

7. Refer to Figure 8-1. If V_{in} = 50 mV p-p, the output voltage is:
   a) 50 mV p-p
   b) 4.4 V p-p
   c) 0.044 V p-p
   d) 440 mV p-p

8. Refer to Figure 8-1. If the measured value of V_{out} was below normal, the problem might be one of the following:
   a) R_D is open
   b) C_2 is shorted
   c) C_2 is open
   d) V_{in} has increased

9. Refer to Figure 8-1. If $V_{in} = 1$ V p-p, the output voltage V_{out} would be:
   a) undistorted
   b) clipped on the negative peaks
   c) clipped on the positive peaks
   d) 0 V

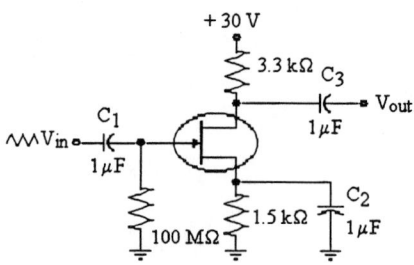

Figure 8-2

10. Refer to Figure 8-2. If $I_D = 6$ mA, the value of V_{GS} is:
    a) 9 V
    b) -9 V
    c) -19.8 V
    d) -10.2 V

11. Refer to Figure 8-2. If $g_m = 6500$ µS and an input signal of 125 mV p-p is applied to the gate, the output voltage V_{out} is:
    a) 2.68 V p-p
    b) 0.8125 V p-p
    c) 1.625 V p-p
    d) 6.25 V p-p

12. Refer to Figure 8-2. If C_2 opened, the output signal would:
    a) increase in value
    b) decrease in value
    c) not change
    d) decrease and then increase

13. Refer to Figure 8-2. If $I_D = 4$ mA, $I_{DSS} = 16$ mA, and V_{GS}(off) = -8 V, V_{DS} would be:
    a) 19.2 V
    b) -6 V
    c) 10.8 V
    d) 30 V

14. Refer to Figure 8-2. If $g_m = 4000\ \mu S$ and a signal of 75 mV rms is applied to the gate, the p-p output voltage is:
    a) 990 mV
    b) 1.13 V p-p
    c) 2.8 V p-p
    d) 990 V p-p

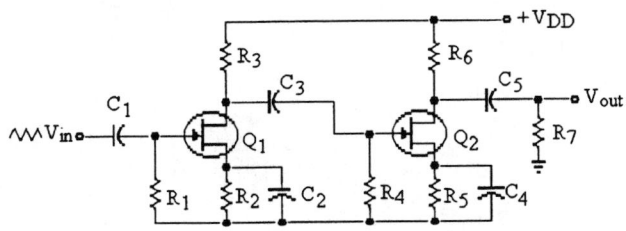

Figure 8-3

15. Refer to Figure 8-3. If C_4 opened, the signal voltage at the drain of Q_2 would:
    a) increase
    b) decrease
    c) remain the same
    d) distort

16. Refer to Figure 8-3. If R_7 were to increase in value, V_{out} would:
    a) increase
    b) decrease
    c) remain the same
    d) distort

17. Refer to Figure 8-3. If C_2 opened, V_{out} would:
    a) increase
    b) decrease
    c) remain the same
    d) distort

18. Refer to Figure 8-3. If R_1 opened, V_{out} would:
    a) increase
    b) decrease
    c) remain the same
    d) distort

19. Refer to Figure 8-3. If C_3 opened, V_{out} would:
    a) increase
    b) decrease
    c) remain the same
    d) distort

20. Refer to Figure 8-3. If R_3 opened, V_{out} would:
    a) increase
    b) decrease
    c) remain the same
    d) distort

21. Refer to Figure 8-3. If R_5 opened, V_{out} would:
    a) increase
    b) decrease
    c) remain the same
    d) distort

22. Refer to Figure 8-3. If the source-drain of Q_2 shorted, the output signal from Q_1 would:
    a) increase
    b) decrease
    c) remain the same
    d) distort

23. Refer to Figure 8-3. If $A_{V1} = 18$ and $A_{Vt} = 288$, the value of A_{V2} would be:
    a) 5184
    b) 18
    c) 49.18
    d) 16

24. Refer to Figure 8-3. If C_4 opened, the signal voltage at the drain of Q_1 would:
    a) increase
    b) decrease
    c) remain the same
    d) distort

25. Refer to Figure 8-3. If V_{in} was increased in amplitude a little, the signal voltage at the source of Q_2 would:
    a) increase
    b) decrease
    c) remain the same
    d) distort

26. What component of an FET operation needs to be at least ten times greater than R_D to ensure maximum voltage gain?
    a) r'_{ds}
    b) R_S
    c) R_s
    d) g_m

27. In a self-biased common-source amplifier (Textbook Fig 8-5), what purpose does resistor R_G serve?
    a) Keeps the gate at approximately zero volts
    b) Develops the gate-source bias current
    c) Prevents loading of the ac signal source
    d) Both a & c

28. A CS amplifier has a voltage gain of:
    a) $g_m R_d$
    b) $g_m R_s$
    c) $\dfrac{g_m R_s}{(1 + g_m R_d)}$
    d) $\dfrac{g_m R_d}{(1 + g_m R_d)}$

29. The common-source JFET amplifier has:
    a) a high input impedance and a relatively low voltage gain
    b) a high input impedance and a very high voltage gain
    c) a high input impedance and a voltage gain less than 1
    d) no voltage gain

30. Compared to a common-emitter amplifier, the voltage gain of a common-source amplifier is:
    a) about the same
    b) much higher
    c) much lower
    d) about 1

31. When used as an amplifier, the JFET should operate:
    a) in the ohmic region
    b) in the current-source region
    c) in the saturation region
    d) in the cut off region

32. A source follower has a voltage gain of:
    a) $g_m R_d$
    b) $g_m R_s$
    c) $\dfrac{g_m R_s}{(1 + g_m R_d)}$
    d) $\dfrac{g_m R_d}{(1 + g_m R_d)}$

33. When the input signal is large, a source follower has:
    a) a voltage gain of less than one
    b) a small distortion
    c) a high input resistance
    d) all of these

34. Changing _____ can control the voltage gain of a common-source amplifier.
    a) the input voltage
    b) g_m
    c) V_{DD}
    d) R_S

35. Enhancement-mode MOSFETS function as active loads when:
    a) the gate is shorted to the source
    b) the source is shorted to the drain
    c) the gate is connected to the drain
    d) the source is left disconnected

36. In IC's, the enhancement MOSFET is used mainly for:
    a) analog switching
    b) digital switching
    c) small signal amplification
    d) dc amplification

37. The power gain of a common-gate amplifier is:
    a) $\cong A_V$
    b) $\cong A_I$
    c) $> A_V$
    d) $> A_I$

38. Most small-signal E-MOSFETs are found in:
    a) heavy-current applications
    b) discrete circuits
    c) disk drives
    d) integrated circuits

39. An E-MOSFET that operates at cutoff or in the ohmic region is an example of:
    a) a current source
    b) an active load
    c) a passive load
    d) a switching device

1. Answer: b Difficulty: 2

2. Answer: b Difficulty: 2

3. Answer: a Difficulty: 2

4. Answer: a Difficulty: 2

5. Answer: c Difficulty: 2

6. Answer: d Difficulty: 2

7. Answer: d Difficulty: 3

8. Answer: c Difficulty: 3

9. Answer: a Difficulty: 2

10. Answer: b Difficulty: 2

11. Answer: a Difficulty: 2

12. Answer: b Difficulty: 2

13. Answer: c Difficulty: 2

14. Answer: c Difficulty: 3

15. Answer: b Difficulty: 2

16. Answer: a Difficulty: 3

17. Answer: b Difficulty: 2

18. Answer: c Difficulty: 3

19. Answer: b Difficulty: 2

20. Answer: b Difficulty: 2

21. Answer: b Difficulty: 2

22. Answer: c Difficulty: 3

23. Answer: d Difficulty: 2

24. Answer: c Difficulty: 3

25. Answer: c Difficulty: 3

26. Answer: a Difficulty: 2 Section: 1

27. Answer: d Difficulty: 3 Section: 2

28. Answer: a Difficulty: 3 Section: 2

29. Answer: a Difficulty: 1 Section: 2

30. Answer: a Difficulty: 2 Section: 2

31. Answer: b Difficulty: 3 Section: 1

32. Answer: b Difficulty: 2 Section: 4

33. Answer: d Difficulty: 1 Section: 4

34. Answer: b Difficulty: 2 Section: 4

35. Answer: c Difficulty: 3 Section: 2

36. Answer: b Difficulty: 2 Section: 2

37. Answer: a Difficulty: 2 Section: 4

38. Answer: d Difficulty: 2 Section: 4

39. Answer: d Difficulty: 2 Section: 4

Chapter 9:   Power Amplifiers

MULTIPLE CHOICE

1. The class A amplifier is usually biased below cutoff.
   a) true
   b) false

2. Darlington pair transistors are often used in power amplifiers because the input impedance is very low.
   a) true
   b) false

3. A class B amplifier conducts _____ of the cycle.
   a) 45°
   b) 90°
   c) 180°
   d) 360°

4. The class of amplifiers that is the most efficient and has the most distortion is class _____ amplifiers.
   a) A
   b) B
   c) C
   d) AB

5. Push-pull amplifiers often use class _____ amplifiers.
   a) A
   b) B
   c) C
   d) AB

6. If a class A amplifier has a voltage gain of 50 and a current gain of 75. The power gain would be:
   a) 50
   b) 75
   c) 1500
   d) 3750

7. If a class A amplifier has R_C = 4.7 kΩ and R_E = 1.5 kΩ and V_{CC} = 24 V, $I_{C(sat)}$ would be:
   a) 5.1 mA
   b) 16 mA
   c) 3.87 mA
   d) 0 mA

8. An application for an amplifier to operate in a linear mode is needed, the most likely choice would be a:
   a) class A
   b) class B
   c) class C
   d) class AB

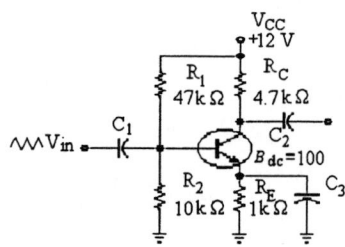

Figure 9-1

9. Refer to Figure 9-1. If R_1 opened, and V_{in} at the base was large, V_{out} at the collector would:
   a) increase
   b) decrease
   c) remain the same
   d) distort

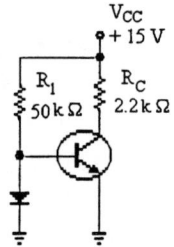

Figure 9-2

10. Refer to Figure 9-2. If the diode opened, this amplifier would be operating as class:
    a) A
    b) B
    c) C
    d) AB

11. Refer to Figure 9-2. The purpose of the diode is:
    a) to bias the amplifier as class A
    b) to bias the amplifier as class B
    c) to bias the amplifier as class C
    d) to bias the amplifier as class AB

12. A typical efficiency for a class A amplifier is about:
    a) 25%
    b) 50%
    c) 75%
    d) 100%

13. The amplifier with the most distortion would be a _____ amplifier:
    a) class A
    b) class B
    c) class C
    d) class AB

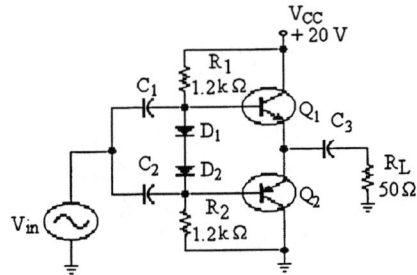

Figure 9-3

14. Refer to Figure 9-3. The emitter voltage with respect to ground is:
    a) 10.7 V
    b) 9.3 V
    c) 0 V
    d) 10 V

15. Refer to Figure 9-3. This amplifier only shows a positive alternation at the output. The possible trouble might be that:
    a) C_3 is shorted
    b) BE_1 is open
    c) BE_2 is open
    d) R_1 is open

16. Refer to Figure 9-3. The dc voltage across R_L was measured at 10 V. A possible problem, if any, might be:
    a) C_1 is open
    b) C_3 is shorted
    c) R_1 is open
    d) C_3 is open

17. Refer to Figure 9-3. During the positive input alternation, Q_1 is _____ and Q_2 is _____.
    a) on, on
    b) on, off
    c) off, off
    d) off, on

18. Refer to Figure 9-3. The purpose for the diodes D_1 and D_2 is:
    a) to apply equal signals to each transistor
    b) to allow the correct bias voltages on the two bases
    c) to maintain constant bias with temperature changes
    d) all of the above

19. Refer to Figure 9-3. The two transistors are called _____ type.
    a) same
    b) complementary
    c) NPN
    d) PNP

20. Refer to Figure 9-3. This circuit is operating as a:
    a) class A push-pull
    b) class B push-pull
    c) class C push-pull
    d) class B

21. An application for a power amplifier to operate at radio frequencies is needed. The most likely choice would be a _____ amplifier.
    a) class A
    b) class B
    c) class C
    d) class AB

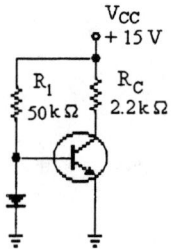

Figure 9-2

22. Refer to Figure 9-2. The approximate voltages on the base, collector, and emitter, respectively, are:
    a) 0.7 V, 6.8 V, 0 V
    b) 0 V, 0 V, 0 V
    c) 0.7 V, 15 V, 0 V
    d) 0.7 V, 0 V, 15 V

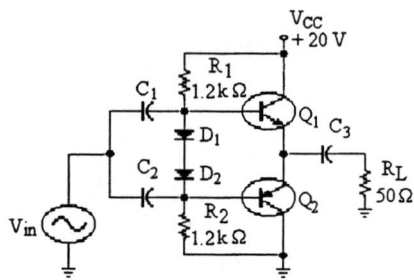

Figure 9-3

23. Refer to Figure 9-3. If R_L shows a zero signal voltage on an oscilloscope, the problem might be that:
    a) C_3 is open
    b) BE_1 is open
    c) BE_2 is open
    d) R_1 is open

24. Refer to Figure 9-3. If there was no output signal, and the measured dc voltage of Q_1 emitter was 0 V, the trouble might be:
    a) D_1 is shorted
    b) D_2 is shorted
    c) R_1 is open
    d) no trouble, everything is normal

25. Refer to Figure 9-3. Class AB amplifier is biased:
    a) at cutoff
    b) slightly above the center of the load line
    c) slightly above cutoff
    d) at the center of the load line

26. In general, an amplifier may be considered to be a power amplifier if the amplifier has to dissipate:
    a) $> 1/4$ W
    b) > 2 W
    c) > 1 W
    d) > 5 W

27. Heat sinks reduce the:
    a) transistor power
    b) ambient temperature
    c) junction temperature
    d) collector current

28. An amplifier has two load lines because:
    a) it has ac and dc collector resistances
    b) it has two equivalent circuits
    c) dc acts one way and ac acts another
    d) all of the above

29. When the Q point is at the center of the dc load line, a maximum _____ signal can be obtained.
    a) class A
    b) class B
    c) class C
    d) none of the above

30. For maximum peak-to-peak output voltage, the Q point should be:
    a) near saturation
    b) near cutoff
    c) at the center of the dc load line
    d) at the center of the ac load line

31. The ac load line is the same as the dc load line when the ac collector resistance equals the:
    a) dc emitter resistance
    b) ac emitter resistance
    c) dc collector resistance
    d) supply voltage divided by collector current

32. For a Q point near the center of the dc load line, clipping is more likely to occur on the:
    a) positive peak of input voltage
    b) negative peak of output voltage
    c) positive peak of output voltage
    d) negative peak of emitter voltage

33. The ac load line usually:
    a) equals the dc load line
    b) has less slope than the dc load line
    c) is steeper than the dc load line
    d) is horizontal

34. For a class "A" CE amplifier, the power dissipation, P_{DQ}:
    a) is maximum when there is no input signal
    b) increases when the peak-to-peak load voltage increases
    c) is zero with no input signal
    d) is maximum when the transistor is driven to cutoff

35. A CE amplifier has a load power of 10 mW and the dc power is 215 mW. The efficiency is:
    a) 46.5%
    b) 4.65%
    c) 25%
    d) 0%

36. To improve the efficiency of an amplifier, you have to:
    a) reduce load power
    b) decrease unwanted power losses
    c) reduce the supply voltage
    d) increase the dc current

37. The quiescent collector current is the same as:
    a) ac collector current
    b) ac load resistor current
    c) dc collector current
    d) none of the above

38. For a class B amplifier, collector current flows for:
    a) 270° of the input cycle
    b) 180° of the input cycle
    c) 360° of the input cycle
    d) 90° of the input cycle

39. In a class B push-pull amplifier, the transistors are biased slightly above cutoff to avoid:
    a) unusually high efficiency
    b) negative feedback
    c) crossover distortion
    d) a low input impedance

40. For a class B push-pull amplifier to work properly, the emitter diodes must:
    a) match the compensating diodes
    b) be germanium and the compensating diodes must be silicon
    c) be silicon and the compensating diodes must be germanium
    d) not match the compensating diodes

41. For a class B push-pull amplifier, diode bias is used to:
    a) allow the transistors to conduct for 360°
    b) ensure thermal runaway
    c) avoid thermal runaway
    d) saturate the output transistors

42. The maximum efficiency of a class B push-pull amplifier is:
    a) 25 percent
    b) 50 percent
    c) 79 percent
    d) 100 percent

43. Under no-signal or quiescent conditions, the transistors of a class B push-pull amplifier:
    a) have excessively high power dissipation
    b) get quite hot
    c) are in saturation
    d) dissipate very little power

44. For certain applications with low-resistance loads, a push-pull amplifier using darlington transistors can be used to decrease the input resistance presented to the driving amplifier and avoid greatly reducing voltage gain.
    a) true
    b) false

45. Power MOSFETs have several advantages over bipolar power transistors. Which of the following statements **is not** correct?
    a) Less signal power from the driver stage
    b) Can switch on/off faster than bipolar power transistors
    c) Can be easily connected in parallel to increase current capacity
    d) Has a low voltage drop across the device under high voltage and current conditions

46. For a class C amplifier, collector current flows for:
    a) 0° of the input cycle
    b) less than 180° of the input cycle
    c) 210° of the input cycle
    d) 360° of the input cycle

47. Class C amplifiers are almost always:
    a) transformer-coupled between stages
    b) operated at audio frequencies
    c) tuned RF amplifiers
    d) wideband

48. The input signal of a class C amplifier:
    a) is negatively clamped at the base
    b) is amplified and inverted
    c) produces brief pulses of collector current
    d) all of the above

49. The collector current of a class C amplifier:
    a) is an amplified version of the input voltage
    b) has harmonics
    c) is negatively clamped
    d) flows for half a cycle

1. Answer: b Difficulty: 2

2. Answer: b Difficulty: 2

3. Answer: c Difficulty: 2

4. Answer: c Difficulty: 2

5. Answer: b Difficulty: 2

6. Answer: d Difficulty: 2

7. Answer: c Difficulty: 2

8. Answer: a Difficulty: 2

9. Answer: d Difficulty: 3

10. Answer: c Difficulty: 3

11. Answer: b Difficulty: 2

12. Answer: a Difficulty: 2

13. Answer: c Difficulty: 2

14. Answer: d Difficulty: 2

15. Answer: c Difficulty: 3

16. Answer: b Difficulty: 3

17. Answer: b Difficulty: 2

18. Answer: d Difficulty: 3

19. Answer: b Difficulty: 2

20. Answer: b Difficulty: 2

21. Answer: c Difficulty: 2

22. Answer: c Difficulty: 2

23. Answer: a Difficulty: 3

24. Answer: c Difficulty: 3

25. Answer: c Difficulty: 3

26. Answer: b Difficulty: 2 Section: 1

27. Answer: c Difficulty: 1 Section: 1

28. Answer: d Difficulty: 3 Section: 1

29. Answer: d Difficulty: 3 Section: 1

30. Answer: d Difficulty: 3 Section: 1

31. Answer: c Difficulty: 3 Section: 1

32. Answer: c Difficulty: 3 Section: 1

33. Answer: c Difficulty: 2 Section: 1

34. Answer: a Difficulty: 2 Section: 1

35. Answer: b Difficulty: 2 Section: 1

36. Answer: b Difficulty: 2 Section: 1

37. Answer: c Difficulty: 2 Section: 1

38. Answer: b Difficulty: 2 Section: 2

39. Answer: c Difficulty: 2 Section: 2

40. Answer: a Difficulty: 2 Section: 2

41. Answer: c Difficulty: 2 Section: 2

42. Answer: c Difficulty: 1 Section: 2

43. Answer: d Difficulty: 2 Section: 2

44. Answer: b Difficulty: 2 Section: 2

45. Answer: a Difficulty: 3 Section: 2

46. Answer: b Difficulty: 2 Section: 3

47. Answer: c Difficulty: 2 Section: 3

48. Answer: d Difficulty: 2 Section: 3

49. Answer: b Difficulty: 2 Section: 3

Chapter 10:   Amplifier Frequency Response

MULTIPLE CHOICE

1. Coupling and bypass capacitors limit the low-frequency response of an amplifier.
   a) true
   b) false

2. High-frequency response is limited by the internal capacitances of a transistor.
   a) true
   b) false

3. At the cutoff frequency, the output is down by 3 dB.
   a) true
   b) false

4. An octave of frequency change is a ten-times change.
   a) true
   b) false

5. The bandwidth is the sum of the two cutoff frequencies.
   a) true
   b) false

6. If an amplifier has an output voltage of 12.7 V p-p at the midpoint of the frequency range, the output voltage at the cutoff frequency would be:
   a) 12.7 V p-p
   b) 4.49 V p-p
   c) 5.89 V p-p
   d) 8.98 V p-p

7. If an amplifier has an input signal voltage of 0.37 mV and an output voltage of 16.8 V, the voltage gain in dB would be:
   a) 45.4 dB
   b) 33.1 dB
   c) 93.1 dB
   d) 46.6 dB

8. If an amplifier has a voltage gain of 54 dB, and an input signal of 22 mV, the output signal voltage would be:
   a) 11 V
   b) 55.3 V
   c) 2.45 V
   d) 24.5 V

9. If an amplifier has a bandwidth of 47 kHz and a higher cutoff frequency of 104 kHz, the lower cutoff frequency would be:
   a) 151 kHz
   b) 57 kHz
   c) 47 kHz
   d) 104 kHz

10. If an amplifier has an R_{in} = 950 Ω, and a coupling capacitor of value 3.3 μF, the approximate cutoff frequency would be:
   a) 508 Hz
   b) 50.8 kHz
   c) 50.8 Hz
   d) 5.08 Hz

11. The f_c of a certain RC network that has values of R = 470 Ω and C = 0.005 μF is:
   a) 67.8 kHz
   b) 425 kHz
   c) 213 kHz
   d) 12 kHz

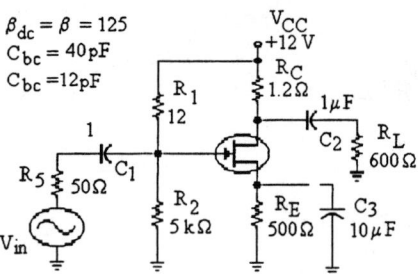

Figure 10-1

12. Refer to Figure 10-1. Low frequency response is affected by:
   a) R_C
   b) C_{BE}
   c) C_3
   d) all of these

13. Refer to Figure 10-1. High frequency response is affected by:
   a) R_C.
   b) C_{BE}.
   c) C_3.
   d) all of these.

14. Refer to Figure 10-1. If the output voltage at the upper cutoff frequency was 7.19 V p-p, the output voltage that would be expected at the lower cutoff frequency is:
   a) 5.08 V p-p
   b) 7.19 V p-p
   c) 10.17 V p-p
   d) 2.11 V p-p

15. Refer to Figure 10-1. The output voltage at f_{c1} = 22 mV. V_{out} at the midpoint frequency would be:
   a) 22 mV
   b) 17 mV
   c) 31.1 mV
   d) not enough data

16. Refer to Figure 10-1. The bandwidth of this amplifier is:
    a) the sum of the upper and lower frequencies
    b) the upper frequency divided by 0.707
    c) the difference between the upper and lower frequencies
    d) the lower frequency times 0.707

17. Refer to Figure 10-1. The capacitance C_{bc} affects:
    a) high-frequency response
    b) low-frequency response
    c) mid-range response
    d) nothing

18. Refer to Figure 10-1. A definite reduction in the output voltage is noticed. The trouble is:
    a) C_3 has shorted
    b) C_1 has opened
    c) C_2 has opened
    d) C_3 has opened

19. Refer to Figure 10-1. The reduction in the output at very high frequencies is due to:
    a) the negative feedback effect of R_E
    b) the negative feedback effect of C_{bc}
    c) the positive feedback effect of V_{BE}
    d) R_L decreasing in value

20. Refer to Figure 10-1. If the output voltage at f_{c1} = 12 mV, the output voltage at the midpoint frequency would be:
    a) 12 mV
    b) 12 mV p-p
    c) 16.97 mV
    d) 8.48 mV

21. Refer to Figure 10-1. If R_L increases in value, the output voltage would:
    a) increase
    b) decrease
    c) remain the same
    d) cannot be determined

22. If an RC network has a roll-off of 40 dB per decade, the total attenuation between the output voltage in the mid-range of the pass-band compared to a frequency of 10f would be:
    a) -3 dB
    b) -20 dB
    c) -23 dB
    d) -43 dB

23. The cutoff frequency of a low pass filter occurs at:
    a) -5 dB
    b) -3 dB
    c) +3 dB
    d) -20 dB

271

24. A high pass filter may be used to:
    a) pass low frequencies
    b) pass high frequencies
    c) pass frequencies between low and high
    d) a or b

25. A roll-off of 20 dB per decade is equivalent to a roll-off of _____ per octave.
    a) 3 dB
    b) 13 dB
    c) 12 dB
    d) 6 dB

26. Which of the following capacitances affects the high frequency response of an amplifier?
    a) Stray wiring capacitance
    b) Internal PN junction capacitance
    c) Coupling and bypass capacitors
    d) Both a and b above

27. At low frequencies, the coupling capacitors produce a decrease in:
    a) input resistance
    b) voltage gain
    c) generator resistance
    d) generator voltage

28. If the value of a feedback capacitor is 50 pF, what is the Miller capacitance when $A_V = 200$ K?
    a) 1 μF
    b) 10 μF
    c) 100 μF
    d) 10 pF

29. The critical frequencies of an amplifier are the frequencies where the output voltage is:
    a) half of V_{OUT}
    b) 0.707 of V_{OUT}
    c) zero
    d) 0.25 of V_{OUT}

30. The voltage gain of an amplifier is 200. The decibel voltage gain is:
    a) 23 db
    b) 46 db
    c) 200
    d) 106

31. If the voltage gain doubles, the decibel voltage gain increases by:
    a) A factor of 2
    b) 3 dB
    c) 6 dB
    d) 10 dB

32. In the midband of a CE amplifier:
    a) the emitter is not at ac ground
    b) the Miller effect kicks in
    c) the voltage gain is maximum
    d) the coupling and bypass capacitors appear open

33. If the power gain doubles, the decibel power gain increases by:
    a) a factor of 2
    b) 3 dB
    c) 6 dB
    d) 10 dB

34. At low frequencies, the emitter-bypass capacitor:
    a) is no longer an ac short
    b) reduces the input voltage
    c) increases the output voltage
    d) increases the voltage gain

35. Raising the frequency of 1 kHz by 2 octaves corresponds to a frequency of:
    a) 2 kHz
    b) 500 Hz
    c) 250 Hz
    d) 2 MHz

36. The frequency response of an amplifier is a graph of:
    a) voltage versus current
    b) voltage versus time
    c) output voltage versus frequency
    d) input voltage versus frequency

37. The voltage gain of an amplifier is 150. If the output voltage doubles (for the same amount of input voltage), the voltage gain equals:
    a) 21.7 db
    b) 43.5 db
    c) 49.5 db
    d) 114 db

38. At the lower or upper cutoff frequency, the voltage gain is:
    a) $0.35A_{mid}$
    b) $0.5A_{mid}$
    c) 0.707_{mid}
    d) 0.995_{mid}

39. Phase shift in the input of an RC circuit will approach 90° when:
    a) frequency approaches zero
    b) frequency approaches maximum
    c) frequency approaches mid-range
    d) frequency approaches cutoff

40. What effect does low frequency have on the emitter bypass RC circuit?
    a) Decreases impedance and increases voltage gain
    b) Increases impedance and decreases voltage gain
    c) Increases impedance and increases voltage gain
    d) Decreases impedance and decreases voltage gain

41. For a lag network above the cutoff frequency, the voltage gain:
    a) decreases at the rate of 20 db per decade
    b) increases at the rate of 6 db per octave
    c) decreases at the rate of 6 db per octave
    d) a and c above

42. Semilog graph paper has:
    a) two (2) linear axis
    b) one vertical linear axis and one logarithmic horizontal axis
    c) one horizontal linear axis and one vertical logarithmic axis
    d) two (2) logarithmic axis

43. To effectively analyze an RC coupled amplifier high frequency response you need only consider the coupling and bypass capacitance, the internal capacitance can be ignored.
    a) true
    b) false

44. The unity-gain frequency (f_T) equals the product of mid-range voltage gain ($A_{V(mid)}$) and the:
    a) compensating capacitance
    b) f_{cu}
    c) BW
    d) load resistance

45. At the unity-gain frequency, the open-loop voltage gain is:
    a) 1
    b) A_{mid}
    c) zero
    d) very large

1. Answer: a   Difficulty: 2

2. Answer: a   Difficulty: 2

3. Answer: a   Difficulty: 2

4. Answer: b   Difficulty: 2

5. Answer: b   Difficulty: 2

6. Answer: d   Difficulty: 2

7. Answer: c   Difficulty: 2

8. Answer: a   Difficulty: 3

9. Answer: b   Difficulty: 2

10. Answer: c   Difficulty: 2

11. Answer: a   Difficulty: 2

12. Answer: c   Difficulty: 2

13. Answer: b   Difficulty: 2

14. Answer: b   Difficulty: 3

15. Answer: a   Difficulty: 2

16. Answer: c   Difficulty: 3

17. Answer: a   Difficulty: 2

18. Answer: d   Difficulty: 3

19. Answer: b   Difficulty: 2

20. Answer: c   Difficulty: 2

21. Answer: a   Difficulty: 2

22. Answer: d   Difficulty: 2

23. Answer: b   Difficulty: 2

24. Answer: b   Difficulty: 2

25. Answer: d   Difficulty: 2

26. Answer: d Difficulty: 1 Section: 1

27. Answer: d Difficulty: 2 Section: 1

28. Answer: d Difficulty: 2 Section: 1

29. Answer: b Difficulty: 2 Section: 2

30. Answer: b Difficulty: 2 Section: 2

31. Answer: b Difficulty: 2 Section: 2

32. Answer: c Difficulty: 2 Section: 2

33. Answer: b Difficulty: 2 Section: 2

34. Answer: a Difficulty: 2 Section: 2

35. Answer: a Difficulty: 2 Section: 3

36. Answer: c Difficulty: 1 Section: 3

37. Answer: c Difficulty: 1 Section: 3

38. Answer: c Difficulty: 1 Section: 3

39. Answer: a Difficulty: 2 Section: 3

40. Answer: b Difficulty: 2 Section: 3

41. Answer: d Difficulty: 3 Section: 3

42. Answer: b Difficulty: 1 Section: 3

43. Answer: b Difficulty: 2 Section: 5

44. Answer: c Difficulty: 2 Section: 5

45. Answer: a Difficulty: 2 Section: 5

Chapter 11: Thyristors and Other Devices

MULTIPLE CHOICE

1. The SCR is a device that can be triggered on by a pulse applied to the gate.
   a) true
   b) false

2. A device that conducts current in only one direction is called a diac.
   a) true
   b) false

3. A device that can be turned on or off by a gate pulse is called an SCS.
   a) true
   b) false

4. A triac can be turned on by a pulse at the gate.
   a) true
   b) false

5. A UJT is turned on by a negative pulse at the base.
   a) true
   b) false

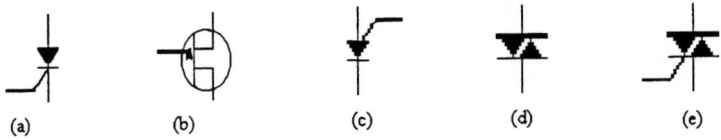

(a)   (b)   (c)   (d)   (e)

Figure 11-1

6. Refer to Figure 11-1 (a). The symbol is for:
   a) a triac
   b) a UJT
   c) a diac
   d) a PUT
   e) an SCR

7. Refer to Figure 11-1 (b). The symbol is for:
   a) a triac
   b) a UJT
   c) a diac
   d) a PUT
   e) an SCR

8. Refer to Figure 11-1 (c). The symbol is for:
   a) a triac
   b) a UJT
   c) a diac
   d) a PUT
   e) an SCR

9. Refer to Figure 11-1 (d). The symbol is for:
   a) a triac
   b) a UJT
   c) a diac
   d) a PUT
   e) an SCR

10. Refer to Figure 11-1 (e). The symbol is for:
    a) a triac
    b) a UJT
    c) a diac
    d) a PUT
    e) an SCR

11. A good choice to trigger atriac would be:
    a) a UJT
    b) an SCR
    c) a diac
    d) a Schockley diode

12. The best choice to operate a small variable speed ac motor is a(n):
    a) triac
    b) diac
    c) SCR
    d) UJT
    e) PUT

13. The best choice to shut down a dc power supply in case of a high voltage condition is a(n):
    a) triac
    b) diac
    c) SCR
    d) UJT
    e) PUT

14. A good choice to turn on a device at a particular voltage would be a(n):
    a) triac
    b) diac
    c) SCR
    d) UJT
    e) PUT

15. The most likely device to be used in an oscillator is a(n):
    a) triac
    b) diac
    c) SCR
    d) UJT
    e) PUT

16. A typical use for an optical coupler might be:
    a) to connect telephone lines to electronic equipment
    b) to transfer signals to a fiber optic cable
    c) to isolate one circuit from another
    d) all of these

17. An SCS has a unique ability to:
    a) be turned on or off with a pulse
    b) be turned off only with a pulse
    c) control a PUT
    d) all of these

18. If an SCR starts to conduct when a gate current is established, what
    will occur when the gate circuit is interrupted?
    a) The SCR will turn off.
    b) The SCR current will increase.
    c) The SCR will continue to conduct.
    d) The SCR gate current will increase.

19. An SCR will turn off when the voltage across it is:
    a) increased to the supply voltage
    b) decreased to near 0 V
    c) timed out
    d) decreased by the value of the gate voltage

20. A triac is used on ac because:
    a) it conducts on both alternations
    b) it is turned off when the ac voltage reaches zero
    c) it can deliver more power to the load in a cycle
    d) all of these

21. A device is needed to trigger an SCR. A good one to use might be:
    a) an SCR
    b) a UJT
    c) a Schockley diode
    d) a PUT

22. The best device to be used to control a dc motor is:
    a) triac
    b) PUT
    c) SCR
    d) diac

23. An SCR is used to control the speed of a dc motor by _____ the _____
    of the pulse delivered to the motor.
    a) varying, width
    b) increasing, amplitude
    c) decreasing, gate width
    d) none of these

24. Which of the following applications would be likely to use a diac?
    a) A battery charger
    b) An oscillator
    c) A high frequency amplifier
    d) A lamp dimmer

25. A light dimmer circuit using an SCR is tested and IG = omA was found. The light is still on. The trouble might be one of the following:
    a) the SCR is open
    b) the switch is faulty
    c) the gate circuit is shorted
    d) this is normal, nothing is wrong

26. A thyristor can be used as:
    a) a resistor
    b) an amplifier
    c) a switch
    d) a power source

27. The minimum input current that can turn on a thyristor is called the:
    a) holding current
    b) switching current
    c) breakdown current
    d) low-current dropout current

28. The minimum current that keeps a latch closed is called the:
    a) pick-up current
    b) critical rate of current rise
    c) trigger current
    d) holding current

29. The only way to close a four-layer diode is with:
    a) a trigger input applied to the gate
    b) forward breakover voltage
    c) low-current dropout
    d) none of the above

30. The only way to stop an SCR that is conducting is by:
    a) a positive trigger
    b) low-current drop out
    c) breakover
    d) reverse-bias triggering

31. A silicon controlled rectifier has:
    a) two external leads
    b) three external leads
    c) four external leads
    d) three doped regions

32. An SCR is usually turned on by:
    a) breakover
    b) a gate trigger
    c) breakdown
    d) holding current

33. SCRs are:
    a) low-power devices
    b) four-layer diodes
    c) high-current devices
    d) bi-directional

34. The trigger voltage of an SCR is closest to:
    a) 0 V
    b) 0.7 V
    c) 4 V
    d) breakover voltage

35. The voltage across a conducting SCR:
    a) equals the breakover voltage
    b) is exactly zero
    c) decreases with more anode current
    d) is quite low

36. Disconnecting the gate lead is a conducting SCR will:
    a) turn it off
    b) not turn it off
    c) destroy it
    d) increase the anode current

37. The angle at which an SCR fires is called the:
    a) displacement angle
    b) firing angle
    c) the peak angle
    d) conduction angle

38. The forced commutation method requires momentarily forcing current in the direction opposite to the reverse conduction so that the net reverse current is reduced below the holding value.
    a) true
    b) false

39. SCR's are:
    a) low-power devices
    b) four-layer diodes
    c) high-current devices
    d) bi-directional

40. Once a diac is conducting, the only way to turn it off is with:
    a) low-current dropout
    b) breakover
    c) a negative gate voltage
    d) a positive gate voltage

41. The diac is equivalent to:
    a) two four-layered diodes in parallel
    b) two SCRs in parallel
    c) two four-layer diodes in series
    d) two triacs in parallel

42. The diac is a:
    a) transistor
    b) unidirectional device
    c) three-layer device
    d) bi-directional device

43. A triac acts like:
    a) two SCRs in parallel
    b) two SCRs in series
    c) two diacs in parallel
    d) a normal transistor

44. A triac:
    a) can trigger only on positive gate voltages
    b) cab trigger only on negative gate voltages
    c) can be triggered by either a positive or a negative gate voltage
    d) cannot be triggered with gate voltages

45. The triac is equivalent to:
    a) a four-layer diode
    b) two diacs in parallel
    c) a thyristor with a gate lead
    d) two SCRs in parallel

46. A silicon-controlled switch:
    a) has only 1 gate lead
    b) has two gate leads
    c) can only be turned off with low-current dropout
    d) is bi-directional

47. A UJT has:
    a) two base leads
    b) one emitter lead
    c) two emitter and one base leads
    d) both a and b above

48. For a UJT, the intrinsic standoff ratio is:
    a) equal to 1
    b) always greater than 1
    c) always less than 1
    d) usually around 1 kω or so

49. For maximum sensitivity to light, the gate of a light-activated SCR, LASCR, should be:
    a) shorted to the cathode
    b) shorted to ground
    c) shorted to both the cathode and the anode
    d) left open

50. The PUT (Programmable Unijunction Transistor) is actually a type of:
    a) thyristor
    b) FET device
    c) triac
    d) SCR

51. An optoisolator is a device containing _____ in a single package.
    a) a photodiode and an optotransmitter
    b) a phototransistor and an optosensor
    c) an optotransmitter and an LED
    d) an optotransmitter and an optosensor

52. The slot type optical sensor (Phototransistor couplers) has a slot
separating _____.
a) a phototransistor and an optosensor
b) a photodiode and an optosensor
c) an optotransmitter and an LED
d) an LED and an optotransistor

1. Answer: a Difficulty: 2

2. Answer: b Difficulty: 2

3. Answer: a Difficulty: 2

4. Answer: a Difficulty: 2

5. Answer: b Difficulty: 2

6. Answer: e Difficulty: 2

7. Answer: b Difficulty: 2

8. Answer: d Difficulty: 2

9. Answer: c Difficulty: 2

10. Answer: a Difficulty: 2

11. Answer: c Difficulty: 2

12. Answer: a Difficulty: 2

13. Answer: c Difficulty: 3

14. Answer: e Difficulty: 2

15. Answer: d Difficulty: 2

16. Answer: d Difficulty: 2

17. Answer: a Difficulty: 2

18. Answer: c Difficulty: 3

19. Answer: b Difficulty: 2

20. Answer: d Difficulty: 2

21. Answer: b Difficulty: 3

22. Answer: c Difficulty: 2

23. Answer: a Difficulty: 3

24. Answer: d Difficulty: 2

25. Answer: d Difficulty: 3

26. Answer: c Difficulty: 2 Section: 1

27. Answer: b Difficulty: 2 Section: 1

28. Answer: d Difficulty: 2 Section: 1

29. Answer: b Difficulty: 3 Section: 1

30. Answer: b Difficulty: 2 Section: 2

31. Answer: b Difficulty: 1 Section: 2

32. Answer: b Difficulty: 2 Section: 2

33. Answer: c Difficulty: 2 Section: 2

34. Answer: b Difficulty: 2 Section: 2

35. Answer: b Difficulty: 2 Section: 2

36. Answer: d Difficulty: 3 Section: 2

37. Answer: b Difficulty: 2 Section: 2

38. Answer: b Difficulty: 3 Section: 2

39. Answer: c Difficulty: 2 Section: 3

40. Answer: a Difficulty: 2 Section: 4

41. Answer: a Difficulty: 3 Section: 4

42. Answer: d Difficulty: 2 Section: 4

43. Answer: a Difficulty: 1 Section: 4

44. Answer: c Difficulty: 2 Section: 4

45. Answer: d Difficulty: 2 Section: 4

46. Answer: b Difficulty: 2 Section: 5

47. Answer: d Difficulty: 2 Section: 6

48. Answer: c Difficulty: 2 Section: 6

49. Answer: d Difficulty: 2 Section: 9

50. Answer: a Difficulty: 2 Section: 7

51. Answer: d Difficulty: 2 Section: 10

52. Answer: d Difficulty: 3 Section: 10

Chapter 12: Operational Amplifiers

MULTIPLE CHOICE

1. A good op-amp has high voltage gain, low output impedance, and high input impedance.
   a) true
   b) false

2. An inverting amplifier has an input resistance equal to the input resistor.
   a) true
   b) false

3. CMRR is the measure of an op-amps voltage gain for an inverting amplifier.
   a) true
   b) false

4. All op-amp configurations must use negative feedback.
   a) true
   b) false

5. A voltage follower has a very high input impedance, and is often used as a high voltage gain amplifier.
   a) true
   b) false

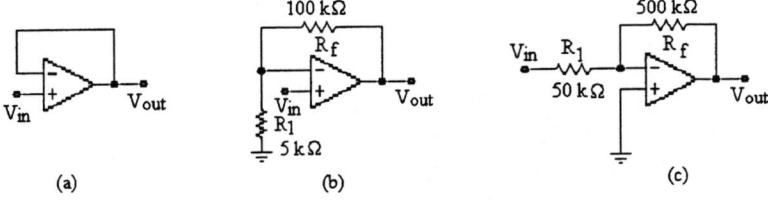

Figure 12-1

6. Refer to Figure 12-1. Which circuit is the inverting amplifier?
   a) (a)
   b) (b)
   c) (c)
   d) None of the above

7. Refer to Figure 12-1. Which circuit is a voltage follower?
   a) (a)
   b) (b)
   c) (c)
   d) None of the above

8. Refer to Figure 12-1. Which circuit is the non-inverting amplifier?
   a) (a)
   b) (b)
   c) (c)
   d) None of the above

9. Refer to Figure 12-1. Which circuit has a voltage gain of 1?
   a) (a)
   b) (b)
   c) (c)
   d) None of the above

10. See Figure 12-1. Which circuit has an input impedance of about 5 kΩ?
    a) (a)
    b) (b)
    c) (c)
    d) None of the above

11. Refer to Figure 12-1. Which circuit has a voltage gain of 10?
    a) (a)
    b) (b)
    c) (c)
    d) None of the above

12. Refer to Figure 12-1. Which circuit has a voltage gain of 20?
    a) (a)
    b) (b)
    c) (c)
    d) None of the above

13. Refer to Figure 12-1 (a). If this circuit has a V_{in} = 12 V p-p, the value of V_{out} would be:
    a) 20 V
    b) -20 V
    c) 8.48 V p-p
    d) 12 V p-p

14. Refer to Figure 12-1 (b). If this circuit has a V_{in} = 0.7, V_{out} would be:
    a) 14.7 V
    b) -14.7 V
    c) 14 V
    d) 0 V

15. Refer to Figure 12-1 (c). V_{in} = -6 V. The value of V_{out} is:
    a) 60 V
    b) -60 V
    c) about -16 V
    d) about 16 V

16. See Figure 12-1. If these three circuits were connected as a multiple-stage amplifier, the total voltage gain would be:
    a) 1
    b) 10
    c) 21
    d) 210

17. Refer to Figure 12-1 (c). If R_f is changed to 1 MΩ, the new Acl would be:
    a) 20
    b) -20
    c) 21
    d) -21

18. Refer to Figure 12-1 (c). If an amplifier with an input impedance of 12 kΩ and the same voltage gain is needed, the new value of R_f would be _____ and the new value of R_F would be _____.
    a) 10 kΩ, 100 kΩ
    b) 13.3 kΩ, 120 kΩ
    c) 12 kΩ, 108 kΩ
    d) 12 kΩ, 120 kΩ

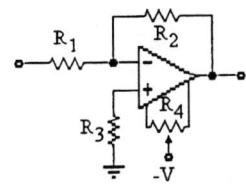

Figure 12-2

19. Refer to Figure 12-2. This op-amp has a slew rate of 1.33 V/μs. How long would it take to change the output voltage from -12 V to +12 V?
    a) 18 μs
    b) 16 μs
    c) -18 μs
    d) 48 μs

20. Refer to Figure 12-2. Which components are used to set input impedance and voltage gain?
    a) R_4
    b) R_3
    c) R_1 and R_2
    d) R_3 and R_4

21. Refer to Figure 12-2. Which components are used for offset voltage compensation?
    a) R_4
    b) R_3
    c) R_1 and R_2
    d) R_2

22. Refer to Figure 12-2. Which components are used for bias current compensation?
    a) R_4
    b) R_3
    c) R_1 and R_2
    d) R_2

23. Refer to Figure 12-2. The purpose of R_1 and R_2 is:
    a) for bias current compensation
    b) for input offset voltage compensation
    c) to set input impedance only
    d) to set input impedance and voltage gain

24. It takes an op-amp 22 μs to change its output from -15 V to +15 V. The slew rate for this amplifier is:
    a) 1.36 V/μs
    b) 0.68 V/μs
    c) -0.68 V/μs
    d) -1.36 V/μs

25. A voltage follower amplifier comes to you for service. You find the voltage gain to be 5.5 and the input impedance is 22 kΩ. The probable fault in this amplifier is, if any:
    a) the gain is too low for this type of amplifier
    b) the input impedance is too high for this amplifier
    c) nothing is wrong. The trouble must be somewhere else
    d) cannot be determined

26. The op amp can amplify:
    a) ac signals only
    b) dc signals only
    c) both ac and dc signals
    d) neither ac nor dc signals

27. The typical input stage of an op amp has a:
    a) single-ended input and single-ended output
    b) single-ended input and differential output
    c) differential input and single-ended output
    d) differential input and differential output

28. The common-mode signal is applied to:
    a) the noninverting input
    b) the inverting input
    c) both inputs
    d) top of the tail resistor

29. If an Op Amp were perfect, the CMRR would be:
    a) zero
    b) infinite
    c) equal to the differential gain
    d) both b and c above

30. In an Op Amp, the CMRR is limited mostly by the:
    a) CMRR of the op amp
    b) gain-bandwidth product
    c) supply voltages
    d) tolerance of the resistors

31. The open-loop voltage gain (A_{ol}) of an Op Amp is the:
    a) external voltage gain the device is capable of
    b) internal voltage gain the device is capable of
    c) most controlled parameter
    d) same as A_{cm}

32. The input offset current is usually:
    a) less than the input bias current
    b) equal to zero
    c) less than the input offset voltage
    d) unimportant when a base resistor is used

33. With both inputs grounded, the only offset that produces an error is the:
    a) input offset current
    b) input bias current
    c) input offset voltage
    d) input short circuit current

34. The input offset current equals the:
    a) difference between two base currents
    b) average of two base currents
    c) collector current divided by current gain
    d) difference between two base-emitter voltages

35. The ideal Op Amp has:
    a) infinite input impedance and zero output impedance
    b) infinite output impedance and zero input impedance
    c) infinite voltage gain and infinite bandwidth
    d) both a and c

36. The two basic ways of specifying input impedance of an Op Amp are:
    a) differential and extremely high
    b) differential and common-loop
    c) differential and common-mode
    d) closed-loop and common-mode

37. The initial slope of a sine wave is directly proportional to the:
    a) slew rate
    b) voltage gain
    c) voltage gain
    d) capacitance

38. When the initial slope of a sine wave is greater than the slew rate:
    a) distortion occurs
    b) voltage gain is maximum
    c) voltage gain is maximum
    d) the op amp works best

39. When slew-rate distortion of a sine wave occurs, the output:
    a) is larger
    b) appears triangular
    c) is normal
    d) has no offset

40. With negative feedback, the returning signal:
    a) aids the input signal
    b) opposes the input signal
    c) is proportional to output current
    d) is proportional to differential voltage gain

41. The closed-loop voltage gain of an inverting amplifier equals:
    a) the ratio of the input resistance to the feedback resistance
    b) the open-loop voltage gain
    c) the feedback resistance divided by the input resistance
    d) the input resistance

42. The noninverting amplifier has a:
    a) large closed-loop voltage gain
    b) small open-loop voltage gain
    c) small closed-loop input impedance
    d) small closed-loop output impedance

43. The voltage follower has a:
    a) closed-loop voltage gain of unity
    b) small open-loop voltage gain
    c) closed-loop bandwidth of zero
    d) large closed-loop output impedance

44. The feedback fraction "B":
    a) is always less than 1
    b) is usually greater than 1
    c) may equal 1
    d) may not equal 1

45. The loop gain $A_{OL}B$:
    a) is usually much smaller than 1
    b) is usually much greater than 1
    c) may not equal 1
    d) is between 0 and 1

46. Current cannot flow to ground through:
    a) a mechanical ground
    b) an ac ground
    c) a virtual ground
    d) an ordinary ground

47. The closed-loop input impedance in a noninverting amplifier is:
    a) much greater than the open-loop input impedance
    b) equal to the open-loop input impedance
    c) sometimes less than the open-loop input impedance
    d) ideally zero

48. The imbalances of the internal circuitry of an op amp are lumped into one value called the _____.
    a) imbalance factor
    b) input offset voltage
    c) output offset voltage
    d) balance offset factor

49. The voltage gain of an op amp is unity at the:
    a) cutoff frequency
    b) unity-gain frequency
    c) generator frequency
    d) power bandwidth

50. For a given op amp, which of these is constant?
    a. $f_{C(CL)}$
    b. feedback voltage
    c. A_{OL}
    d. $A_{OL} f_{c(OL)}$

51. If the unit-gain frequency is 10 MHz and the mid-band open-loop voltage gain is 200,000, the cutoff frequency is:
    a) 5 kHz
    b) 50 Hz
    c) 5 Hz
    d) 25 MHz

1. Answer: a Difficulty: 2

2. Answer: a Difficulty: 2

3. Answer: b Difficulty: 2

4. Answer: b Difficulty: 2

5. Answer: b Difficulty: 2

6. Answer: c Difficulty: 2

7. Answer: a Difficulty: 2

8. Answer: b Difficulty: 2

9. Answer: a Difficulty: 2

10. Answer: d Difficulty: 3

11. Answer: c Difficulty: 2

12. Answer: d Difficulty: 2

13. Answer: d Difficulty: 2

14. Answer: a Difficulty: 2

15. Answer: a Difficulty: 2

16. Answer: d Difficulty: 2

17. Answer: b Difficulty: 2

18. Answer: d Difficulty: 2

19. Answer: a Difficulty: 2

20. Answer: c Difficulty: 2

21. Answer: a Difficulty: 3

22. Answer: b Difficulty: 2

23. Answer: d Difficulty: 2

24. Answer: a Difficulty: 2

25. Answer: d Difficulty: 3

26. Answer: c Difficulty: 1 Section: 1

27. Answer: c Difficulty: 1 Section: 1

28. Answer: c Difficulty: 1 Section: 2

29. Answer: c Difficulty: 2 Section: 2

30. Answer: a Difficulty: 2 Section: 2

31. Answer: b Difficulty: 2 Section: 2

32. Answer: a Difficulty: 2 Section: 2

33. Answer: c Difficulty: 2 Section: 2

34. Answer: a Difficulty: 2 Section: 2

35. Answer: a Difficulty: 2 Section: 1

36. Answer: c Difficulty: 2 Section: 2

37. Answer: a Difficulty: 2 Section: 2

38. Answer: a Difficulty: 2 Section: 2

39. Answer: b Difficulty: 2 Section: 2

40. Answer: b Difficulty: 2 Section: 3

41. Answer: c Difficulty: 2 Section: 4

42. Answer: c Difficulty: 2 Section: 4

43. Answer: a Difficulty: 2 Section: 4

44. Answer: a Difficulty: 2 Section: 4

45. Answer: b Difficulty: 2 Section: 4

46. Answer: c Difficulty: 2 Section: 4

47. Answer: a Difficulty: 2 Section: 4

48. Answer: b Difficulty: 2 Section: 6

49. Answer: b Difficulty: 2 Section: 6

50. Answer: d Difficulty: 3 Section: 6

51. Answer: b Difficulty: 1 Section: 6

Chapter 13:   Basic Op-Amp Applications

MULTIPLE CHOICE

1. An op-amp comparator has an output dependent upon the polarities of the two inputs.
   a) true
   b) false

2. The output voltage of a summing amplifier is proportional to the product of the input voltages.
   a) true
   b) false

3. Integration is a mathematical process for determining the area under a curve.
   a) true
   b) false

4. A square wave input to an op-amp integrator will produce a sine wave output.
   a) true
   b) false

5. Bounding allows the op-amp to have unlimited output voltage.
   a) true
   b) false

6. An op-amp has an open-loop gain of 100,000. V_{sat} = +/-12 V. A differential signal voltage of 150 μV p-p is applied between the inputs. What is the output voltage?
   a) 12 V
   b) -12 V
   c) 12 V p-p
   d) 24 V p-p

7. A summing amplifier can:
   a) add dc voltages
   b) add ac voltages
   c) add dc to ac voltages
   d) all of these

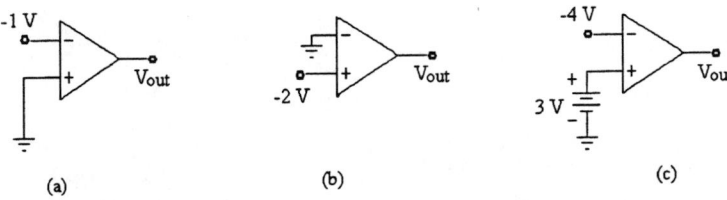

(a)   (b)   (c)

Figure 13-1

297

8. Refer to Figure 13-1 (a).   If V_{CC} = 15 V, the approximate output voltage is:
   a) 1 V
   b) -1 V
   c) 13 V
   d) -13 V

9. Refer to Figure 13-1 (b).   If V_{sat} = +/-12 V, the approximate output voltage is:
   a) 12 V
   b) -12 V
   c) 2 V
   d) -2 V

10. Refer to Figure 13-1 (c).   If V_{sat} = +/-10 V, the approximate value of V_{OUT} is:
    a) -1 V
    b) 1 V
    c) -6 V
    d) none of the above

11. Refer to Figure 13-1 (c).   With the inputs shown, the output voltage would be:
    a) 7 V
    b) -7 V
    c) $+V_{sat}$
    d) $-V_{sat}$

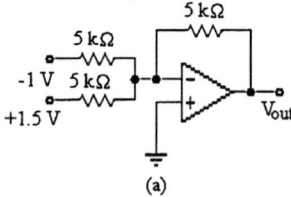

(a)

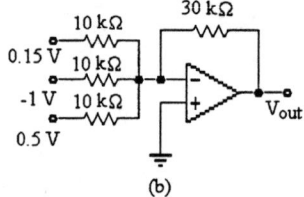

(b)

Figure 13-2

12. Refer to Figure 13-2 (a).   If a solder splash shorted the two ends of the feedback resistor to each other, the output voltage would be:
    a) 0.5 V
    b) -0.5 V
    c) 0 V
    d) $-V_{sat}$

13. Refer to Figure 13-2 (b).   A voltmeter placed from the inverting input to ground would read:
    a) -0.925 V
    b) -2.775 V
    c) 2.775 V
    d) $\approx$ 0 V

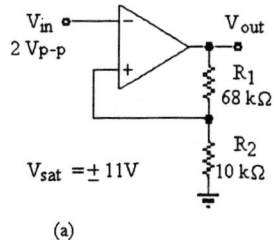 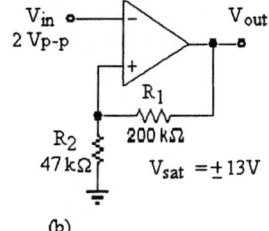

Figure 13-3

14. Refer to Figure 13-3 (a). This circuit is known as:
    a) a multivibrator
    b) a zero level detector
    c) a non-zero level detector
    d) a non-inverting amplifier

15. Refer to Figure 13-3 (b). This type of circuit will usually have:
    a) a square wave output if the input is a sine wave
    b) a triangle wave output
    c) a ramp output for a square wave input
    d) none of these

16. Refer to Figure 13-3 (b). The output voltage with the inputs as shown is:
    a) $+V_{sat}$
    b) $-V_{sat}$
    c) 26 V_{p-p}
    d) 17.06 V_{p-p}

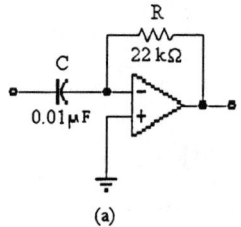 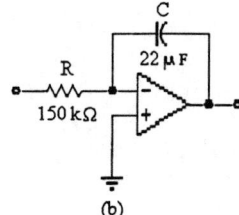

Figure 13-4

17. See Figure 13-4. This circuit is known as:
    a) a non-inverting amplifier
    b) an integrator
    c) a differentiator
    d) a summing amplifier

18. Refer to Figure 13-4. Which of these circuits is known as a differentiator?
    a) (a)
    b) (b)
    c) None of these

19. Refer to Figure 13-4 (b). A square wave input is applied to this amplifier. The output voltage is most likely to be:
    a) a square wave
    b) a triangle wave
    c) a sine wave
    d) no output

20. A Schmitt trigger is:
    a) a comparator with hysteresis
    b) a comparator with one trigger point
    c) a comparator with two trigger points
    d) a and c

21. An op-amp has an open-loop gain of 90,000. V_{sat} = +/-13 V. A differential voltage of 0.1 V_{p-p} is applied between the inputs. The output voltage is:
    a) 13 V
    b) -13 V
    c) 13 V_{p-p}
    d) 26 V_{p-p}

22. The output of a Schmitt trigger is a:
    a) triangle wave
    b) sine wave
    c) sawtooth
    d) square wave

23. An integrated circuit:
    a) uses a capacitor in its feedback circuit
    b) produces a ramp voltage at its output for a step input voltage
    c) uses an inductor in its feedback circuit
    d) a and b

24. A differential circuit:
    a) uses a resistor in its feedback circuit
    b) uses a capacitor in its feedback circuit
    c) produces a ramp voltage at its output for a step input voltage
    d) a and c

25. Hysteresis voltage is defined as:
    a) the voltage of the lower trigger point
    b) the voltage of the upper trigger point
    c) the difference in voltage between the upper and the lower trigger points
    d) the sum of voltages of the upper and the lower trigger points

26. A comparator is an example of a(n):
    a) active filter
    b) current source
    c) linear circuit
    d) nonlinear circuit

27. If the input to a comparator is a sine wave, the output is a:
    a) ramp voltage
    b) sine wave
    c) rectangular wave
    d) sawtooth wave

28. A zero crossing detector is a:
    a) comparator with a sine-wave output
    b) comparator with a trip point referenced to zero
    c) peak detector
    d) limiter

29. A window comparator:
    a) has only one usable threshold
    b) uses hysteresis to speed up response
    c) clamps the input positively
    d) detects an input voltage between two limits

30. A Schmitt trigger has:
    a) only one trip point
    b) only negative feedback
    c) two slightly different trip points
    d) a triangular output

31. A Schmitt trigger is a comparator with:
    a) negative feedback
    b) positive feedback
    c) neither a nor b
    d) both a and b

32. The _____ circuit overcomes the problem of false switching caused by noise on the input(s).
    a) input buffer
    b) Schmitt trigger
    c) input noise rejecter
    d) differentiator

33. The amount of hystersis in a Schmitt trigger is defined by the _____ of the two trigger levels.
    a) difference $V_{UTP} - V_{LTP}$
    b) product $V_{UTP} \times V_{LTP}$
    c) division $\dfrac{V_{UTP}}{V_{LTP}}$
    d) sum $V_{UTP} + V_{LTP}$

34. Output Bounding is the process of _____ the output voltage range of a comparator.
    a) extending
    b) limiting
    c) comparing
    d) filtering

35. If all the resistors in a summing amplifier are equal, the output will be equal to the _____.
    a) average of the individual inputs
    b) inverted average of the individual inputs
    c) sum of the individual inputs
    d) inverted sum of the individual inputs

36. If the value of resistor R_f in a averaging amplifier circuit is equal to the value of one input resistor divided by the number of inputs, the output will be equal to:
    a) average of the individual inputs
    b) inverted average of the individual inputs
    c) sum of the individual inputs
    d) inverted sum of the individual inputs

37. The _____ input makes the summing amplifier circuit possible.
    a) virtual ground at the noninverting
    b) virtual ground at the inverting
    c) low voltage
    d) high voltage

38. A D/A converter is an application of the:
    a) adjustable bandwidth circuit
    b) noninverting amplifier
    c) voltage-to-current converter
    d) scaling adder

39. In an op-amp integrator, the current through the input resistor flows into the:
    a) inverting input
    b) noninverting input
    c) bypass capacitor
    d) feedback capacitor

40. A mathematical operation that determines the rate of change of a curve is called _____.
    a) differentiation
    b) integration
    c) curve averaging
    d) linear regression

41. A mathematical operation for finding the area under the curve of a graph is called _____.
    a) differentiation
    b) integration
    c) curve averaging
    d) linear regression

42. The formula $I_C = \left[\dfrac{V_C}{t}\right] C$ shows that for a given capacitor, if the voltage changes at a constant rate with respect to time, then current will:
   a) increase
   b) decrease
   c) be constant
   d) decrease logarithmically

43. The output of an op-amp differentiator with a rectangular input is a:
   a) series of positive and negative spikes
   b) sine wave
   c) ramp voltage

1. Answer: a   Difficulty: 2

2. Answer: b   Difficulty: 2

3. Answer: a   Difficulty: 2

4. Answer: b   Difficulty: 2

5. Answer: b   Difficulty: 2

6. Answer: d   Difficulty: 2

7. Answer: d   Difficulty: 2

8. Answer: c   Difficulty: 2

9. Answer: b   Difficulty: 2

10. Answer: a   Difficulty: 2

11. Answer: c   Difficulty: 2

12. Answer: c   Difficulty: 3

13. Answer: d   Difficulty: 3

14. Answer: c   Difficulty: 2

15. Answer: a   Difficulty: 2

16. Answer: c   Difficulty: 3

17. Answer: b   Difficulty: 2

18. Answer: a   Difficulty: 2

19. Answer: b   Difficulty: 2

20. Answer: d   Difficulty: 2

21. Answer: d   Difficulty: 3

22. Answer: d   Difficulty: 2

23. Answer: d   Difficulty: 2

24. Answer: a   Difficulty: 2

25. Answer: c   Difficulty: 2

26. Answer: d Difficulty: 2 Section: 1

27. Answer: c Difficulty: 2 Section: 1

28. Answer: b Difficulty: 2 Section: 1

29. Answer: d Difficulty: 2 Section: 1

30. Answer: c Difficulty: 2 Section: 1

31. Answer: b Difficulty: 2 Section: 1

32. Answer: b Difficulty: 2 Section: 1

33. Answer: a Difficulty: 3 Section: 1

34. Answer: b Difficulty: 2 Section: 1

35. Answer: b Difficulty: 2 Section: 2

36. Answer: b Difficulty: 3 Section: 2

37. Answer: b Difficulty: 3 Section: 2

38. Answer: d Difficulty: 2 Section: 2

39. Answer: d Difficulty: 2 Section: 3

40. Answer: a Difficulty: 2 Section: 3

41. Answer: b Difficulty: 2 Section: 3

42. Answer: a Difficulty: 3 Section: 3

43. Answer: a Difficulty: 2 Section: 3

Chapter 14:   Special-Purpose Op-Amp Circuits

MULTIPLE CHOICE

1. A basic instrumentation amplifier has three op-amps.
   a) true
   b) false

2. One of the key characteristics of an instrumentation amplifier is its low input impedance.
   a) true
   b) false

3. The voltage gain of an instrumentation amplifier is set with an external resistor.
   a) true
   b) false

4. A basic isolation amplifier has two electrically isolated sections.
   a) true
   b) false

5. Most isolation amplifiers use transformer coupling for isolation.
   a) true
   b) false

6. OTA stands for operational transistor amplifier.
   a) true
   b) false

7. A log amplifier has a JFET in the feedback loop.
   a) true
   b) false

8. An antilog amplifier has a BJT in series with the input.
   a) true
   b) false

9. The main purpose of an instrumentation amplifier is to amplify common mode voltage.
   a) true
   b) false

10. The OTA is a voltage-to-current amplifier.
    a) true
    b) false

11. The OAT has a _____ input impedance and a _____ CMRR.
    a) high, low
    b) low, high
    c) high, high
    d) low, high

306

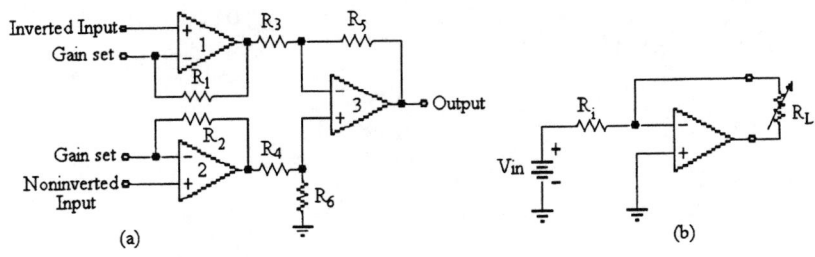

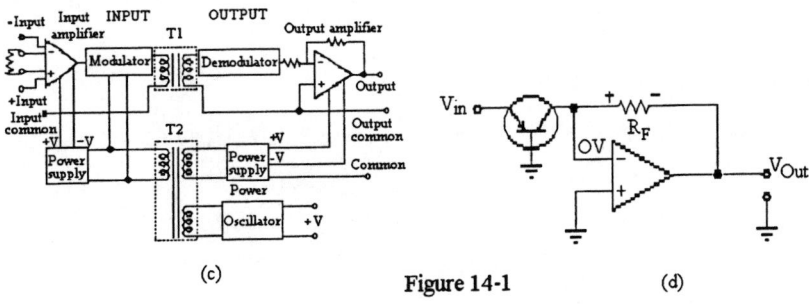

Figure 14-1

12. Refer to Figure 14-1. Which of these circuits is known as an antilog amplifier?
    a) (a)
    b) (b)
    c) (c)
    d) (d)

13. Refer to Figure 14-1. Which of these circuits is known as a constant-current source?
    a) (a)
    b) (b)
    c) (c)
    d) (d)

14. Refer to Figure 14-1. Which of these circuits is known as an isolation amplifier?
    a) (a)
    b) (b)
    c) (c)
    d) (d)

15. Refer to Figure 14-1. Which of these circuits is known as an instrumentation amplifier?
    a) (a)
    b) (b)
    c) (c)
    d) (d)

16. Refer to Figure 14-1 (a).   If $R_1 = R_2 = 30$ kΩ and the closed loop gain is 450, the value of the external gain-setting resistor R_G is:
    a) 133.64 kΩ
    b) 133.64 Ω
    c) 13.364 Ω
    d) none of the above

17. Refer to Figure 14-1 (a).   If $R_1 = R_2 = 28$ kΩ and $R_G = 100$ Ω, the A_{cl} would be:
    a) 5.51
    b) 55.1
    c) 551
    d) 550

18. Refer to Figure 14-1 (b).   If $V_{in} = 5$ V and $R_{in} = 22$ kΩ, the current thru the load R_L would be:
    a) 227.27 mA
    b) .227 μA
    c) 22.72 mA
    d) 227.27 μA

19. Refer to Figure 14-1 (d).   If $V_{in} = 200$ mV, $R_F = 52$ k, and $I_{EBO} = 50$ nA, the V_{out} would be:
    a) 77.5 V
    b) 7.75 mV
    c) 7.75 V
    d) 775 mV

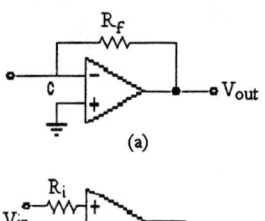

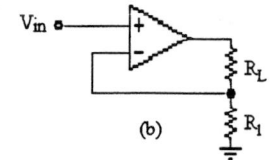

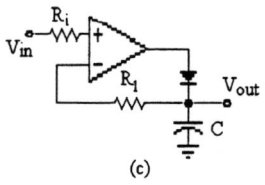

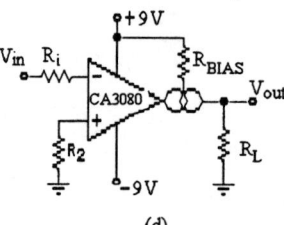

Figure 14-2

20. Refer to Figure 14-2.   Which of these circuits is known as a voltage-to-current converter?
    a) (a)
    b) (b)
    c) (c)
    d) (d)

21. Refer to Figure 14-2. Which of these circuits is known as a current-to-voltage converter?
    a) (a)
    b) (b)
    c) (c)
    d) (d)

22. Refer to Figure 14-2. Which of these circuits contains an OTA?
    a) (a)
    b) (b)
    c) (c)
    d) (d)

23. Refer to Figure 14-2. Which of these circuits is known as a peak detector?
    a) (a)
    b) (b)
    c) (c)
    d) (d)

24. Refer to Figure 14-2 (b). If R_L = 20 k, R_1 = 1.2 k, and V_{in} = 2.5 V, the load current I_L would be:
    a) 20.83 mA
    b) 2.083 mA
    c) 2.083 A
    d) 208.3 µA

25. Refer to figure 14-2 (d). If g_m = 25 mS and R_L = 25 kΩ, the voltage gain would be:
    a) 625
    b) 62.5
    c) 6.25
    d) not enough information

26. The input signal for an instrumentation amplifier usually comes from:
    a) an inverting amplifier
    b) a transducer
    c) a differential amplifier
    d) a wheatstone bridge

27. In the classic three op-amp instrumentation amplifier, the differential voltage gain is usually produced by the:
    a) first stage
    b) second stage
    c) mismatched resistors
    d) output op amp

28. An instrumentation amplifier has a high:
    a) output impedance
    b) power gain
    c) CMRR
    d) supply voltage

29. An input transducer converts:
    a) voltage to current
    b) current to voltage
    c) an electrical quantity to a nonelectrical quantity
    d) a nonelectrical quantity to an electrical quantity

30. In some respects an isolation amplifier is nothing more than an elaborate:
    a) op amp
    b) instrumentation amplifier
    c) rectifier and filter
    d) both a and b

31. The primary function of the oscillator in an isolation amplifier is to:
    a) convert dc to high frequency ac
    b) convert dc to low frequency ac
    c) rectify high frequency ac to dc
    d) produce dual polarity dc voltages for the input to the demodulator

32. The voltage gain of an OTA can be calculated using the formula:
    a) $A_V = \dfrac{R_f}{R_i}$

    b) $A_V = g_m R_L$

    c) $A_V = \left[\dfrac{R_f}{R_i}\right] + 1$

    d) $A_V = \dfrac{2R_f}{R_i}$

33. If an operational transconductance amplifier (OTA) is used as a nonlinear mixer and an audio signal is mixed with an RF signal, the output will be a(n) _____ signal.
    a) square wave
    b) triangular wave
    c) frequency modulated (FM)
    d) amplitude modulated (AM)

34. When using an OTA in a Schmitt-trigger configuration, the trigger points are controlled by:
    a) the I_{OUT}
    b) the I_{BIAS}
    c) the V_{OUT}
    d) both a and b

35. A logarithmic characteristic, when placed in the feedback loop, will produce a natural logarithm?
    a) true
    b) false

36. An antilog amplifier is formed by connecting a PN junction (diode or BJT) to the:
    a) input
    b) output
    c) feedback loop
    d) inverting and noninverting inputs

37. To scale down large signal voltages without obscuring lower signal voltages, _____ should be used.
    a) signal compression
    b) logarithmic signal compression
    c) natural logarithmic signal compression
    d) antilogarithmic signal compression

38. A voltage-to-current converter is used in applications where its necessary to have an output load current that is controlled by _____.
    a) input voltage
    b) input resistance
    c) output resistance
    d) input frequency

39. The output of a peak detector is always:
    a) 70.7% of input
    b) equal to the max value of the peak level received since the last reset pulse
    c) equal to the min value of the peak level received since the last reset pulse
    d) none of the above

40. The precision rectifier circuit is designed to _____.
    a) rectify precision waveforms
    b) amplify and rectify waveforms
    c) rectify waveforms with very small voltage swings
    d) rectify waveforms with very large voltage swings

1. Answer: a Difficulty: 2

2. Answer: b Difficulty: 2

3. Answer: a Difficulty: 2

4. Answer: b Difficulty: 2

5. Answer: a Difficulty: 2

6. Answer: b Difficulty: 2

7. Answer: b Difficulty: 2

8. Answer: a Difficulty: 2

9. Answer: b Difficulty: 2

10. Answer: a Difficulty: 2

11. Answer: c Difficulty: 2

12. Answer: d Difficulty: 2

13. Answer: b Difficulty: 2

14. Answer: c Difficulty: 2

15. Answer: a Difficulty: 2

16. Answer: b Difficulty: 2

17. Answer: c Difficulty: 2

18. Answer: d Difficulty: 2

19. Answer: c Difficulty: 2

20. Answer: b Difficulty: 2

21. Answer: a Difficulty: 2

22. Answer: d Difficulty: 2

23. Answer: c Difficulty: 2

24. Answer: b Difficulty: 2

25. Answer: a Difficulty: 2

26. Answer: d Difficulty: 2 Section: 1

27. Answer: a Difficulty: 3 Section: 1

28. Answer: c Difficulty: 2 Section: 1

29. Answer: d Difficulty: 2 Section: 1

30. Answer: d Difficulty: 2 Section: 2

31. Answer: a Difficulty: 3 Section: 2

32. Answer: b Difficulty: 2 Section: 2

33. Answer: d Difficulty: 3 Section: 2

34. Answer: d Difficulty: 3 Section: 2

35. Answer: b Difficulty: 3 Section: 4

36. Answer: a Difficulty: 3 Section: 4

37. Answer: b Difficulty: 3 Section: 4

38. Answer: a Difficulty: 3 Section: 5

39. Answer: b Difficulty: 2 Section: 5

40. Answer: c Difficulty: 2 Section: 5

Chapter 15: Active Filters

MULTIPLE CHOICE

1. The bandwidth of a band-pass filter is the difference between the two cutoff frequencies.
   a) true
   b) false

2. Butterworth filters have a roll-off of 40 dB/decade and a widely varying output in the pass-band.
   a) true
   b) false

3. A high-pass filter passes high frequencies easily and attenuates all others.
   a) true
   b) false

4. A low-pass filter attenuates low frequencies.
   a) true
   b) false

5. A band-reject filter passes all frequencies above and below a band.
   a) true
   b) false

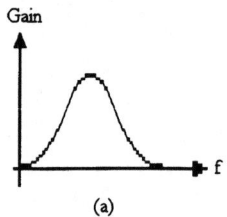
(a)

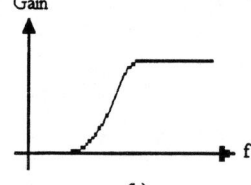
(b)

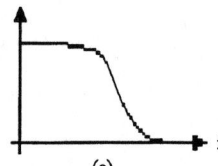
(c)

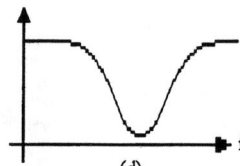
(d)

Figure 15-1

6. Refer to Figure 15-1 (a). This is the frequency response curve for a:
   a) low-pass filter
   b) high-pass filter
   c) band-pass filter
   d) band-stop filter

7. Refer to Figure 15-1 (b). This is the frequency response curve for a:
   a) low-pass filter
   b) high-pass filter
   c) band-pass filter
   d) band-stop filter

8. Refer to Figure 15-1 (c). This is the frequency response curve for a:
   a) low-pass filter
   b) high-pass filter
   c) band-pass filter
   d) band-stop filter

9. Refer to Figure 15-1 (d). This is the frequency response curve for a:
   a) low-pass filter
   b) high-pass filter
   c) band-pass filter
   d) band-stop filter

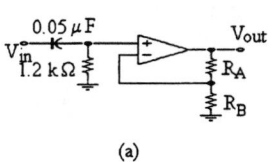

(a)

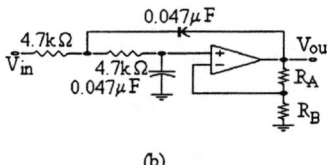

(b)

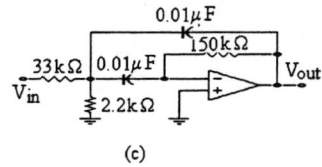

(c)

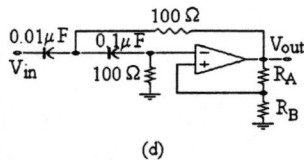

(d)

Figure 15-2

10. Refer to Figure 15-2. Identify the active single-pole high-pass filter.
    a) (a)
    b) (b)
    c) (c)
    d) (d)

11. Refer to Figure 15-2. Identify the high-pass filter with a 40 dB/decade roll-off.
    a) (a)
    b) (b)
    c) (c)
    d) (d)

12. Refer to Figure 15-2. The low-pass filter with a 20 dB/decade roll-off is:
    a) (a)
    b) (b)
    c) (c)
    d) none of the above

13. Refer to Figure 15-2. The band-pass filter is:
    a) (a)
    b) (b)
    c) (c)
    d) (d)

315

14. Refer to Figure 15-2. The low-pass filter with a roll-off of 40 db/decade is:
    a) (a)
    b) (b)
    c) (c)
    d) (d)

15. Refer to Figure 15-2 (a). This circuit was checked for proper operation and f_C was correct but the voltage gain is 1. The cause of this problem might be:
    a) the 1.2 kΩ resistor is open
    b) the capacitor is shorted
    c) R_A is open
    d) R_B is open

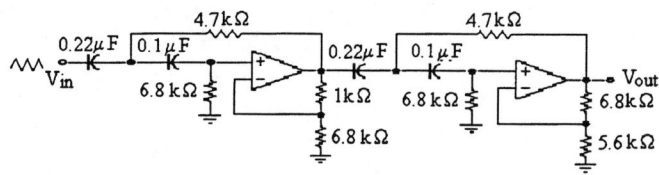

Figure 15-3

16. Refer to Figure 15-3. This circuit is known as a _____ and the roll-off rate is _____.
    a) low-pass filter, 60 dB/decade
    b) high-pass filter, 20 dB/decade
    c) high-pass filter, 80 dB/decade
    d) band-pass filter, 80 dB/decade

17. Refer to Figure 15-3. The cutoff frequency for the first filter section is _____ the cutoff frequency for the second section.
    a) equal to
    b) higher than
    c) lower than
    d) none of these

18. Refer to Figure 15-3. This filter has a roll-off rate of:
    a) 20 dB/decade
    b) 40 dB/decade
    c) 60 dB/decade
    d) 80 dB/decade

19. A high-pass filter has a cutoff frequency of 1.23 kHz. The bandwidth of this filter is:
    a) 2.46 kHz
    b) 1.23 kHz
    c) 644 Hz
    d) none of these

20. A low-pass filter with a roll-off rate of 60 dB/decade is needed. The best combination to use is:
    a) a 2-pole filter followed by another 2-pole
    b) two single-pole filters in series
    c) a 2-pole filter followed by a 1-pole
    d) none of these

21. A high-pass filter has R = 47 kΩ and C = 0.002 μF. The cutoff frequency is:
    a) 1.694 kHz
    b) 10.6 kHz
    c) 3.39 Hz
    d) none of these

22. A pole is a network that contains:
    a) a resistor and a capacitor
    b) a resistor and an inductor
    c) a capacitor and an inductor
    d) two resistors and one inductor

23. A maximally flat frequency response is a common name for:
    a) Chebyshev
    b) Bessel
    c) Butterworth
    d) Colpitts

24. An RC circuit produces a roll-off rate of:
    a) -20 dB/decade
    b) -6 dB/octave
    c) -40 dB/decade
    d) a and b

25. A low-pass filter has a cutoff frequency of 1.23 kHz. Determine the bandwidth of the filter.
    a) 2.46 kHz
    b) 1.23 kHz
    c) 644 Hz
    d) not enough information given

26. Above the f_c cutoff frequency of a low-pass filter, the output voltage _____.
    a) does not change
    b) doubles for every 1 kHz increase in frequency
    c) increases
    d) decreases

27. The center frequency of a bandpass filter is always equal to the:
    a) bandwidth
    b) geometric average of the cutoff frequencies
    c) bandwidth divided by Q
    d) 3-dB frequency

28. Bandpass filters are designed to pass a band of frequencies between _____.
    a) f_{c1} and f_{c2}
    b) a bandstart and bandstop
    c) 1 kHz and 10 kHz
    d) 1 kHz and 10 MHz

29. Low—Q filters are _____ circuits, and high—Q filters are _____ circuits.
    a) bandpass, bandstop
    b) wide bandpass, narrow bandpass
    c) low pass, high pass
    d) low order, high order

30. A notch filter is a(n):
    a) all-pass filter
    b) bandpass circuit
    c) bandstop circuit
    d) time-delay circuit

31. The type of filter response with a rippled passband is the:
    a) Butterworth
    b) Chebyshev
    c) Inverse Chebyshev
    d) Bessel

32. The approximation that distorts digital signals the least is the:
    a) Butterworth
    b) Chebyshev
    c) Elliptic
    d) Bessel

33. The filter with the slowest roll-off rate is the:
    a) Butterworth
    b) Chebyshev
    c) Elliptic
    d) Bessel

34. The damping factor (DF) of an active filter determined by:
    a) the positive feedback of the circuit
    b) the negative feedback of the circuit
    c) the number of poles
    d) the Q of the circuit

35. If a Butterworth filter has 9 second-order stages, its rolloff rate is:
    a) 20 dB per decade
    b) 40 dB per decade
    c) 180 dB per decade
    d) 360 dB per decade

36. Sallen-Key filters are also called:
    a) VCVS filters
    b) multiple feedback filters
    c) biquadratic filters
    d) state-variable filters

37. By cascading low-pass filters, _____ can be improved.
    a) band-width
    b) roll-off rate
    c) Q-rating
    d) phase shift

38. A multiple-feedback bandpass filter _____.
    a) uses a minimum of two op amps
    b) is used for a narrow band (high Q) filter
    c) is used for a wide band (low Q) filter
    d) is also known as a Sallen-Key filter

39. The state-variable filter:
    a) is difficult to tune
    b) uses fewer than three op amps
    c) has high component sensitivity
    d) has a low-pass, high-pass and bandpass output

40. The Q of a state-variable filter is controlled by the:
    a) ratio of $\dfrac{R_5}{R_6}$
    b) product of $R_5 \times R_6$
    c) ratio of the feedback resistors
    d) both a and c

41. How does the multiple-feedback bandstop filter differ from the multiple-feedback bandpass filter?
    a) both the inverting and noninverting inputs use feedback and input resistors
    b) both have input and feedback capacitors
    c) both inverting and noninverting inputs have ac applied
    d) both a and b

1. Answer: a Difficulty: 2

2. Answer: b Difficulty: 2

3. Answer: a Difficulty: 2

4. Answer: b Difficulty: 2

5. Answer: a Difficulty: 2

6. Answer: c Difficulty: 2

7. Answer: b Difficulty: 2

8. Answer: a Difficulty: 2

9. Answer: d Difficulty: 2

10. Answer: a Difficulty: 2

11. Answer: d Difficulty: 2

12. Answer: d Difficulty: 2

13. Answer: c Difficulty: 2

14. Answer: b Difficulty: 2

15. Answer: d Difficulty: 3

16. Answer: c Difficulty: 3

17. Answer: a Difficulty: 2

18. Answer: b Difficulty: 2

19. Answer: d Difficulty: 2

20. Answer: c Difficulty: 2

21. Answer: a Difficulty: 2

22. Answer: a Difficulty: 2

23. Answer: c Difficulty: 2

24. Answer: d Difficulty: 3

25. Answer: b Difficulty: 3

26. Answer: d Difficulty: 3 Section: 1

27. Answer: b Difficulty: 1 Section: 1

28. Answer: a Difficulty: 2 Section: 1

29. Answer: b Difficulty: 2 Section: 1

30. Answer: c Difficulty: 2 Section: 1

31. Answer: b Difficulty: 2 Section: 2

32. Answer: b Difficulty: 3 Section: 2

33. Answer: a Difficulty: 2 Section: 2

34. Answer: b Difficulty: 2 Section: 2

35. Answer: d Difficulty: 1 Section: 2

36. Answer: a Difficulty: 2 Section: 4

37. Answer: b Difficulty: 2 Section: 3

38. Answer: c Difficulty: 3 Section: 5

39. Answer: d Difficulty: 2 Section: 5

40. Answer: d Difficulty: 3 Section: 5

41. Answer: d Difficulty: 3 Section: 6

Chapter 16:   Oscillators

MULTIPLE CHOICE

1. To operate properly, an oscillator requires an external ac input signal.
   a) true
   b) false

2. An oscillator can produce many types of outputs, such as sine, triangle, or square waves.
   a) true
   b) false

3. Positive feedback is required for an oscillator to operate properly.
   a) true
   b) false

4. Crystal oscillators are very stable.
   a) true
   b) false

5. An RC phase-shift oscillator uses feedback from a tank circuit.
   a) true
   b) false

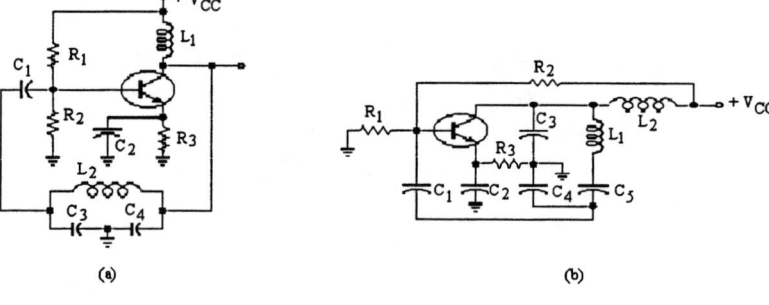

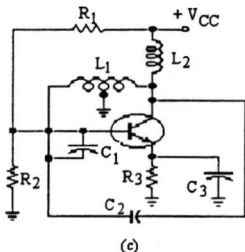

Figure 16-1

6. Refer to Figure 16-1. Which of these circuits is known as a Clapp oscillator?
   a) (a)
   b) (b)
   c) (c)
   d) none of these

7. Refer to Figure 16-1. Which of these circuits is known as a crystal oscillator?
   a) (a)
   b) (b)
   c) (c)
   d) none of these

8. Refer to Figure 16-1. Which of these circuits is known as an Armstrong oscillator?
   a) (a)
   b) (b)
   c) (c)
   d) none of these

9. Refer to Figure 16-1. Which of these circuits is known as a Colpitts oscillator?
   a) (a)
   b) (b)
   c) (c)
   d) none of these

10. Refer to Figure 16-1. Which of these circuits is known as a Hartley oscillator?
    a) (a)
    b) (b)
    c) (c)
    d) none of these

11. Refer to Figure 16-1 (a). The resonant frequency is determined by:
    a) L_1, C_1
    b) L_2, C_1, C_2
    c) L_1, C_3, C_4
    d) L_2, C_3, C_4

12. Refer to Figure 16-1 (c). The main frequency determining components are:
    a) L_2, C_2.
    b) L_1, C_1.
    c) L_1, C_2.
    d) L_2, C_1.

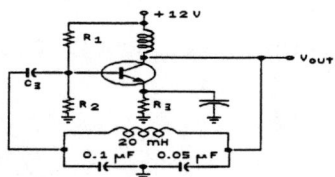

Figure 16-2

13. Refer to Figure 16-2. If the 20 mH inductor were increased to 100 mH, the resonant frequency would:
    a) increase
    b) decrease
    c) remain the same
    d) cannot be determined

14. Refer to Figure 16-2. This circuit operates easily as a:
    a) variable frequency oscillator
    b) fixed frequency oscillator
    c) a crystal oscillator
    d) none of these

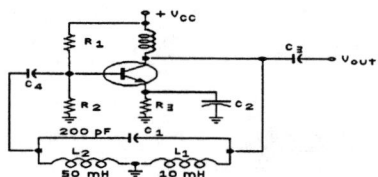

Figure 16-3

15. Refer to Figure 16-3. This circuit is known as:
    a) a Clapp oscillator
    b) a Colpitts oscillator
    c) an Armstrong oscillator
    d) a Hartley oscillator

16. Refer to Figure 16-3. This type of oscillator utilizes _____ feedback to control the oscillation. The voltage gain is _____.
    a) negative, low
    b) positive, high
    c) positive, low
    d) negative, high

17. An op-amp differentiator with a linear ramp voltage as its input, will have ____ output.
    a) dc
    b) a square wave
    c) a sine wave
    d) a triangle wave

18. A very stable oscillator is needed to operate on a single frequency, a good choice might be:
    a) a Hartley
    b) a Colpitts
    c) a crystal
    d) a Clapp

19. Refer to Figure 16-3. If C_1 decreases in value, the resonant frequency will:
    a) increase
    b) decrease
    c) remain the same
    d) cannot be determined

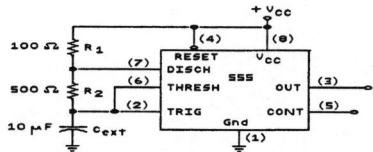

Figure 16-4

20. Refer to Figure 16-4. If the value of V_{CC} = 5 V, the output voltage would be:
    a) a square wave of 10 V_{p-p}
    b) a square wave that varies between 0 V and 5 V
    c) a sine wave
    d) 5 V dc

21. Nonsinusoidal oscillators produce:
    a) sine waves only
    b) triangle waves only
    c) square waves only
    d) either b or c

22. The 555 timer contains:
    a) 2 comparators
    b) 3 comparators
    c) 4 comparators
    d) 5 comparators

23. The most stable type of oscillator is:
    a) the Clapp oscillator
    b) the Hartley oscillator
    c) the Crystal oscillator
    d) the Colpitts oscillator

24. Refer to Figure 16-4. To reduce the duty cycle to less than 50%, the following circuit change would be necessary:
    a) reduce the size of R_1
    b) reduce the size of R_2
    c) increase the size of R_1
    d) connect a diode in parallel with R_1

25. A circuit that can change the frequency of oscillation with an application of a dc voltage is sometimes called:
    a) a voltage-controlled oscillator
    b) a crystal oscillator
    c) a Hartley oscillator
    d) an astable multivibrator

26. Which of the following is not an essential requirement of a feedback oscillator?
    a) Positive feedback network
    b) Negative feedback network
    c) Phase shift around the feedback loop of 0°
    d) Amplifier circuit

27. In order to sustain oscillations in a feedback oscillator, the gain should be _____ so the product of A_V x B equals _____.
    a) reduced, one
    b) reduced, less than one
    c) increased, more than one
    d) increased, much greater than one

28. The voltage that starts a feedback oscillator is caused by:
    a) ripple from the power supply
    b) thermal noise in resistors
    c) the input signal from a generator
    d) positive feedback

29. A Wien-bridge oscillator uses:
    a) positive feedback
    b) negative feedback
    c) both types of feedback
    d) an LC tank circuit

30. The RC feedback network used in the Wein-bridge oscillator has a maximum output voltage when:
    a) $X_C = X_L$
    b) $X_L = R$
    c) $R_1 = R_2$ and $X_{C1} = X_{C2}$
    d) $R = 0 \ \Omega$

31. The closed-loop voltage gain, A_{CL}, for a Wien-bridge oscillator is:
    a) 3, after the oscillations have built up
    b) slightly greater than 1
    c) less than 1
    d) exactly 1

32. In order for feedback oscillators to have any practical value, the gain has to be:
    a) 1/4
    b) self-adjusting
    c) stabilized
    d) non-linear

33. The phase-shift oscillator usually has:
    a) two lead or lag circuits
    b) three lead or lag circuits
    c) a lead-lag circuit
    d) a twin-T filter

34. The Twin-T Oscillator is a popular choice because it works well over a wide range of frequencies.
    a) true
    b) false

35. A sure way to recognize a Colpitts oscillator is by:
    a) the tapped inductors in the tank circuit
    b) the tapped capacitors in the tank circuit
    c) the three lag networks in the feedback path
    d) the lead/lag network in the feedback path

36. A sure way to recognize a Hartley oscillator is by the:
    a) transformer used for feedback
    b) three lead networks in the feedback path
    c) tapped capacitors in the tank circuit
    d) tapped inductors in the tank circuit

37. When Q decreases in a Colpitts oscillator, the frequency of oscillation:
    a) decreases
    b) remains the same
    c) increases
    d) becomes erratic

38. The Hartley oscillator uses:
    a) negative feedback
    b) two inductors
    c) a tungsten lamp
    d) a tickler coil

39. Of the following, the one with the most stable frequency is the:
    a) Armstrong
    b) Clapp
    c) Colpitts
    d) Hartley

40. Which type of LC oscillator uses a tickler coil in the feedback path?
    a) Colpitts
    b) Hartley
    c) Armstrong
    d) Clapp

41. Which of the following LC oscillators is least affected by the transistor and stray capacitances?
    a) Twin-T oscillator
    b) Hartley oscillator
    c) Colpitts oscillator
    d) Clapp oscillator

42. In a Colpitts oscillator, which component(s) determine the feedback fraction, B?
    a) The resistors R_1 and R_2 in the base circuit
    b) The RF choke in the collector circuit
    c) The capacitors C_1 and C_2 in the tank circuit
    d) The inductor in the tank circuit

43. The Q of a crystal:
    a) is extremely low
    b) is about 10 or so in most cases
    c) is extremely high
    d) none of the above

44. For a crystal, the series resonant frequency, and the parallel resonant frequency, are:
    a) very far apart
    b) usually within 1 kHz
    c) usually 10 MHz apart from each other
    d) exactly the same

45. The higher resonant frequencies of a crystal are called:
    a) undertones
    b) overtones
    c) octaves
    d) decades

1. Answer: b Difficulty: 2

2. Answer: a Difficulty: 2

3. Answer: a Difficulty: 2

4. Answer: a Difficulty: 2

5. Answer: b Difficulty: 2

6. Answer: b Difficulty: 2

7. Answer: d Difficulty: 2

8. Answer: d Difficulty: 2

9. Answer: a Difficulty: 2

10. Answer: c Difficulty: 2

11. Answer: d Difficulty: 3

12. Answer: c Difficulty: 2

13. Answer: b Difficulty: 2

14. Answer: b Difficulty: 3

15. Answer: d Difficulty: 2

16. Answer: c Difficulty: 3

17. Answer: a Difficulty: 2

18. Answer: c Difficulty: 2

19. Answer: a Difficulty: 2

20. Answer: b Difficulty: 2

21. Answer: d Difficulty: 2

22. Answer: b Difficulty: 2

23. Answer: c Difficulty: 2

24. Answer: d Difficulty: 2

25. Answer: a Difficulty: 2

26. Answer: b Difficulty: 2 Section: 1

27. Answer: a Difficulty: 2 Section: 1

28. Answer: b Difficulty: 1 Section: 2

29. Answer: c Difficulty: 2 Section: 3

30. Answer: c Difficulty: 3 Section: 3

31. Answer: c Difficulty: 2 Section: 3

32. Answer: b Difficulty: 2 Section: 2

33. Answer: b Difficulty: 2 Section: 3

34. Answer: b Difficulty: 2 Section: 3

35. Answer: b Difficulty: 2 Section: 4

36. Answer: d Difficulty: 2 Section: 4

37. Answer: a Difficulty: 2 Section: 4

38. Answer: b Difficulty: 2 Section: 4

39. Answer: b Difficulty: 2 Section: 4

40. Answer: c Difficulty: 2 Section: 4

41. Answer: d Difficulty: 2 Section: 4

42. Answer: c Difficulty: 3 Section: 4

43. Answer: c Difficulty: 2 Section: 4

44. Answer: b Difficulty: 2 Section: 4

45. Answer: b Difficulty: 2 Section: 4

Chapter 17: Communications Circuits

MULTIPLE CHOICE

1. Combining an audio signal with an RF carrier in a non-linear device is called _____.
   a) neutralization
   b) demodulation
   c) heterodyning
   d) modulation

2. The process of modifying a high frequency carrier by the information to be transmitted is called _____.
   a) modulation
   b) multiplexing
   c) carrier transmission
   d) discrimination

3. Mixing two signals by a nonlinear process is called _____.
   a) sum and product frequencies
   b) heterodyning
   c) spectrum modulation
   d) bandwidth discrimination

4. The outline of the peaks of the modulated carrier has the shape of the information signal, and is called the _____.
   a) envelope
   b) lower-side frequency
   c) RF index
   d) duty cycle

5. Both FM and AM are examples of which type of modulation?
   a) Phase
   b) Amplitude
   c) Angle
   d) Duty Cycle

6. Higher modulating frequencies are amplified more than the lower frequencies at the transmitting end of an FM system by a process called _____.
   a) pre-emphasis
   b) full duplex
   c) de-emphasis
   d) filtering

7. The quadrant classification of a linear multiplier indicates the number of _____ that the multiplier can handle.
   a) input polarity combinations
   b) output polarity combinations
   c) transfer characteristics
   d) scale factors

8. What is the purpose of a balanced modulator?
   a) To eliminate the upper sideband
   b) To eliminate the lower sideband
   c) To eliminate both sidebands
   d) To eliminate the carrier

9. The product of two sinusoidal signals is called:
   a) balanced modulation
   b) lower side frequency
   c) suppressed-carrier modulation
   d) both a and c

10. Balanced modulation is used in certain types of communications such as AM broadcast systems, but is not used in single side-band systems.
    a) true
    b) false

11. If you receive an AM signal modulated by a pure sinusoidal signal in the audio frequency range, you will hear:
    a) a single tone
    b) static
    c) distortion
    d) nothing

12. A mixer is basically a:
    a) frequency doubler
    b) frequency converter
    c) frequency demodulator
    d) frequency modulator

13. A basic IF Amplifier always has:
    a) a tuned (resonant) circuit on the input
    b) a tuned (resonant) circuit on the output
    c) a tuned (resonant) circuit on both the input and output
    d) none of the above

14. The main difference between an FM receiver and an AM receiver is the:
    a) method used to recover the audio signal from the modulated IF
    b) method used to recover the audio signal from the carrier
    c) method used to recover the audio signal from the mixer
    d) method used to recover the audio signal from the detector

15. The phase detector in a PLL is followed by a low-pass filter. The low-pass filter passes the _____ and rejects all other frequencies.
    a) input signal
    b) feedback signal
    c) sum of the input and feedback signals
    d) difference of the input and feedback signals

16. In a PLL, to obtain lock, the signal frequency must come within the:
    a) lock range
    b) less than f_{cap}
    c) capture range
    d) greater than f_{cap}

17. For a PLL the capture range is:
    a) always greater than the lock range
    b) always the same as the lock range
    c) usually less than the lock range
    d) always two times the lock range

18. A PLL can be used as a(n):
    a) series voltage regulator
    b) FM demodulator
    c) pulse width modulator
    d) both b & c

19. A phase detector has:
    a) one input signal and two output signals
    b) two input signals and one output signal
    c) no input signals
    d) three output signals

20. The bandwidth of the low-pass filter in a PLL determines the:
    a) capture range
    b) lock range
    c) free-running frequency
    d) phase difference

21. Most VCO's used in PLL's operate on the principle of _____.
    a) variable power
    b) variable inductance
    c) variable reactance
    d) phase detection

22. If a PLL is designed to operate in the RF range and the input to the PLL is connected to an audio signal, the output will be a(n) _____ signal.
    a) square wave
    b) triangular wave
    c) frequency modulated (FM)
    d) amplitude modulated (AM)

1. Answer: d Difficulty: 2 Section: 1

2. Answer: a Difficulty: 2 Section: 1

3. Answer: b Difficulty: 3 Section: 1

4. Answer: a Difficulty: 2 Section: 1

5. Answer: c Difficulty: 2 Section: 1

6. Answer: c Difficulty: 3 Section: 1

7. Answer: a Difficulty: 3 Section: 2

8. Answer: d Difficulty: 2 Section: 3

9. Answer: d Difficulty: 2 Section: 3

10. Answer: b Difficulty: 2 Section: 3

11. Answer: a Difficulty: 2 Section: 3

12. Answer: b Difficulty: 2 Section: 4

13. Answer: c Difficulty: 2 Section: 6

14. Answer: a Difficulty: 2 Section: 7

15. Answer: d Difficulty: 2 Section: 8

16. Answer: c Difficulty: 2 Section: 8

17. Answer: c Difficulty: 2 Section: 8

18. Answer: d Difficulty: 2 Section: 8

19. Answer: b Difficulty: 2 Section: 8

20. Answer: a Difficulty: 2 Section: 8

21. Answer: c Difficulty: 2 Section: 8

22. Answer: c Difficulty: 2 Section: 8

MULTIPLE CHOICE

1. Switching regulators are very efficient.
   a) true
   b) false

2. A Zener diode is sometimes used as a voltage regulator.
   a) true
   b) false

3. Line regulation is the percentage change in input voltage for a given change in output voltage.
   a) true
   b) false

4. In a shunt regulator, the control element is in series with the load.
   a) true
   b) false

5. Most voltage regulators include some kind of protection circuitry.
   a) true
   b) false

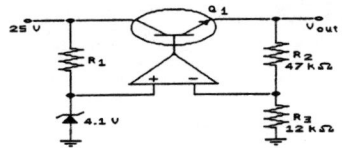

Figure 18-1(a)

6. Refer to Figure 18-1 (a). If the Zener had a voltage rating of 3.7 V, V_{out} would be:
   a) 25 V
   b) 20.2 V
   c) 18.2 V
   d) 7.1 V

7. Refer to Figure 18-1 (a). If a wire clipping were to short Q_1 emitter to collector, the problem that might result is:
   a) R_2 would open
   b) V_{OUT} would increase to 25 V
   c) Q_1 would fail
   d) the Zener would open

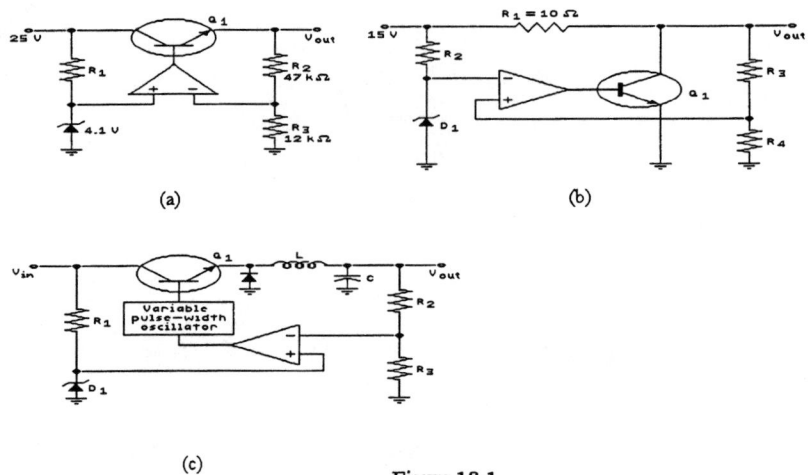

(a)   (b)

(c)

Figure 18-1

8. Refer to Figure 18-1. Which of these circuits is known as a shunt regulator?
   a) (a)
   b) (b)
   c) (c)
   d) (a) or (b)

9. Refer to Figure 18-1. Which of these circuits is known as a step-up switching regulator?
   a) (a)
   b) (b)
   c) (c)
   d) none of these

10. Refer to Figure 18-1. Which of these circuits is known as a series regulator?
    a) (a)
    b) (b)
    c) (c)
    d) none of these

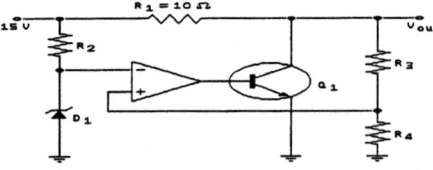

Figure 18-1(b)

11. Refer to Figure 18-1 (b). The purpose for the op-amp is:
    a) to supply a reference voltage
    b) to sense the error signal
    c) to limit the input voltage to the circuit
    d) to amplify the error signal

12. Refer to Figure 18-1 (b). An increase in V_{OUT} will cause Q_1:
    a) to conduct less
    b) to conduct the same
    c) to conduct more
    d) to open

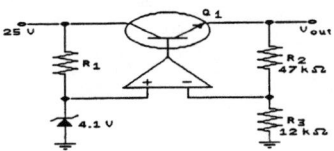

Figure 18-1(a)

13. Refer to Figure 18-1 (a). To increase the current handling capability of this regulator, beyond the 5 A rating of the transistor, the reasonable thing to do would be:
    a) place another transistor in series with Q_1
    b) increase the value of the Zener diode
    c) place another transistor in parallel with Q_1
    d) change the values of R_2 and R_3

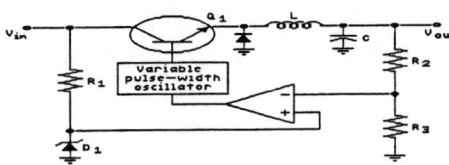

Figure 18-1(c)

14. Refer to Figure 18-1 (c). If the output voltage tends to increase due to a decrease in load current, the transistor will conduct for _____ time each cycle.
    a) a longer
    b) a shorter
    c) the same
    d) exactly half the

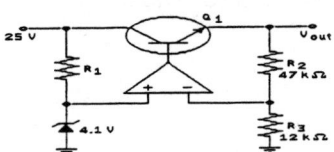

Figure 18-1(a)

15. Refer to Figure 18-1 (a). This circuit is brought in for repair. The measured output voltage was 25 V under all load conditions. A possible cause of this symptom might be:
    a) R_2 has opened
    b) Q_1 base-emitter has opened
    c) R_3 has opened
    d) V_{in} has decreased

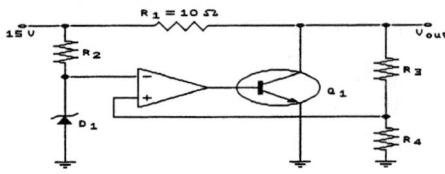

Figure 18-1(b)

16. Refer to Figure 18-1 (b). If R_1 opened, V_{OUT} would:
    a) increase
    b) decrease
    c) remain the same
    d) cannot be determined

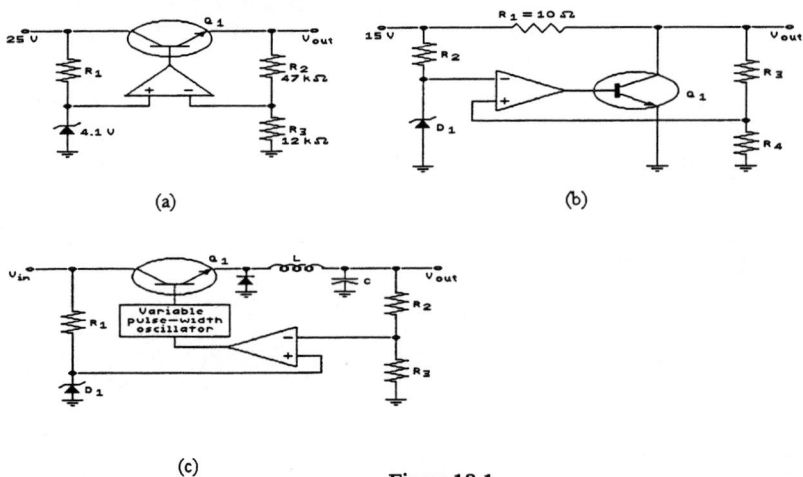

(a)   (b)

(c)   Figure 18-1

17. Refer to Figure 18-1. In all of these circuits, the Zener is used:
    a) to sense the change in output voltage
    b) as a reference voltage
    c) to supply the op-amp with V_{CC}
    d) to regulate the output voltage directly

18. Refer to Figure 18-1. The circuit that will also regulate the output voltage when V_{in} varies is:
    a) (a)
    b) (b)
    c) (c)
    d) all of the above

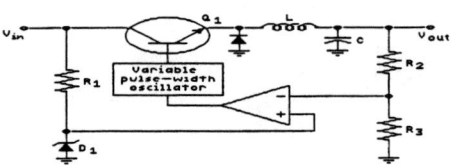

Figure 18-1(c)

19. Refer to Figure 18-1 (c). This circuits operates at a _____ frequency and its efficiency is _____.
    a) low, low
    b) low, high
    c) high, high
    d) high, low

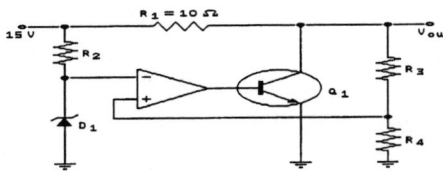

Figure 18-1(b)

20. Refer to Figure 18-1 (b). The purpose for the diode D_1 is:
    a) to supply a reference voltage
    b) to amplify the error signal
    c) to sense the error signal
    d) to limit the input voltage to the circuit

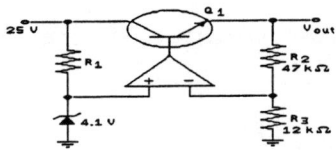

Figure 18-1(a)

21. Refer to Figure 18-1 (a). If a solder splash shorted the ends of R_1 to each other, the result would be:
    a) the op-amp would fail
    b) that Q_1 would open
    c) the output voltage would not change
    d) the Zener would fail

22. A voltage regulator with a no-load dc output of 15 V is connected to a load with a resistance of 12 Ω. If the load voltage decreases to 14.5 V, the percent regulation would be:
    a) 96.7%
    b) 3.33%
    c) 3.45%
    d) 100%

23. An advantage of a switching regulator is:
    a) the filter components are small
    b) the circuit is very efficient
    c) voltages can be stepped-up or stepped-down
    d) all of these
    e) none of these

24. A voltage regulator has a no-load output of 18 V and a full load output of 17.3 V. The percent load regulation is:
    a) 0.25%
    b) 96.1%
    c) 4.05%
    d) 1.04%

25. A voltage regulator with a no-load output dc voltage of 12 V is connected to a load with a resistance of 10 Ω. If the load resistance decreases to 7.5 Ω, the load voltage will decrease to 10.9 V. The load current will be _____ and the percent load regulation is _____.
    a) 1.45 A, 90.8%
    b) 1.45 A, 9.17%
    c) 1.6 A, 90.8%
    d) 1.6 A, 9.17%

26. An increase of line voltage into a power supply usually produces:
    a) a decrease in load resistance
    b) an increase in load voltage
    c) a decrease in efficiency
    d) less power dissipation in the rectifier diodes

27. _____ is a measurement of how well the power supply maintains a constant output voltage with changes in input voltage.
    a) voltage control
    b) load voltage control
    c) load regulation
    d) line regulation

28. If the output of a voltage regulator varies from 15 to 14.7 V between the minimum and maximum load current, the load regulation is:
    a) 0
    b) 1%
    c) 2%
    d) 5%

29. If the output of a voltage regulator varies from 20 to 19.8 V when the line voltage varies over its specified range, the source regulation is:
    a) 0
    b) 1%
    c) 2%
    d) 5%

30. A series regulator is an example of a:
    a) linear regulator
    b) switching regulator
    c) shunt regulator
    d) ac-to-dc converter

31. Without current limiting, a shorted load will probably:
    a) produce zero load current
    b) destroy diodes and transistors
    c) have a load voltage equal to the Zener voltage
    d) have too little load current

32. Simple current limiting produces too much heat in the:
    a) Zener diode
    b) load resistor
    c) pass transistor
    d) ambient air

33. With foldback current limiting, the load voltage approaches zero, and the load current approaches:
    a) a small value
    b) infinity
    c) the Zener current
    d) a destructive level

34. If the load is shorted, the pass transistor has the least power dissipation when the regulator has:
    a) foldback limiting
    b) low efficiency
    c) buck topology
    d) a high Zener voltage

35. The input current to a shunt regulator is:
    a) variable
    b) constant
    c) equal to load current
    d) used to store energy in a magnetic field

36. An advantage of shunt regulation is:
    a) built-in short-circuit protection
    b) low power dissipation in the pass transistor
    c) high efficiency
    d) little wasted power

37. To get more output voltage from a step-down switching regulator, you have to:
    a) decrease the duty cycle
    b) decrease the input voltage
    c) increase the duty cycle
    d) increase the switching frequency

38. A _____ maintains a constant output voltage by controlling the duty cycle of a switch in series with the load.
    a) shunt regulator
    b) linear regulator
    c) series regulator
    d) switching regulator

39. Switching regulators have _____ than linear regulators.
    a) longer life
    b) simper circuitry
    c) a higher cost in all cases
    d) greater efficiency

40. In a step-up regulator, the output voltage is filtered with a:
    a) choke-input filter
    b) capacitor-input filter
    c) diode
    d) voltage divider

41. The 7800 - 12 produces a regulated output voltage of:
    a) 3 V
    b) 4 V
    c) 12 V
    d) 40 V

42. The 7800 series of voltage regulators produces an output voltage that is:
    a) positive
    b) negative
    c) either positive or negative
    d) unregulated

43. Shunt regulators require:
    a) shorted-load protection
    b) load voltage sampling
    c) high-frequency protection
    d) open-load protection

1. Answer: a Difficulty: 2

2. Answer: a Difficulty: 2

3. Answer: b Difficulty: 2

4. Answer: b Difficulty: 2

5. Answer: a Difficulty: 2

6. Answer: c Difficulty: 2

7. Answer: b Difficulty: 3

8. Answer: b Difficulty: 2

9. Answer: d Difficulty: 2

10. Answer: a Difficulty: 2

11. Answer: d Difficulty: 2

12. Answer: c Difficulty: 3

13. Answer: c Difficulty: 2

14. Answer: b Difficulty: 2

15. Answer: a Difficulty: 3

16. Answer: b Difficulty: 2

17. Answer: b Difficulty: 2

18. Answer: a Difficulty: 2

19. Answer: c Difficulty: 2

20. Answer: a Difficulty: 2

21. Answer: d Difficulty: 3

22. Answer: c Difficulty: 2

23. Answer: d Difficulty: 2

24. Answer: c Difficulty: 2

25. Answer: b Difficulty: 2

26. Answer: b Difficulty: 2 Section: 1

27. Answer: d Difficulty: 2 Section: 1

28. Answer: c Difficulty: 2 Section: 2

29. Answer: b Difficulty: 2 Section: 2

30. Answer: a Difficulty: 2 Section: 2

31. Answer: b Difficulty: 2 Section: 2

32. Answer: c Difficulty: 2 Section: 2

33. Answer: a Difficulty: 3 Section: 2

34. Answer: a Difficulty: 2 Section: 2

35. Answer: b Difficulty: 2 Section: 3

36. Answer: a Difficulty: 2 Section: 3

37. Answer: c Difficulty: 3 Section: 4

38. Answer: d Difficulty: 2 Section: 4

39. Answer: d Difficulty: 2 Section: 4

40. Answer: b Difficulty: 2 Section: 4

41. Answer: c Difficulty: 2 Section: 5

42. Answer: a Difficulty: 2 Section: 4

43. Answer: b Difficulty: 2 Section: 3